FOLK TALES
OF
MALLORCA

A selection from
L'Aplec de Rondaies Mallorquines
de
Mossèn Antoni M. Alcover

Translated by
David Huelin

Editorial Moll
Palma de Mallorca
1999

Primera edició: Març 1989
Segona edició molt ampliada: Desembre 1999

D.L.: PM-2317-99
ISBN: 84-273-0822-1

Tipografia: Colophon, Oxford

Fotolits: Litho & Digital Impressions Ltd.
Witney, Oxford

Impressió: Gràfiques Miramar,s.a.
Palma de Mallorca

Propietat de l'edició:
Editorial Moll
Torre de l'Amor, 4
Palma de Mallorca
Spain

Contents

Page

FOLK TALES
OF
MALLORCA

Preface

ANTONI MARIA ALCOVER i SUREDA was born in 1862, the fourth child among six of a modest tenant farmer at Santa Cirga, near the town of Manacor in the island of Mallorca. It was a rural patriarchal family with deeply rooted religious beliefs. Antoni left home at the age of fifteen to enter the Seminary in the City (Palma), but he never lost his love of the country and its people and their tales – known in the island as *Rondaies*. When he was still a student the young Alcover developed a talent for writing which he exercised in recording *Rondaies* that he remembered from his childhood.

Alcover was ordained priest in 1886 and became Vicar of the parish of Manacor. After only two years he was summoned to the City by the Bishop to be appointed Vicar General of the Diocese. He later held several academic chairs at the Seminary. Despite his ecclesiastical and academic responsibilities he found time to hear, to write down, and to publish over three hundred tales related by some two hundred and fifty narrators from the City and from Manacor – his parents and others – representing most of the island's regions.

Mossèn Alcover was a poor preacher but he was eloquent and forceful on paper; his writings include sixty-four published and five unpublished major works, substantial contributions to specialist journals, and innumerable polemic and ephemeral articles. As a country lad who had developed a good literary style and a keen interest in language, he was uniquely fitted to hear, to enjoy, and to record on paper the legacy of the island's folk-tales. In 1896 he published the first volume of *L'Aplec de Rondaies Mallorquines* – the collection of island tales – which was the beginning of his life-long self-imposed task of rescuing Mallorca's folk-lore from neglect and oblivion.

Along with Alcover's delight in *Rondaies* and the language in which they were told went his interest in the philology of Catalan in its several branches. He made copious notes which later became the groundwork of his most ambitious undertaking, the *Diccionari Català-Valencià-Balear*. The first of ten volumes of this massive work appeared in 1930.

In the monumental task of compiling the *Diccionari* Alcover had the dedicated and highly qualified help of his friend and pupil Francesc de Borja Moll, who edited and published the subsequent nine volumes as well as keeping up the editing of *Rondaies*. He in turn handed on the torch to his son Francesc de B. Moll Marquès, who has made many further contributions to Balearic culture.

Alcover was convinced that the island's wealth of country tales and seafaring legends was rapidly disappearing, and he was anxious to preserve, in writing, as much of it as possible. In spite of his ecclesiastical and family obligations, he succeeded in hearing tales from most of the regions of Mallorca.

For Alcover the collecting of *Rondaies* developed its own momentum. It was, he said, like a kite that would take as much line as it was given. He estimated that the whole *Aplec* would run to eleven or twelve volumes, and indeed it did. He often heard a tale more than once; he would then select the best passages from each version and reassemble the *Rondaia* in its most dramatic or amusing form. His critics – mostly foreign folklorists – accused him of "corrupting" or falsifying these tales with his erudition, but he was able to retort that he was himself a countryman and capable of preserving the authentic language and style of indigenous narrators. He was in fact, the ideal, perhaps the only, writer for the task of rescuing Rondaies; he was himself as "authentic" as it is possible to be.

When the Good Jesus was creating the World the Devil too tried his hand at it

WHEN THE GOOD JESUS was creating the world and was making things, the Devil did not want to be left out of it – envious and arrogant as he is – and tried to do the same as the Good Jesus did; but of course everything that the Devil made came out botched and badly done.

As soon as the Good Jesus had made pigs, the Devil thought he too would make some; but when he had done messing about at it he produced only hedgehogs, which are small and feeble with spines instead of bristles, though it is true they have little noses in the shape of a snout like piglets have. The Devil was furious and would have smashed them to bits if he had been able.

Another day he saw the Good Jesus making sheep, and he was so overcome with envy that he could not help saying:

"Let's see if I can't make some too."

He threaded his needle and worked away at the job. He did his very best, but instead of sheep he turned out goats; he was so pleased with himself, the proud fellow, that when he had finished his goats and looked them over he said:

"Aha! They have come out better finished than his animals! I'll be hanged if they're not seven times better!" But when he had looked at them more closely, and had seen the sheep again, he could not deny that the goats were a long way from being as good as the sheep. He was furiously angry.

But what do you think? Later on, when he saw the Good Jesus was making vines, he again wanted to try his hand.

"Well", he said. "I can make a vine quicker and better than he does. Cut off my horns if I can't".

No sooner said than done, and he worked away hammer and tongs. He sweated hard, I can tell you, and put in several full days' work on the job. But do you think he managed to make a vine? What came out were brambles, all over thorns and as clinging as he is, always trying to cling to our souls. It is true that bunches of blackberries have some resemblance to grapes, and bramble shoots are something like vine tendrils, but the Devil saw he had made a mess of it; cursing and swearing and breathing fire through his nose, he said in his rage:

"A fine maker of vines I have turned out to be! But then making good things seems to be something I am not very clever at."

Even then the Devil had not learned his lesson. When he saw the Good Jesus making oxen he at once wanted to do the same, of course. He went at it as hard as he could and almost burst with the effort.

You will never guess what came out... Snails.

Of course they have ample horns because, as we all know, the Devil may be short of many things but never of horns. All male snails have such long wide-apart horns that we call them ox-snails. What a let-down for the Devil these snails were. But don't think he was put off, even then. He can't help it, the silly fool; he always wants to be equal with the Good Jesus, come what may. He always gets the worst of it, but he is as he is.

After some time the Devil saw the Good Jesus was making apple trees. They were coming out beautifully, bearing delicious shiny fruit with a smell to make you ecstatic. The Devil – naturally! – wanted to make some too.

He went at it tooth and nail and put all his guts into it; but if it went badly for him the other times, it was worse this time. Instead of apple trees he made deadly nightshade, and instead of apples, nightshade berries. I cannot tell you how furious he was. He kicked himself, and kicked hard; he bit his own tail, and he bashed his head against the wall. Bits of horn flew off and some landed a couple of miles away.

Still the Devil could not match the Good Jesus; and he never will, though the sky were to kiss the earth.

How it is there are Rich and Poor in the World

WHEN ADAM AND EVE had been knocking about the world for some years the Good Jesus appeared one day and said to them:

"Where are your children?"

"Scattered about," they replied. "They are out looking after the animals."

"Very good; on such and such a day let them all be here at sunrise. I want to see them."

"They shall be here, God willing – never fear," said Adam and Eve. They had twenty-four children, and Eve was ashamed to bring out the whole brood. "That will be enough if we present twelve," she said when she had thought it over. The day came. The Good Jesus appeared at sunrise and said to Eve:

"Come on, let's see these children of yours."

Eve brought out twelve of them.

"Are these all you have?" the Good Jesus asked her.

"They are all," said Eve. "Don't you think they are enough?"

"Very well," he replied. "Come with me." He led them away and he divided the world among them.

When Eve realized what was happening she cried out as if she had been stung.

"This is too much! And what about the other twelve; are they not to have anywhere of their own, even to lie down and die?"

She dashed off to find the Good Jesus, and she said:

"Lord, we have twelve more children!"

"Then why did you tell me you had only these twelve?"

"It's true I told you so," said Eve. "but I was ashamed to bring you twenty-four children."

"You should be ashamed of doing bad things," said the Good Jesus, "but not of showing me all the children you have. The world is now shared out, and what is done must be taken as done. These other twelve children will just have to earn their living by working on the lands of the first twelve; so each will live by helping the other, and they can all do well if they want to."

And that is why there are rich and poor in the world. The rich are descended from the twelve children whom Eve first presented to the Good Jesus, and the poor come from the other twelve, brought out when the sharing of the world had already been done.

So the poor need the rich, and the rich need the poor; and they can all do well if they want to.

Why it is that Women have less Brain than Men

WHEN THE GOOD JESUS was creating the world and was making men, Saint Peter came up and said: "Master, tell me if you would like me to help you."

"That's a good idea," the Good Jesus replied. "Here is the cauldron of brains; put a spoonful into each man's head."

It was a cauldron, full to the brim with fresh new brain-juice. Saint Peter took up the spoon and, as soon as the Good Jesus had finished forging a man, he put a spoonful of brain-juice – *splash*– into the man's nut, and the fellow went off thinking away. And so you would suppose, with brand-new brain-juice!

The Good Jesus went on forging men, and Saint Peter sploshed a good spoonful into each one's head. At first he did it with the spoon good and full, and of course the juice in the cauldron began to go down.

"How are we getting on, Peter?" asked the Good Jesus. "Are you going to run short? You had better eke it out a bit."

Saint Peter then put in smalller spoonfuls, and still more and more men kept coming along for a spoonful in the head so as to be able to think properly.

"Well," said Peter when he saw this. "I shall have to eke it out even more if there is to be enough for everybody." And he put only half a spoonful into each man's head.

At length the men were finished, and Saint Peter heaved a big sigh.

But then came the women. The Good Jesus began forging them and sending them over to Saint Peter, who exclaimed:

"What is this now?"

"What do you think?" said the Good Jesus. "It's the women, and you must give them a spoonful of brain-juice in the coconut; they too will need it to do things properly."

"I don't know what we are going to do, Master" said Saint Peter. "There's not much more than the dregs left in the cauldron."

"Come on!" replied the Good Jesus. "You must manage to work it out somehow."

"Very well," said Saint Peter; "there's nothing for it but to add a drop of water."

He tipped in a couple of pitchers of water and stirred it well. It came out a bit thin, but it was good enough. And then he went on putting spoonfuls into the women's heads. So many women came along that it was only by eking out the juice still further that he had enough for all of them.

And so it is that there are some men very well favoured with brain-juice, and others less so; and women, if they have any brain-juice at all, have it pretty thin.

What happens is that, even though women may be a little short of brains, they use what they have better than many men do.

So look out!

The Stones, or what happened to Saint Peter with the Good Jesus and the other Apostles

IN THE DAYS WHEN THE GOOD JESUS was walking about the world with Saint Peter and the other Apostles, it happened that they had been three days without swallowing anything but their own spittle, and as you may imagine they were beginning to be seriously hungry.

The Good Jesus all at once took to the mountain, and up he went; and he said to the Apostles:

"Each of you pick up a stone and follow me with it."

The Apostles all did so. The one who picked up the smallest stone was Saint Peter, because he thought it would be easier to carry.

When they reached the top of the mountain, what do you think the Good Jesus did? He blessed those stones and they all turned into bread. The Apostles tucked into that bread – and so I should think! – seeing they were desperately hungry.

The unlucky one was Saint Peter; because he had carried up such a small stone, to save himself the effort, his loaf of bread was the smallest. The poor fellow, seeing himself caught out like this, exclaimed:

"I shall know better next time."

Would you believe it? A couple of days later the Good Jesus again took to the mountain with the Apostles and Saint Peter, and he said to them:

"Come, pick up a stone again and follow me."

The other Apostles each took a stone like the time before; but Saint Peter, not to be cheated by having the smallest loaf of bread, picked up a stone three or four times the size of the others.

The trouble was getting that great boulder to the top of the mountain. When they got there Saint Peter was running with sweat and gasping for breath.

And what do you think the Good Jesus said to the Apostles then? He said:

"Put your stones on the ground and sit down on them."

The other Apostles, without a word. sat down on their stones, and very good seats they found them, tired as they were after climbing the mountain with such a load.

Saint Peter was caught out again; he had felt sure the Good Jesus would make a loaf of bread from the huge stone that had cost him so much effort to bring up. But the poor fellow was careful not to open his mouth, for fear that the Good Jesus might come out with one of those sayings that leave a man stunned.

Which side of a Mattress to lie on

WHEN THE GOOD JESUS AND SAINT PETER were about the world it happened once that towards evening they came to a farm-house, and the Good Jesus called out in greeting,:

"Praised be the Lord."

"For ever," replied a voice from inside the house. It was the farmer's wife doing her chores, and she came out to see who it was.

The Good Jesus said: "Could you put us up for the night?"

"Yes, certainly," she replied. "But there is one thing, friends: we are so short of space that we can only offer you a mattress on the floor in a corner of grandpa's room. And, to tell you the truth, he is a bit short-tempered."

"Anything will do for us," said the Good Jesus. "Whatever you give us, we will accept it gladly, and be grateful for it."

"The straw in the mattress is fresh and well stuffed, I know," said the woman, "because I think nobody has slept on it since we changed the straw."

"We shall be as comfortable as the Pope!" said Saint Peter.

"The only thing is," the woman went on, "the mattress is on the floor, because we have not been able to afford the boards and posts to make a bed to put it on."

"That's nothing," said the Good Jesus. "You must have heard the saying: *If you want to be rich be poor in your desires.*"

"Indeed, my friend, I have heard it, and very true it is."

The Good Jesus and Saint Peter were chatting away with her when the farmer and his men came back from their work; they very much liked the conversation of the Good Jesus as you may well imagine. Saint Peter's voice was hardly heard, because when the Good Jesus was speaking he usually kept his mouth shut, for the same reason that the Rector said: "*When I am preaching the organ does not play.*"

It was soon dark; they told the Rosary and said a good string of *Pater Nosters* to all the Saints and Lady Saints in Heaven, they had their supper, and they went to bed, the farm hands in the hay-loft, the farmer and his wife in their room, grandfather in his bed, and the Good Jesus and Saint Peter on the mattress in the corner of grandfather's room.

Grandfather said his four bed-time *Pater Nosters* as usual, and – *thump* – he was in bed. The poor old fellow suffered from being a very light sleeper; a mere nothing was enough to keep him from going to sleep, or to wake him if he managed to go off. There was trouble over this because the Good Jesus and Saint Peter, sitting on the mattress, began reciting their bed-time *Pater Nosters*; and there they were, saying one Our Father after another.

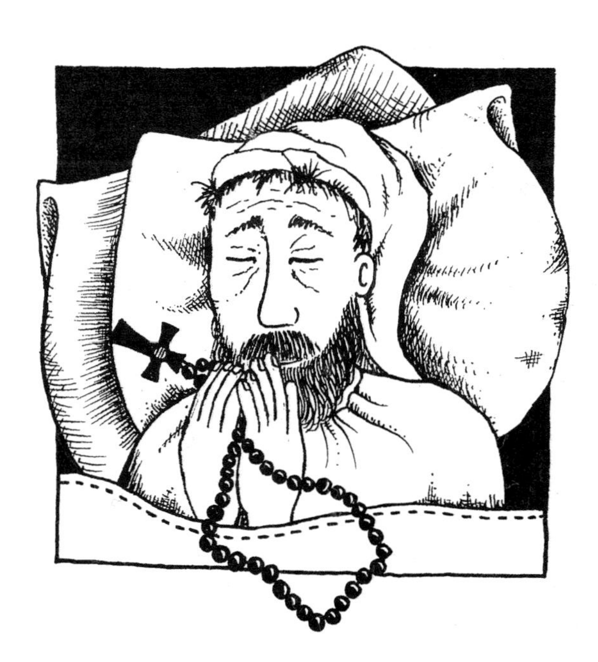

The Good Jesus said his prayers very softly, but Saint Peter was not so quiet, and the Good Jesus warned him:

"Peter! Not so loud. You'll keep grandpa from going to sleep, and that's not good in a strange house." At first Peter said his prayers a bit more quietly, but after a little his whispering got louder.

Grandfather heard him well enough; at first he said nothing, from politeness as they were strangers. But when it seemed the whispering was never going to stop he could bear it no longer and called from his bed:

"Aren't you ever going to shut up? Don't you realize you are keeping other people from going to sleep?"

"You see, Peter?" said the Good Jesus very softly. "Didn't I tell you to say your prayers more quietly?"

"You are right, Master," Saint Peter answered, "but I raised my voice without knowing it."

Saint Peter went on saying his *Pater Nosters* very very quietly, but he soon began to raise his voice once more. When Grandfather heard it again he lost his temper altogether; he jumped out of bed, grabbed some straps that he kept handy just in case, and went over to the corner of the room. There he laid into the people on the mattress who were keeping up all the whispering.

It was bad luck for Saint Peter that he was on the outer side of the mattress, and the Good Jesus on the inside; all Grandfather's blows fell on Saint Peter and none on the Good Jesus.

When Grandfather was tired of thrashing he went back to bed. Then Saint Peter, feeling very sore, said to the Good Jesus very very softly, so that even his collar could hardly have heard him:

"Master, let me go next to the wall; I don't think it's right for me to be lying in front of you."

"Move over, then," said the Good Jesus. "And let's see if you can manage not to whisper so loud saying your *Pater Nosters*."

Saint Peter had not finished saying the number of prayers that he usually said, so he went on with his task, as quietly as he could.

And would you believe it? Without realizing it he let his whispering get louder. When that bad-tempered Grandfather heard it yet again he could not bear it any longer; he jumped out of bed, grabbed his straps, and went over to the mattress saying:

"Last time the one on the outside got it; now it shall be the one on the inside." And he thrashed away at the one on the inside, next to the wall; and if he hit hard the first time he hit much harder the second time, and he went on till he was out of breath.

Saint Peter felt as beaten about as a woodman's donkey, and he gave up saying his *Pater Nosters*. As best he could he went to sleep, and afterwards never again wanted to sleep in a room with a bad-tempered grandfather.

And if you don't believe it, go and find out for yourself.

The Empty Purse and the Cloth

THERE WAS ONCE A COUPLE who had one son, a small farm and a house. The son was called Johnny, and he was a very good lad.

The wife suffered a bit from Saint Peter's trouble; she was short of wits, like land without rain in April. The man never went out in the evenings unless it was for a particular purpose, and his silly wife used to say:

"Aren't you going out?"

"And where should I go?" he would ask.

"To the tavern," would be her stupid reply.

At last one evening she managed to persuade him, and he went to the tavern. He found a game of cards going on; the players invited him to join them, and he did so. He staked his farm on a card, and he lost it.

You can imagine what a blow that was. He went home miserable, silent, crest-fallen.

"Well?" said his wife when she saw him like that.

"That was fine advice you gave me, to go to the tavern. I should never have gone there."

"Well, what happened?"

"They were playing cards; they made me join them, and I lost the farm."

"All this fuss just for that?" she said. "Go again tomorrow and you may win it back."

Would you believe it? He went, and instead of winning back the farm he lost the house.

The poor man thought he would go out of his mind, he was hitting himself on the head; he could not see straight.

"Well," he said to his wife, "how are we going to manage now? Thanks to you we have lost all we had; how are we going to eat?"

"Do you know what?" said his wife. "We'll go begging, and there will be no more worries."

Each of the three took a basket, and the woman said:

"It's best if we separate; we shall get more that way."

They came to a crossing with three roads leading out of it; each of them took a road, and off they went begging.

Johnny soon got tired of this kind of life, and he said:

"What I will do is get a job with a farmer."

He came to a farmhouse: the farmer and his wife seemed good people, so he took a job as ploughman. He was soon the best-liked hand on the farm – as he deserved to be.

In those days the Good Jesus and Saint Peter were walking about the world, and one day they came through the field where Johnny was ploughing.

The Good Jesus said to Saint Peter:

"Look at that young fellow, Peter. Isn't he handsome?"

"Yes, he is." Saint Peter replied.

"You won't believe it," the Good Jesus went on, "but the kernel is even better than the skin. You think you are the one who loves me best, but you should know this young fellow loves me more than you do."

"That's not very likely!" said Saint Peter

"It's quite likely," replied the Good Jesus. "Look, he has not yet eaten anything today: he has his breakfast in his knapsack. I will ask him for something, and you shall see how readily he gives, without hesitating."

"That's rather hard to believe," said Saint Peter.

"You shall see for yourself." And with that they came up to Johnny.

"The Lord be praised, young man!" said the Good Jesus.

"Be he praised for ever!" Johnny responded.

"How goes the ploughing?" the Good Jesus asked.

"Well enough so far, if it pleases God and the farmer."

"And – er – what was I going to say..." said the Good Jesus. "... Have you had breakfast?"

"No, not yet. Have you?"

"No, we haven't, either," said the Good Jesus.

"Well, take mine," said the lad. "You are older than I am, and you're travelling; you need it more than I do."

He went to his knapsack, brought out his breakfast, and insisted that the Good Jesus should take it.

The Good Jesus took it, and they went on their way.

"Well, Peter?" he said.

Saint Peter was amazed; he could not believe his senses.

The next day they again passed by the plough-land. It was bitterly cold – almost unbearable.

"You see that young man?" the Good Jesus said to Saint Peter. "I tell you he is a very good lad. You think you are the one who loves me best, but he loves me more."

"So we are back on that story!" said Saint Peter. "You seem to be seized with the idea."

"Never mind if I am. Think how cold it is today; that lad is wearing two pairs of trousers, and I bet you he will give me one pair if I just tell him I am cold."

"I'll believe that when I see it," Saint Peter replied.

"You shall see at once." He went up to Johnny and greeted him: "Good day, and a good year to you, young man."

"May God make it so, but not so cold."

"It certainly is keen, this wind," said the Good Jesus.

"A bit too keen! Even ploughing I am still shivering a bit, and I am wearing two pairs of trousers at that."

"Imagine then how cold I am with only one pair."

"Only one pair?" cried the lad. "We can't allow that."

Would you believe it? He took off his top pair and insisted that the Good Jesus put them on.

Then the Good Jesus said to him:

"Look, tomorrow they are going to auction the farm and the house that your father lost gambling. You should go to the auction and keep above all the others, no matter how high they may go."

"But how do I pay?" Johnny asked.

"Take this purse. When you want money just turn it inside out, and don't fear; there will be all you need."

Johnny's hair stood on end with amazement when he heard this. He took the purse and put it away, saying:

"A thousand thanks, my friend; God repay your kindness."

"Amen," said the Good Jesus. "And by the way, wouldn't you like to see your father and mother?"

"That would please me more than anything, apart from going to heaven."

"Well, look," said the Good Jesus. "Take this cloth. When you have possession of the farm and the house, spread the cloth out and say to it: 'O Cloth, take me to where my father and mother are.' It will take you there at once. And if you want something to eat say: 'Oh Cloth, bring us such and such dishes', and it will bring them."

Johnny was then even more amazed and astonished. He took the cloth and put it away, and said to the Good Jesus:

"A thousand thousand thanks, my friend; may God repay you."

"Amen," said the Good Jesus, and he went on his way with Saint Peter.

"You see, Peter, what a kind heart that lad has."

"Indeed, he has," Saint Peter replied, "but all the same you have paid him handsomely."

"Surely you must know," the Good Jesus said, " I don't remain idle when I can reward good deeds."

That evening, when Johnny returned from his ploughing, he asked the farmer's leave to be absent the next day, as he had pressing business in the town; the farmer readily agreed. Next day the lad went to where they were auctioning the farm and the house that his father had lost gambling.

There were several men bidding. When they heard Johnny putting his oar in, they were quite taken aback – and even more so as he pushed up the bids. There came a point where, cursing and swearing, they had to give up. Johnny outbid them all easily, and both the properties were knocked down to him.

"Now we shall see if the young fool can pay," they said.

"He may have a bag full of money, but he does not look as if he had. He looks pretty poor."

But they got a big surprise when Johnny brought out his purse and turned it inside out. There was a cascade of gold coins – the brightest and the best-looking that you ever saw.

The people who had held the auction counted the money; there was enough to cover the price of the farm and the house, with a handful of coins left over.

Johnny then owned the farm and the house. And what do you think he did? He spread out the cloth and said: "Cloth, take me to where my father and mother are."

He had hardly said it when – *zoom* – the cloth took flight, and in the time it takes to say one *Ave Maria* they were on a hilltop; a man and a woman were lying there by the roadside, without the will or the strength to move, half dead from starvation.

"Father! Mother!" cried Johnny when he saw them.

"Son!" they said. "We are dead; hunger has finished us. It's all over with us."

"Don't bother to talk." said Johnny. "We must have a bite first."

He spread out the cloth and said: "O Cloth, bring us a dish of saffron rice such as the angels sing of, and then some chicken fricassee that would make a saint break his fast, and also a flagon of wine of the kind that will bowl a man over or bring the dead back to life."

At once there appeared on the cloth a tremendous dish of saffron rice such as the angels might sing of, so good it looked; then a chicken fricassee, and I can't tell you how enticing it was. If saints were not so resolute in fasting, any of them would have broken his fast just to taste that chicken – and so I should think! As for the flagon of wine, words fail me; it was red, bright, and cheerful. It would not have been humanly possible to see it and not take a good mouthful of it.

When the old couple saw all this they began to recover. Both of them, with Johnny, tucked in till there was not a lick of the rice left, nor the chicken; and as for the wine, they went at it to the very last drop.

Meanwhile Johnny told them about the farm and the house. And they all went back there, happy and content. Johnny found himelf a cheerful, pretty, clever girl; they were married and they lived in peace and happiness for years and years. And they are still alive if they are not dead.

And if you don't believe it, go and find out for yourself.

Acorns and Pumpkins, and Saint Peter

WHEN THE GOOD JESUS AND SAINT PETER were walking about the world, they one day passed by an orchard where there was a long row of pumpkin plants with a crop of enormous pumpkins. There were some as big as the baskets used for grape-picking, and that's the truth. Then they went through an oak-wood where the trees were laden with acorns.

Saint Peter had an idea, and he could not help saying it out loud:

"Master," he said, "what about these oak trees, so thick and strong, with such massive trunks, and their tiny acorns, and those pumpkin plants with their feeble thin stalks and such huge fruit weighing more than the plant? Wouldn't it be better if the oak trees bore pumpkins, which are so heavy, and the pumpkin plants had acorns, which are quite light?"

"Do you mean you think it would be better that way round?" said the Good Jesus.

"Of course it would be, Master; a great deal better."

"Very well.," the Good Jesus replied. "It shall be as you want it." At once the pumpkins in the orchard turned into acorns, and all the acorns on the oak trees turned into pumpkins. It was an amazing sight, I can tell you.

Saint Peter, as you may imagine, stood with his mouth open gazing at this tremendous array of pumpkins.

"There's certainly enough of them, Master!" he said in astonishment.

But the Good Jesus, without pausing, walked slowly on, and he got some distance ahead of Saint Peter. When Saint Peter noticed this he hurried to catch up. He had to pass under an oak tree with pumpkins,that were getting ripe; one of them was quite ripe and it said:

"Down we go!"

It came off its stalk and – *crash* – fell on Saint Peter's head just as he was walking beneath it.

"Ow!" cried the poor fellow. At first he thought the whole tree had fallen on him. It was an enormous pumpkin, and if it had been a little bigger it would have smashed his skull; as it was he lost sight of the world for a moment and, got a couple of big lumps on his head.

"Ow!" he said. "Ow! Ow!"

The Good Jesus, pretending to know nothing, turned round and said:

"What's the matter? Has something happened?"

"Too much has happened," said Saint Peter. "A pumpkin has fallen on my head – as if it had nowhere else to fall."

"Do you still think," the Good Jesus asked him, "that it is better for oak trees to bear pumpkins and pumpkin plants to have acorns?"

Saint Peter was thoroughly ashamed. He hung his head and replied:

"I think it was better as it was before – the way you made it."

"Well, another time don't try and be too clever," said the Good Jesus, "and don't stupidly try to alter what has been made."

And all the pumpkins hanging on the oak trees turned back into acorns, and the acorns in the orchard back into pumpkins, and things remained just as the Good Jesus had first made them. And, however you look at it, that is the way things are best.

The Good Jesus and Saint Peter, and Brutus

IN THOSE DAYS when the Good Jesus and Saint Peter were walking about the world, they once stopped at a farmhouse at harvesting time. The farmer thought they were just ordinary men and he offered them a job of reaping.

"Shall we, Peter?" said the Good Jesus.

Saint Peter was making faces at the idea, but seeing the Good Jesus appeared to want to do it, he did not like to refuse. They struck a deal on the largest wheat-field, agreeing to do the job for thirty pounds.

"You can go there now," said the farmer. "The water-girl will bring you your dinner and reeds for tying the sheaves."

"Then we will wait for her there," said the Good Jesus. And he went off towards the wheat-field, with Saint Peter plodding along behind, putting on a miserable face.

They reached the wheat-field, which was a joy to see, very large, with wheat up to your chest and in places taller than a man, with ears a hand-span long and bulging with grain.

"Look, what lovely wheat!" the Good Jesus exclaimed.

"For the farmer," said Saint Peter, "but for us it will be pretty tough."

"No, man, don't be afraid of it. Things are not so frightening if you will only look at them close up."

"No, it will be worse close up than it is from far away," said Saint Peter. "If I didn't have to attack it with a sickle I should not be in the least afraid of it, I assure you."

"Alright," the Good Jesus said. "If you don't mind too much, let's sit down for a while and cool off."

"Mind?" replied Saint Peter. "I shall be very pleased to, and even for two whiles, or three and all."

They sat down and chatted away until mid-day. The water-girl appeared with their dinner and some reeds; they had their dinner and went on with their conversation sitting there in the shade of a walnut tree; wonderfully cool it was, fit for a king.

Saint Peter could not understand why the Good Jesus did not say: "Come on, let's do some reaping." But he was careful not to say a word on the matter. And there they were chatting away, as comfortable as you please.

An hour before sunset the water-girl came again with their supper of salad, and more reeds; she found them still sitting under the walnut tree, with no sign that they had picked up a sickle or touched an ear of wheat. She looked at them wide-eyed with amazement. She very nearly gave them a good talking-to.

"Look," the Good Jesus said to her, "please tell the farmer we will not come to the house tonight. We will sleep under this walnut tree; it will be cooler here than in your hay-loft."

"I will tell him," she replied,and went back to the house, where she said to the farmer: "Fine reapers you have contracted!"

"Have they cut a lot?"

"A lot? Such a lot that they have not touched a single ear. Sitting under the walnut tree I found them when I took their dinner, and still sitting there when I went again with their supper; and there I left them without any sign that they intended to get at the wheat with a sickle."

"Damnation!" said the farmer. "It will be a fine to-do if these men turn out to be good-for-nothings."

The next morning the water-girl went to the field with the men's breakfast and another bunch of reeds; and what do you think? She found them sitting in the shade under the walnut tree. At mid-day she took their dinner, and towards evening their salad supper; and every time she found them in the cool under the walnut tree, without any sign of their having picked up a sickle or touched an ear of wheat.

The girl could bear it no longer, and she was on the point of giving them a really sharp scolding; but so many things came to the tip of her tongue, and she was so indignant, that she did not know where to begin.

When they had finished their salad Saint Peter managed to say: "Master, are we going to reap or are we not going to reap?"

"It's for you to say," the Good Jesus replied. "Are you still so much afraid of this wheat?"

"I shall go on being afraid of it until it is reaped, if it is we who have to reap it; but I am worried about these people finding us all the time sitting under this walnut tree."

"Don't worry about that," said the Good Jesus. "The point is this: for us to start reaping you must be no longer afraid of it. Never mind; it is not worth starting today, as it is so late. Let's wait till tomorrow."

I cannot tell you of the outburst of the water-girl when she told the farmer about the men contracted for the big field. The farmer was beginning to be anxious, and he decided to go down there the next day after dinner; if he found them with no reaping done he would tell them what he thought of them, call them some bad names and kick them out.

The next morning the Good Jesus said to Saint Peter: "Come on, take a good look at this wheat; you have all the morning. After dinner we will get to work, and we must do the job pretty quickly as we have to make up for lost time."

"Well, if we have to get down to it later," said Saint Peter, "it would almost be worth starting now."

"Don't be so impatient. After dinner it is to be."

About eight o'clock the water-girl brought their breakfast and a bunch of reeds, and she found them still in the shade of the walnut tree. The farmer had forbidden her to say anything if she found them idle; otherwise she would have slaughtered them with her tongue, she was so indignant. And I cannot tell you about mid-day, when she brought their dinner and saw them still there. She put down the reeds and the dinner and went off in a fury.

They had their dinner, and afterwards the Good Jesus said:

"Come on, Peter; you can start by putting out these bundles of reeds; undo the ties so they are all ready when the time comes."

"But, Master," said Saint Peter, "don't we have to reap first?"

"You do as I say and don't worry."

Saint Peter obeyed, and there he was distributing bundles of reeds, undoing the ties and spreading the reeds out; and all the time he was saying to himself: "I wonder where this will get us."

What do you think? The Good Jesus took a flint, made fire, and set light to a corner of the wheat-field. There was soon a fierce blaze and a terrible smoke, and the more it burned the fiercer it got. In the time it takes to say three *Pater Nosters* the whole field was alight, with clouds and clouds of smoke.

The farmer, who had heard what the water-girl had to say, was on his way with his mind made up, and when he saw all the smoke and the whole field on fire he left off walking to run, shouting like mad to everybody to come and fight the fire, and calling on the Good Jesus, Holy Mary, and all the Saints to stop the terrible conflagration.

Everybody on the farm and in the neighbourhood made for the fire, running as hard as they could. They got there almost as soon as the farmer himself. Then they all stood there thunder-struck, with their hair standing on end, utterly amazed – and the farmer most of all – because when they reached the field they found no fire and hardly any smoke. The wheat was all reaped, made into sheaves and tied, and so well placed that the stooks made lines in all directions.

The Good Jesus and Saint Peter went up to the farmer, and the Good Jesus said. "This was our agreement with you. Will you accept our reaping as properly done?"

The farmer said *Yes* as well as he could, but he was quite stunned and he started crossing himself at the astonishing event. He went back to the house and fetched the thirty pounds, which he gave them. And they went off leaving everybody amazed and dumbfounded.

As they walked and walked along nightfall caught them near Brutus's inn, so they stopped there for the night. The next morning, to pay the inn-keeper's wife, the Good Jesus brought out the thirty pounds. When the woman saw all that money her eyes nearly jumped out of her head, and the Devil – *whoosh!* – came at once to tempt her to break the Seventh and the Ninth Commandments.

The temptation was so strong that, when the Good Jesus and Saint Peter were leaving, she had the bad manners to ask them which way they were going. They told her, and she went to find her husband.

"Look," she said to him, "there is a nice catch to be had with those two who have just left. When they paid me they brought out a huge great bag of money; and they have told me which way they are going. What you must do is put on a mask, and with your blunderbuss go and hold them up; relieve them of their bag of money and we can live more comfortably."

The stupid Brutus did as his beastly wife said. He masked himself carefully, and with his blunderbuss over his shoulder he trotted off to get in front of the Good Jesus and Saint Peter. He was soon ahead of them; then he jumped out into the road before them, pointed his blunderbuss at their chests and cried:

"Your money or your..."

He could not finish saying it because the Good Jesus made the sign of the cross at him, and he turned into a white donkey, with a good chain round his neck.

"Well I never," said Saint Peter. "Where did this donkey come from? And wasn't there a man who jumped out at us? Or am I seeing double?"

"Never mind," said the Good Jesus. "Take the chain and bring Snowy along; he may do us good service."

"And so I should think!" Saint Peter exclaimed. "Do you suppose he is rideable? It would not be at all inconvenient if we could ride a little."

"Alright," said the Good Jesus, "get on him if you are tired."

Saint Peter mounted the donkey – *Gee-up Snowy* – and whacked him with the chain.

They passed a farm where a new house was being built. "Masters," said the Good Jesus to the stonemasons "would you care to hire this donkey to carry blocks and stones or mortar?"

"Yes, certainly," the master-mason replied, and they agreed on a price of thirty pounds, with the masons keeping the donkey until the building was finished. Saint Peter handed Snowy over to the master-mason and then went off with the Good Jesus to walk about the world.

I can assure you that Snowy had a really hard time of it; he had to bear endless blows and loads of work and hunger; they even grudged him straw and water, and beans or oats he never saw, still less came near any.

They made him carry things in panniers, across his back, and they loaded him so heavily that he came to have no hair on his back because it all went, stuck to the blocks, stones, and baskets of mortar. So much hair went that, as it was white, the house came out white, and it still is. Imagine how poor Snowy's back must have been.

Anyway, when the building work was just finishing, the Good Jesus and Saint Peter came by, and the master-mason said:

"Hey! Have you come to take Snowy?"

"If you have done with him, yes," said the Good Jesus.

"You can take him," the master-mason said. "We can manage for the small jobs still to be done. Wait, I will pay you."

And he gave them thirty pounds. Saint Peter took the donkey by the chain and went off with the Good Jesus.

The Good Jesus led them towards the spot where Brutus had held them up with his blunderbuss. When they got there he made the sign of the cross over Snowy, and Snowy turned back into Brutus, who stood there looking hang-dog and thoroughly ashamed.

"Look, Brutus," said the Good Jesus. "Two years ago just here you waylaid us to take from us thirty pounds that we had, which were not yours. Here is another sum of thirty pounds, which you have earned in these two years working at the farmhouse. This money is yours and you will profit from it."

Brutus took the money and went off home. From that day on he was a proper man, working for himself or for others and making all his family follow the light, beginning with his wife, who certainly needed to do so.

The Mother of God and Pilate's Wife

THEY SAY THAT when the Mother of God heard how the Scribes and Pharisees had brought her son Jesus before Pilate, for him to sign the death sentence, she went straight there.

She got to Pilate's house and was looking about, when at one of the windows she saw a lady, who also noticed her, all distraught as she was. This woman had a kind heart, and she said to the Mother of God:

"Lady, are you in trouble?"

"Indeed I am," replied the Blessed Virgin. "My only son has been arrested and brought here, I am told, for the judge to sentence him to death."

"I saw them bringing in a man," said the lady. "He was about thirty, a good-looking man, the most decent-looking I have ever seen, I thought when I saw him. It's not possible this young man could have committed any crime. I should not be surprised if it had something to do with the envy and hatred of a bad gang."

"It is just as you say, I can assure you," said the Virgin Mary. "And, Lady, you seem to have a kind heart; can you tell me what I should do to speak with the Judge?"

"Look," the lady replied, "I am the judge's wife, and I myself will go and speak for your son and for you."

She went to Pilate and told him that on no account should he condemn the prisoner who had been brought in, because she was sure the man was innocent; that Pilate would regret it if he condemned the man; and that the man's mother was waiting outside to speak for him.

When Pilate heard all this pleading he was more confused than ever; he could not see straight, his head was in a whirl, and he thought he was going mad.

"If I condemn him," he said to himself, "I shall be doing an injustice. If I don't condemn him they will tell Caesar, and I shall lose my job as a judge."

And the fellow was more interested in staying on as judge than in defence of an innocent man; so in the end he said to his wife:

"My dear, I am very sorry, but there is no way out. Tell the man's mother that I have no choice; I must sign the sentence as the Scribes and Pharisees want."

The lady leaned out of the window in tears and said to the Mother of God:

"Dear lady, I bring you bad news. My husband says there is no way out and it is impossible to save your son from death."

Imagine how anguished the Mother of God must have been. Pilate's wife, who had no part in it, was in tears, how must the Blessed Virgin have wept for her only Son.

And so the song goes:

> As Mary went away
> She clapped her hands and cried:
> 'You mothers who have sons,
> Come and help me weep!'

Saint Vincent Ferrer* and the Charcoal-Burner

SAINT VINCENT FERRER was once making for a port to take ship. When he was nearly there, going through a wood, he came on a Charcoal-Burner, who was looking after his kiln.

They greeted each other, and Saint Vincent asked him:

"Do you ever pray to the Good Jesus?"

"Yes, Father, just a bit," said the Charcoal-Burner.

"And what do you say to the Good Jesus?"

"Well," he replied, "a prayer that my mother taught me when I was a small boy."

"Yes; and what is this prayer?"

"I'll tell you. Every morning when I get up, and in the evening when I go to bed, I say: 'O Lord, may I ever offend thee and may I never love thee. May I ever offend thee and may I never love thee'."

"Good God!" exclaimed Saint Vincent when he heard such monstrous words. "Don't say that any more, my friend! Don't say it like that; you have got it the wrong way round. You should say: 'O Lord, may I ever love thee and may I never offend thee'."

"Do you mean I must say it like that from now on?" the Charcoal-Burner asked.

"Yes, my friend, just as I have said it to you." And Saint Vincent made him repeat it after him.

* Dominican friar born in Valencia 1350, died in Vannes, Brittany, 1419; preached extensively in Spain, France, and Italy; visited Mallorca 1413-14; canonized 1455.

"Very well, I will say it like that!" replied the Charcoal-Burner.

Saint Vincent went on his way and was soon at the port; he got on board the ship, and it put out to sea.

The trouble was that the Charcoal-Burner after a little said to himself:

"Let's see now; how was it the good friar said I was to say the prayer? 'O Lord, may I ever... offend... love... offend...' And now I don't remember how that holy man of God said I was to say it. What a mess I have made of it! I had better run after him and get him to tell me again."

No sooner said than done, and off he went as fast as he could to the port. He caught sight of the ship, already well out to sea and making good way.

"Oh well," he said, "I'll run till I catch up with it."

He got to the shore and kept on running. Without taking any notice of the sea he went striding over the water as if it had been flat land; and on he went towards the ship, shouting like mad:

"Hey, sailors! Ship ahoy! Stop a moment! You must stop, for God's sake."

The sailors on board eventually heard him, and when they saw him running towards them on the water they stood with their hair on end. They called Saint Vincent so that he too should see. When Saint Vincent looked out and saw the fellow just reaching the ship, he said:

"What's this, my friend? Are you in trouble?"

"I certainly am," answered the Charcoal-Burner. "I can't remember how you told me to say that prayer."

When Saint Vincent saw the miracle of the Charcoal Burner's faith, which made him able to walk on the water, without sinking in at all, he said:

"Don't worry about it any more, my friend. Say it the way you have always said it. It is quite clear that God is well pleased with it."

"Very well," said the Charcoal-Burner, "I'll go back to my kiln." And he turned round and went racing back till he got to the rocks, and then in a few strides he was back at his kiln.

And he went on saying his prayer the wrong way round, as before, until he died and went to Heaven. May we all meet him there.

Amen.

How the Father Prior forbade Saint Vincent Ferrer to do any Miracles

IT SEEMS THAT SAINT VINCENT was doing miracles right and left, day in day out, and so many people came to the monastery seeking his help that it became unbearable; you could not hear yourself speak. The other brothers went to the Father Prior and said:

"Father Prior, this business of Brother Vincent doing so many miracles cannot go on. The monastery has become worse than a market-place; the crowds allow us no peace; we cannot pray, nor say our Office, nor any blessed thing. It is necessary that Your Paternity regulate the matter."

"Very well," said the Father Prior. "We will forbid Brother Vincent to do any more miracles, and that will settle it."

No sooner said than done. He called Brother Vincent and said to him:

"You have done enough miracles! No more, now, without my permission."

"Very good, Father Prior," Saint Vincent said. "I am the very embodiment of obedience."

Saint Vincent kept his obedience, and to all the people who came asking him to do a miracle for them he replied:

"My children, the Father Prior has forbidden me to do any more miracles."

Some days went by like this until God so arranged it that they had to repair the roof-tiles on the monastery. The builders went up on the roof, and there they were straightening the tiles moved by the wind and replacing those that were broken or cracked.

And, believe it or not, one of the men coming and going across the roof, replacing tiles here and there, stumbled and fell; he rolled down the slope, reached the edge of the roof, and plunged over.

The other builders supposed he would be smashed and dead as soon as he hit the ground, but they saw Saint Vincent at a window and they all cried out:

"Brother Vincent! Do a miracle for God's sake!"

And Saint Vincent said to the falling builder:

"Stop a moment, and I will go and ask the Father Prior's permission."

The builder had almost reached the ground, but he stopped in the air, and Saint Vincent went off to find the Father Prior and ask his permission to do a miracle.

When the Father Prior heard the story he ran to see the builder in the air. He stood with his hair on end, naturally enough, and he exclaimed:

"Brother Vincent, you have already done the miracle. Now that you have gone so far, you may finish it!"

So Saint Vincent told the builder to come down slowly. He did so, and as soon as his feet touched the ground he threw himself on his knees before Saint Vincent, thanking him a thousand times for having saved his life.

Then the Father Prior said to Saint Vincent:

"Brother Vincent, I take back the order that I made forbidding you to do any more miracles. Do as many as the Good Jesus wishes."

And Saint Vincent went on doing miracles without ceasing.

The Soldier of the Marines

THERE WAS ONCE A SOLDIER in the Marines who served the King for forty years as if it were nothing. When he was no longer any good for active service the Officers found they had to give him a large amount of money for so many years' wages – because they had never paid him a penny all that time.

They began reciting lists of the faults he had committed and of the things he had damaged or lost, putting on him the blame for everything that had gone wrong in the barracks during all the forty years he had served. For each of these things they took off a good slice of the money that they ought to have given him.

Need I go on? They sent him off with only four coins and a loaf of bread. You can imagine how he left, light of pocket and purse, and he kept saying:

"Well, well! After serving the King for forty years all I get is four coins and a loaf of bread! I can't believe the King would let me go like this if he knew about it." But he was a really good man, and when he had done turning it over in his head he ended by saying:

"Never mind! Patience! It's the will of God! Let's be good, and God will never fail us!" He had a truly kind heart – kinder than I can say – as you will see from what happened to him.

As he went on his way towards home, he chanced to meet the Good Jesus and Saint Peter, who were walking about the world without letting themselves be known, seeming to be two pilgrims, with ragged clothes and looking thin and starved.

They came up to the Marine and said:

"Can you spare us something, please?"

"You're out of luck!" the Marine exclaimed. "Here I am after forty years' service, and now that I am no good for anything they have packed me off home with four coins and a loaf of bread. I ask you now, whether I am able to give alms to anybody. I should be asking rather than giving"

The Good Jesus and Saint Peter, seeming to take no notice of this rigmarole, again said:

"Can you spare us something, please?"

"Very well," said the Marine. "I see you won't be satisfied until I have given you something; what can I do for you? Here's half the loaf of bread that they gave me at the King's place." No sooner said than done; he gave half the loaf to the Good Jesus and Saint Peter. And because he liked a joke he nicknamed the Good Jesus Tatters, and Saint Peter he called Scrawny.

They then disappeared in another direction. The Marine soon came to an inn where he could have supper and sleep the night under the porch roof. And do you know what he did?

With two of his coins he bought wine, with one of them some olives, and with the fourth some cigarettes. The olives he ate with half of the bread that he had left, then he took a good drink of wine and lay down in a corner under the porch that the inn had in front of it, where the inn-keeper was kind enough to let him sleep free.

In the morning at daybreak the Marine got up, thanked the inn-keeper, and went trudging off towards home. About nine o'clock he saw two men coming towards him, and he exclaimed: "Who can they be – those two tramps?"

As they came nearer and nearer, he recognized them.

"Can you believe it?" he cried. "Here we have Tatters and Scrawny on the dance again!"

With that they were quite close; they came up and said:

"Can you spare us something please?"

"Yes!" the Marine exclaimed. "You think I'm a good touch. Yesterday you got half a loaf of bread out of me, and now you want another taste. Won't you ever be satisfied?"

The Good Jesus and Saint Peter took no notice of this broadside, and again they said, very humbly: "Can you spare us something please, for the love of God?"

What do you think? The Marine's heart was so touched by the humility of the two pilgrims that he exclaimed:

"Very well, we won't argue about it. Here's half of what is left of the bread." He broke the bread in two and gave half to the Good Jesus and Saint Peter, who thanked him very much for his kindness and went on their way. And the Marine went on his way homewards, saying every now and then:

"Well, well! Now I can go with an easy mind and no fear of thieves! Any who tried to rob me now would be thoroughly cheated. What a disappointment it would be for them!"

He walked and walked; after dark he came to an inn, and he asked if they would let him sleep the night free; they said they would, so he ate the last of the bread with a handful of dried figs that the inn-keeper's wife gave him out of kindness, and he lay down in a corner under the porch roof that the inn had in front of it. In the morning, at daybreak he took his leave of the inn-keeper, thanking him for letting him sleep there free, and set off trudging homewards. He was wide-awake and as bright as a spark, for you will never find anything to sharpen a man's wits so much as going about with empty pockets.

Would you believe it? About nine o'clock the Marine again spied two figures some way off, coming nearer and nearer as he walked along. He began to say:

"Can it be those two? I believe it's Tatters and Scrawny again. They will be out of luck this time. They won't squeeze much juice out of me now!"

The two were coming closer and closer, and when the Marine was sure who they were he made a great to-do, crying:

"Well, if it isn't Tatters and Scrawny! You seem to have got a taste for me! But today you've struck unlucky; do you think there's no end to what I can give? Didn't you see, these past two days, that I had next to nothing? But never mind; just to show you, come and feel my pockets. Put your hands in where you like, and I'll be hanged if you find anything on me but my clothes, which are as old as the hills and not worth a bad penny on a good market day."

As he was saying all this, the Marine put his hands in his pockets and turned them inside out. Would you believe it: there fell to the ground three cigarettes. When he saw them he fairly danced for joy, saying:

"Well I never! I had forgotten I had these three old cigarettes; they are left from some that I bought the night before last at an inn. Well now, to show you that what I say I really mean, with all my heart – here are three cigarettes; we'll have one each."

And he gave one to the Good Jesus and one to Saint Peter, and he kept one for himself, saying: "Come on, let's smoke them! We have no bread, but at least we can satisfy ourselves with a bit of smoke. It's better than nothing."

Just as the Marine was going to light up, the Good Jesus blessed the three cigarettes; one of then turned into a loaf of bread, of the largest; another into a cheese, a really big one; and the third into a red sausage, of the fattest.

When the Marine saw this his hair stood on end with amazement; he began crossing himself, not knowing what to do. Then he began to be happy; he danced and jumped about and threw his cap in the air, and kept on saying:

"That's wonderful – marvellous! Hoorah! Hoorah! Well done, Tatters! You're the very Devil! Good old Tatters! Good! Good! Good!"

"It's nothing," said the Good Jesus. "Let's sit down and have a bite."

"Good idea, Tatters! A very good idea!" said the Marine.

And the three sat down there and ate their fill; the one who ate the most was the Marine, who stuffed himself. Then he became dreadfully sleepy, and so too did Saint Peter.

"Master," said Saint Peter, "couldn't we have a little siesta now?"

"Yes, of course," the Good Jesus replied.

Saint Peter and the Marine lay down, and you could soon have heard them snoring their loudest. They had a tremendous sleep.

When they opened their eyes they saw the Good Jesus had gone some way off; then the Marine said to Saint Peter:

"Tell me, Scrawny, why do you call Tatters 'Master'?"

"Because. he is the Master," Saint Peter replied. "It surprises me that you can ask such a question after seeing him perform the feat of turning your three cigarettes into a loaf of bread, a cheese, and a red sausage. And look, there is another thing I should like to say: I don't mind if you call me Scrawny – or Starveling, if you like – but it's not at all right you should call the Master 'Tatters', because he could cover you with clothes, and all your family. And, moreover, politeness costs nothing."

The Marine listened carefully to Saint Peter, and he was thoughtful for a while; then he said: "You are quite right, my friend. Forgive me; I didn't mean any harm by it. The thing is I like a bit of fun, and I joke with everyone I meet. From now on I too will call him Master; and I won't call you Scrawny any more but your own rightful name. And what is it, if I may ask?"

"Peter, at your service," said Saint Peter.

"Well," said the Marine, "I had an idea – if our Master and you would allow it – to go along with you; because, if you don't already know it, I have served the King for forty years, and now they have sent me home empty-handed. I am sure all my people are dead and buried by now; and even if they are alive, imagine what a reception they would give me if I were to turn up penniless and stony broke, just when they should be receiving rather than giving, and are needing someone to bear their burden rather than having to support a useless old man like me. So I think, if you will have me, it would be much better for me to go along with you than to go back to my village."

To this Saint Peter replied: "It must be the Master who shall say if he wants you. If he wants you, I want you. I am not, nor do I wish to be, more than his follower."

With that the Good Jesus came back towards them. The Marine summoned up his courage and approached him, asking if he would have him as a companion. The Good Jesus made the Marine go over his life, and when he had heard it all he said: "You may come with us if you wish, but you must submit to our way of life."

"Yes, of course, and willingly," said the Marine.

And so he went along with Saint Peter, following in the steps of the Good Jesus. They walked and walked, and when it was beginning to get dark they came to some cliffs, which had a lot of small caves in them. The Good Jesus said:

"We could spend the night in these little caves, if you like."

"Good idea! Good idea!" exclaimed Saint Peter and the Marine.

"I suppose," the Good Jesus said, "you are not hungry for supper after the lunch we had with that loaf of bread, that cheese, and that sausage."

"No, I'm not hungry just at the moment," said Saint Peter.

"Nor am I," added the Marine.

"Very well then," the Good Jesus went on. "Let us cross ourselves and say the Rosary."

"That's a good idea," said the Marine. "It will suit me very well, because in all these forty years of scraping my bottom around the barracks, I can tell you, I never had a chance to say any Rosaries or Our Fathers."

"Did the officers forbid you to say any?" the Good Jesus asked.

"No, Master, but life in the barracks does not make for saying Rosaries or Our Fathers. Marines tell other stories."

Well, they told the Rosary and said a good string of *Our Fathers*, and then they lay down, each in a little cave, and they were soon sleeping like logs.

Next morning at daybreak the Good Jesus called Saint Peter and the Marine, and they went on their way. They walked and walked, and about ten o'clock the Good Jesus asked the Marine:

"Do you think, you could do with a little lunch?"

"I have a feeling I could," the Marine answered.

"Do you see that flock of sheep down there?" said the Good Jesus. And there was indeed a flock grazing about half a mile away. "Yes, I see them," said the Marine.

"Well then, go down there and say to the shepherd: 'My Master sends me to ask if you could spare us a lamb to stay our hunger a bit.' If he says you may take whichever lamb you like, choose one, bring it back here, and you shall see how good it will be."

The Marine wasted no words. He set off towards the flock; he went up to the shepherd and said:

"Friend, my Master sends me to ask if you would let us have a lamb to stay our hunger a bit."

"If it's the Master who sends you," said the shepherd, "you may pick for yourself the animal you like best."

So the Marine began feeling the lambs, to see which had the best flesh on it. At length he found a black one that was as round as a barrel and looked very good indeed.

"May I take this one?" he asked.

"Yes, certainly," said the shepherd. "And please commend me well to the Master, and tell him that we and all our goods are always at his service."

"Very many thanks, on his behalf," the Marine replied. And he picked up the black lamb and went back with it to the Good Jesus and Saint Peter who were waiting for him near some farm cottages.

When the Marine reached them he exclaimed: "Master, the shepherd must be a very good friend of yours. When he heard it was you who sent me, he at once told me to pick the lamb that I liked best. And I chose this black one which I can tell you is heavy and should have meat of the very best."

"And you, now; would you know how to cook this animal?" the Good Jesus asked.

"I most certainly would!" the Marine replied. "Don't worry on that score, Master. You can leave it to me. I will make you a meal out of this animal that will have you sucking your fingers afterwards."

"Very well," said the Good Jesus. "You are in charge of cooking the lamb, and meanwhile we will go and beg a little bread from these houses."

"If everybody hereabouts is as much your friend as that shepherd, we shall certainly do well in these parts!"

The Good Jesus and Saint Peter went off towards the farm buildings. The Marine killed the black lamb, skinned it, gutted it, turned out the innards and put them on the hot coals – because of course he had first of all made a fire. If you will believe it, when the innards were cooking they gave off such a good smell that the Marine could not resist having a taste; he found it so good that he went on having tastes until, before he realized it, he had finished off the innards altogether.

"Well, I'll be blowed!" he exclaimed. "And what am I to say when those two come back? What can I tell them about the innards? That somebody stole them? That I have pickled them in salt water? He thought about it for a while, and at length he said to himself: "I know what I will do! I'll say this lamb, being black, did not have any innards. Then I can get out of the muddle like a man."

What do you think? The Marine cooked the lamb wonderfully well but there were no innards. When the Good Jesus and Saint Peter returned with a couple of loaves that had been given to them at the farm houses, they found the lamb just ready, and the three of them went at it for all they were worth. As they were taking their last bites the Good Jesus exclaimed to the Marine:

"You have turned out to be a good cook! You certainly know how to do it to perfection. But I notice you have not given us any innards."

"How could I?" said the Marine. "Don't you know that black lambs don't have any."

"Oh, really?" the Good Jesus replied. "You mean to say that black lambs don't have any innards? That's rather strange, isn't it?" He pretended to believe it, and Saint Peter swallowed it with the best faith in the world. Then the three of them went on their way, blown out like bagpipes; and on they went, trudging along.

And if you will believe it, the Good Jesus and Saint Peter and the Marine walked so far that they came to a great city, and they found it all in a turmoil. There were circles of men and groups of women everywhere, all talking and discussing and hitting themselves on the head; it seemed they were all going mad.

"What can all this be about?" Saint Peter and the Marine kept asking each other. Then they saw some notices on the street corners, which said:

"The King is dying. The doctors have said there is no cure for him; a fire has entered his body and will leave him cooked; and then it will plague the whole City. Any person who has the courage to treat the King, and heals him, shall be loaded with as much money as he wants."

You can imagine how Saint Peter and the Marine exclaimed when they saw these notices.

"Oh, if I were the Master," cried Saint Peter, "I would soon cure this King?"

"So would I!" the Marine chimed in.

"Master, do this miracle!" Saint Peter kept saying. "Do it to please us "

"Yes, do it, Master!" the Marine was adding.

At length the Good Jesus exclaimed:

"Very well, we'll do it, just to keep you quiet."

He went and called at the King's house with his two assistants, and asked to see the Queen. The Queen came and the Good Jesus said to her:

"Would you like us to cure the King? Is that what you would wish?"

"I should say it is!" the Queen cried.

"Very well," said the Good Jesus. "Everybody is to leave the Royal Bedchamber, and the patient is to be left alone there with only us three; we shall shut ourselves in with him. Meanwhile, have three bundles of firewood and three panniers of straw brought in to us."

The Queen at once gave orders for everything to be done just as required by the new foreign doctor who had appeared. Neither the Queen nor anybody in the City knew it was the Good Jesus. That was the last thing they would have thought.

If the Queen had not been worried to her wits' end she would hardly have listened to the new doctor who gave such seemingly crazy orders; but the poor woman was distraught, and she would have seized hold of a red-hot iron to save the King's life. She ordered everybody out of the Royal Bedchamber, leaving only the King and the three strangers, with the three bundles of firewood and the panniers of straw.

Once they were locked in there with all this stuff, they saw that the King was not conscious and did not know which world he belonged in.

And what do you think the Good Jesus did? Well, he set fire to the three panniers of straw, which of course burned fiercely, and then he threw on the three bundles of firewood, which caught and burned like pitch. And – would you believe it? – when all that firewood was well burnt and was all hot coals, the Good Jesus took the King from his bed and without ceremony threw him on the fire. He soon began to sizzle, then he caught alight, and soon he was all embers like the firewood; and after a while all was ashes.

And what do you think the Good Jesus did then? He blessed the ashes, and at once the King came out of them, fit and well. He fell on his knees before the Good Jesus, saying:

"It is you who have saved me! Yours is the reward!" Then the Good Jesus said to Saint Peter and the Marine:

"Open the doors wide."

They opened up, and the Queen and all the court saw the King kneeling before the Good Jesus, and they saw he was fit and well, as if he had never been ill.

The Good Jesus raised the King, who then embraced the Queen, and the whole court hugged him, and everyone was in floods of tears with sheer joy.

"But who is this new doctor?" they were all asking. "Who is he? Where did he come from? He is no earthly doctor; he must be a doctor from Heaven."

The King took the Good Jesus aside from the people and said to him:

"Promises are promises, and a King cannot belie his own word. The edict said that whoever should heal me would be loaded with as much money as he wanted. You have healed me, so let's go to the Treasury and you shall take all you want."

The Good Jesus did not want to go, but the King was so insistent that there was no way out of it. In the Treasury they saw seven piles of coins of the yellowest gold, and each pile was of thirty or forty bushels.

Imagine how Saint Peter and the Marine goggled at this amazing amount of gold!

"Master, take plenty now you are here," said the Marine very softly.

"Let him be," said Saint Peter. "He knows what he is doing. He is grown up and does not need to be led by the hand."

"That's true," the Marine replied; "but now he is here he should load up. And if he does not want any money for himself he can give it to us. We could use it, I can tell you!"

And there the Good Jesus stood, not budging, refusing to take anything, with the King determined that he should take a good load. At length the Good Jesus stretched out his hand to one of those seven piles and took four gold coins. The King begged him, but could not make him take any more.

Then the Good Jesus took his leave of the King, and with Saint Peter and the Marine set off for another place. When they were out of the town the Good Jesus said:

"Look, I think we should share out the money we have been given. Come, the division is quite easy." he put the four gold coins on a stone and said: "There! Four coins, four shares – one each."

"Master," said the Marine, "I think you've made a mistake."

"How do you mean?"

"You have set out four shares, but we are only three," said the Marine.

"No, my friend," the Good Jesus replied. "The shares are right: one for me, one for Peter, one for you, and one for the fellow who ate the innards of the black lamb."

"It was me" cried the Marine, carried away by greed at the idea of having two gold coins.

"There you are, then," said the Good Jesus. "You get two shares. And didn't you tell us the black lamb had no innards because it was black?"

The Marine did not reply, from shame. He took the two gold coins and, with the excuse that he was homesick for his people and thought of going back to his village, he left the Good Jesus and Saint Peter and went his own way with the two gold coins, thinking they would be enough for him to live in revelry for the rest of his days.

He stopped at a city that he came to, where he began to live like a lord, roistering and playing; but almost before he realized it the two gold coins had flown – because, you know, money is flighty; if you are not very careful with it, if you do not lead it by the nose, if you do not watch it closely, it will suddenly disappear – and good-bye!

If you will believe it, when the Marine was wondering what to do, having finished even the small change, he heard of an edict saying the King's daughter was so ill that the doctors could find no cure for her, and that anyone who might heal her would be loaded with money, as much as he wanted.

"I'm saved!" cried the Marine. "I'll go straight away, and I'll do the same with her as the Master did with that King."

No sooner said than done, and he set off to see the King whose daughter was so ill. He found her breathing her last, and he offered to have her fit and well in less than an hour.

"Is that really true?" said the King when he heard it.

"It's perfectly true! It's the surest thing in the world."

"Very well then," the King replied. "Tell us what you need to carry out this cure."

"What I need," said the Marine, "is that everybody leave the Bedchamber, except the patient, and that you send in three panniers of straw and three bundles of firewood."

This struck people as very strange, but the King made them all leave the Bedchamber, except his daughter, and he ordered three panniers of straw and three bundles of firewood to be taken in.

The Marine went alone into the Bedchamber, locked the door with the key, and then set light to the straw, with the firewood on top. He soon had a tremendous blaze. When it was all hot coals he took up the King's daughter, who did not know which world she belonged in and was unconscious, and threw her on the pile of hot coals. She caught fire all over – and so I should think! – and she was soon burned, quite burnt up, and there was nothing left of her but a heap of ashes.

And what do you think the Marine did then? The same as the Good Jesus had done; he began blessing the heap of ashes, to make the King's daughter rise up fit and well. But what a hope! He went on blessing away, but the heap of ashes gave no sign of anything, and the King's daughter certainly did not appear.

By this time the hour had passed; the King had been waiting, watch in hand, for the time to be up, so then he went to the door of his daughter's bedroom and went *Knock-knock!*

"Who is it?" called the Marine inside.

"It's me," said the King. "It is now an hour that you have been shut in there. How is my daughter? Have you cured her, or what?"

"Wait a moment longer, my lord King, for God's sake!" cried the Marine.

The King waited, but he began to have nasty thoughts that the new doctor would no more heal his daughter than the Man in the Moon.

And there was the Marine still blessing the heap of ashes; but the heap of ashes did nothing, just as if it had never been blessed at all. The Marine came over hot and cold; he began to tremble all over; his teeth chattered and chattered violently.

"It's all over with me!" the poor fellow cried. "And I deserve it, and worse, for being a beast and an ass! Who ever made me a doctor or a healer that I should come here to cure the King's daughter? I am a fool seven times over for wanting to be as much as the Master! And I shall pay for it dearly, because the King will get impatient and he will knock down the door; and when he sees this mess-up of his daughter burned to ashes what will he do to me? I am done for, finished, as good as dead..."

And he went on like this, saying the same sort of thing, until he had the idea of calling on the Master, who was so good and so powerful, and whom he had been beastly enough to leave.

"Oh, Master!" he began. "I see all too well I have been horrible to you, and I am not worthy that you should hear me; but you are so good – have pity on me! Come, for the love of God, and pull me out of the mud! I repent with all my heart that I ever left you and I promise never to leave you again but to follow you always, whatever may happen. Come, Master, for if you don't come it is all up with me. The King will sentence me to death, without appeal – and I well deserve it... But come, Master, for the love of God!"

What do you think? The Good Jesus took pity on the Marine, seeing him so penitent and calling with such devotion. He suddenly appeared, with Saint Peter, at the King's house.

"My Lord King," he said, "please let me into your daughter's bedchamber if you want to see her fit and well immediately."

The King said *Yes*, and so I should think! The Good Jesus went and knocked on the door and said:

"It is me."

The Marine knew him and opened the door to him. The Good Jesus blessed the heap of ashes, and at once the King's daughter rose up, fit and well. She hugged her father and mother, and everybody wept for happiness, and there was no stopping them.

The King wanted to give loads of money to the people who had healed his daughter, but the Good Jesus would not take anything; neither would the Marine, who said:

"I won't have anything to do with money! I want only my Master. It is enough for me to have him, and I want nothing else – not even the thought of it."

And the Marine went away with the Good Jesus and Saint Peter, and never more left them.

Let us do the same, because there is no other way on earth; we should go with the Good Jesus if we want to end our lives in peace and not fall into the clutches of the Devil, from whom God preserve us all.

Amen.

Veronica and Gamus her Husband

VERONICA was a very devout woman. She heard the great noise of the people who were taking the Good Jesus, bearing his cross, along the road to Calvary; and she came out of her house to see what was happening.

She saw the Good Jesus in the middle of that horde of man-eating wolves, bowed under the weight of the cross, a crown of thorns on his head, a halter round his neck, and his most holy face all bruised and covered with spittle, and running with sweat. How could such a sight not rend her heart? How could she fail to pity him, with all her soul?

What do you think she did? She summoned up her courage; she took off the kerchief that she was wearing round her head, and she folded it into three; then, forcing her way through the crowd, she came up to the Good Jesus and with her kerchief she wiped the sweat from his face as best she could. Then, fearing those foul-minded torturers might do her some mischief, she dashed back to her house as fast as she could.

She looked at her kerchief – and what a shock she had! On each of the three folds was imprinted the face of the Good Jesus, as well traced, as if the world's greatest painter had put his utmost into painting it.

Veronica's husband Gamus was a real hot-head; she had seen him following in the crowd, along with many others of the same kind, shouting and making a noise like everybody else; and she thought:

"If he saw me and didn't like what I did, he will make a terrible row about it: and it will be even worse if he sees these three faces painted here. What's more, they could get us into trouble if the Scribes and Pharisees came to know about it."

So what did she do? She got a bowl of water and began washing the kerchief to see if the three faces would come out, but the more she rubbed the stronger and brighter they became. Then she heard her husband coming in, shouting and making a noise; not to be caught red-handed, she emptied the bowl in a corner of the yard.

Would you believe it? As soon as the water touched the earth there sprang up from that very spot a large vine bearing three ripe grapes as big as chestnuts, just asking to be eaten. Veronica, as you may imagine, stood rooted to the ground; she could not make it out at all. Her husband appeared, shouting to know what she had done to the man who was being taken to be crucified on Calvary.

The poor woman, all trembling, told him everything that had happened; when Gamus saw the three faces on her kerchief, and the vine with its three ripe grapes so out of season, he turned pale and said:

"God must be in this; we must take it seriously." He thought for a moment and then he said to Veronica: "Look, not a word about this to anybody! If you say one word I'll flay you. Hide the kerchief carefully, and don't leave the house until I come back."

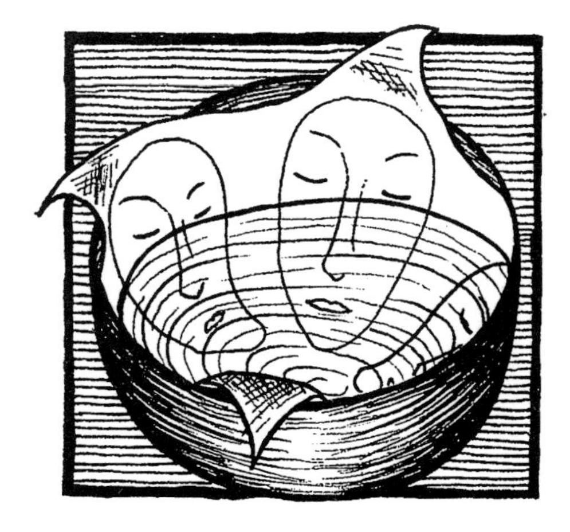

And what did he do? He picked the three grapes and went off towards the crowd surrounding the Good Jesus. He soon caught up with them and began shouting and waving his arms.

"Let me through! Let me through! I want to give him one that he well deserves!"

The people thought he wanted to strike the Good Jesus or spit in his face, and of course they made way. Gamus went right up to the Good Jesus and, pretending to pull his beard, secretly put one of the grapes into his mouth, which refreshed him wonderfully.

They went on towards Calvary, and after a little Gamus began making the same row, shouting like a madman:

"Let me through! Let me through! I want to let him have it properly!"

They made way for him, to see what he would do. He went up to the Good Jesus as if to take hold of his beard to pull it, and secretly put another grape into his mouth, which refreshed him beyond measure.

They went on a little farther, and Gamus began shouting:

"Let me through! This time I will pull his beard right out – what there is left of it!"

They made way for him; he went up close to the Good Jesus and, pretending to seize his beard, put the last grape into his mouth.

Then the Good Jesus said, as the song has it:

> For this great kindness, Gamus,
> That you have done for me
> Three times shall your name be heard
> Whenever Mass is said.*

Gamus, in sheer terror, took to his heels and sped off home like a rocket, and it was some time before he dared show his face outside, in case the Scribes and the Pharisees should play some dirty trick on him.

*Mossèn Alcover suggests in a footnote that the origin of this may be found in the preliminary words of the Preface: *Gratias agamus Domino Deo Nostro*; and in the expressions of the Gloria: *Glorificamus te* and *Gratias agimus tibi*.

The Rosemarian Flower

THERE WAS ONCE A KING who had three sons. When they were still small they used to play in the garden, where they had captive a large eagle, tied by one leg with a cord to the trunk of an orange tree; it was there for the boys to play with.

The two elder boys used to poke the eagle with canes and sticks, and from time to time they would suffer a good peck or a scratch from the bird's talons, which would draw blood. The third boy, Bernard, was quite different; he made friends with the eagle and used to go and caress it and take it good things to eat. He could not bear his brothers when he saw them tormenting the bird as they did.

"This cannot go on," he said one day. So at night, when he saw everybody was asleep, he went into the garden and said to the eagle:

"I have come to untie you, so my brothers shall not be able to torment you any more."

He untied the eagle, who was deeply grateful and said:

"May God repay you for what you have done for me! But I too would like to repay you. Look; pull out the longest feather in my right wing; with the hollow quill make a whistle, and don't lose it. If you ever find yourself in difficulty or in trouble, blow the whistle and I will come and help you."

Bernard did as he was told; the eagle gave three jumps to take flight, spread his wings, and was up and away, to be seen no more.

The next day the King's other sons were in tears the whole time, kicking and throwing themselves on the ground because the eagle had escaped, they did not know how.

Some time later a war began, and the King had to fight; he had to do his utmost to win. He was a very brave man, afraid of nothing and always wanting to be in the lead. So he came back with a good many wounds.

The doctors did their best to cure him, and all went well except for one large wound in his leg, which did not heal; the more they treated it the worse it got.

At length the doctors said: "Unless the Rosemarian Flower can be applied to this wound, it will never heal."

"And where is this flower to be found?" the King asked.

"That is something we don't know," they replied. "We only know it is a flower that cures everything – if our books are telling the truth."

The King then summoned his three sons and said:

"My sons, you see how it is. The doctors say that unless the Rosemarian Flower can be applied to this wound of mine there is no curing it. Nobody knows this flower; so it is up to you boys to go searching for it until you find it. Whichever of you brings it shall inherit the Crown when I die."

Each of the three brothers took a large bag of money and a horse, and they set off. They came to a meeting of three roads, and they said:

"Let us each take a road; and a year and a day from now we will meet again here."

They agreed on that; each one took his road and went off searching and searching for the Rosemarian Flower, asking everybody about it; but nobody was able to tell them anything.

They travelled over one land after another; weeks and months went by, and they knew no more today than they did yesterday; nowhere could they find any clue to the source of this blessed flower.

They were in the twelfth month of their search when Bernard at length remembered what the eagle had said to him: that if he found himself in difficulty he was to blow the whistle he had made from the quill of the eagle's wing-feather.

He blew the whistle, and at once the eagle appeared.

"What do you want, Bernard?"

"What don't I want! My father has a wound in his leg which will not heal unless the Rosemarian Flower can be applied to it; and he has sent me and my two brothers to search for this flower. The one who brings it back will inherit the Crown. For eleven months I have been searching everywhere, and I have not been able to find the flower. Perhaps you know and can tell me where it is to be found."

They were on the shore; out to sea in the distance there was an enormous rock, four or five belfries high, in the shape of a beak – sheer, misty, whitish. It looked like the main-mast of a huge sunken ship.

"Do you see that rock?" said the eagle.

"Yes," Bernard replied.

"Well, at the top of it there grows a kind of rosemary that does not grow anywhere else, and that particular kind bears the Rosemarian Flower that you are looking for."

Bernard was altogether discouraged and said:

"But how is it possible to get there? There is no boat here, and even if there were one, who is able to climb that rock and reach the top?"

"Easy, my friend! Don't worry. We shall soon be there. Get on my back – and hold on tight, because if you were to fall off we should never see you again; but don't be afraid."

So Bernard mounted the eagle and held on tight.

"Are you ready?"

"Yes, I am ready."

The eagle gave a jump, and up they went, and up and up towards the rock. The eagle kept going until they were on the very summit.

There was barely space enough for the eagle and Bernard; he was holding the eagle tight and trembling like an aspen leaf. He was afraid to let go lest he should become dizzy or his foot should slip; he would have plunged down bouncing from crag to crag until he ended, broken to bits, in a mighty dive into the sea, which was roaring away down there, rough and angry. The waves were so violent that each breaker made the rock shake.

"Oh, Blessed Mary! Oh, my Good Jesus'" Bernard cried in tears. "What a place you have brought me to! I shall never live through this! It is all up with me!"

"Rubbish, man!" said the eagle, to give him courage. "Don't be afraid! Don't be cowardly! It is not as bad as all that!"

Just by Bernard's feet there was a crevice, which went deep down.

"Look down into this crevice," said the eagle, "and tell me what you see."

Bernard looked in, and after a while he said:

"Oh, what a lovely thing! What a pretty thing I see! A flower – the most beautiful flower I have ever seen! And what a delightful scent it is giving off! Even right down there I can smell it."

"Well, that is the Rosemarian Flower!" said the eagle. "Let us see if you can get into this crevice and reach it."

Bernard worked his way head first into the crevice, using his hands to advance; he went so far into it that he could no longer be seen; but the crevice became narrower as it went down, and there came a point where the boy could go no farther. He was about a hand's breadth short of the Rosemarian Flower.

In vain he stretched and wriggled; the blessed flower was still a hand's breadth away.

"I cannot get it," he said at length. "It is a hand's breadth beyond my reach."

"Then come out," said the eagle.

Bernard came out; then the eagle held out a leg and amazed him by saying:

"Look, cut off my leg near the thigh; crawl back with it into the crevice where you have just been, and with the leg you will be able to reach the flower; the talons will seize it by the stem. When you have hold of it like this, pull, and it will be yours."

"Would you have me cut off your leg?" Bernard exclaimed. "That I will never do – not for anything in the world. Me, cripple you for life? Never!"

"Do as I say, Bernard; obedience shows good breeding. I am telling you what to do, and you need not worry about me. And don't be anxious about my leg; when we have the Rosemarian Flower it will be restored just as it is now."

The eagle insisted so much that at length Bernard drew out a knife that he carried, took hold of the eagle's leg and cut it off near the thigh; then he went back into the crevice with the leg, and down he went. When he again reached the point that was as far as he could go, he fully stretched out his hand holding the eagle's leg. This time he was not short of reaching the flower; he was touching it. The eagle's talons at once grasped it by the stem, Bernard gave a tug, and came back out of the crevice with the flower.

He was soon outside with the flower in his hands. How lovely and pretty he found it! With what delight he looked at it and smelled it! He devoured it with his eyes and could not take it away from his nose. What a wonderful flower! It was a cluster of three small sky-blue flowers, the most noble sight, with three groups of leaves, finely shaped, strongly made, bright and fresh, and all dusted with a fine, very fine, powder like frost.

"Pull off one of those three flowers," said the eagle; "rub it on the cut and put my cut-off leg against it."

Bernard did this, and as soon as the leg touched the cut it joined up with the thigh and there was no trace of its ever having been severed.

Bernard's hair stood on end with amazement.

"You see?" said the eagle. "There was no need to worry about my leg. Now, don't be afraid; if you do as I say, you will be alright. You must separate these two remaining flowers and hide them both away, well hidden; and never show or give more than one. And look: be careful not to make use of them, because once they have been used they lose their power."

"I only need them to cure my father's leg."

"We don't know that you may not need them for other things as well. Never mind; now you can get on my back again and we will be off, so you will not be late."

Bernard separated the two flowers, hid them away carefully, and mounted the eagle, who then gave a jump, spread his great wings, and carried Bernard back to the land. There the eagle left him and flew up and away.

Bernard fetched his horse, which was under the pine-trees where he had tied it, and he made for the cross-roads as quickly as he could.

He arrived there an hour before dawn on the day that completed the year-and-a-day when the three brothers had agreed to meet. There was nobody there.

About mid-day the eldest brother arrived.

"Bernard!" he said when he saw him. "So you are here already and you have beaten us both. And I come empty-handed. In vain have I travelled everywhere and asked everybody, and I am nearly dead with searching and asking. I have not found this beast of a flower, nor any clue to it. And how have you fared, Bernard?"

"I have found it, thanks be to God, and I have it," the lad replied.

"What? And you have it? Let me see it"

"Here it is," said Bernard, and he brought out one of the two flowers.

"Oh, how pretty it is! Oh, I say!" cried the eldest brother with his eyes starting out of his head.

At that moment envy possessed him and began slyly speaking poison into his ear: "You are finished! You can see the Crown a long way off! You can see it, but will you ever touch it? You are more likely to be struck by lightning. You can forget about being the eldest son. The world is upside-down now; the youngest will rule and the eldest can go to the Devil, if the Devil will have him!"

This fear so obsessed the eldest brother, and he was so anxious to escape from it as quickly as possible, that he seized Bernard and took the flower from him; then he killed him and buried him in a sand-quarry that there was near-by.

In the evening the second brother turned up.

"You have not found it, have you?" the eldest said from a little distance.

"No," he replied.

"I have got it, and I should have it, being the eldest."

"And what about Bernard?"

"To Hell with him! Let's go, and he can catch us up if he wants to. We don't have to drop dead waiting for him here. He should have been on time, as we were!"

They went home; when they arrived the eldest brother presented the Rosemarian Flower, and as soon as it was applied to the King's leg the wound dried up and closed, leaving only the stitches to be seen.

The King was very pleased, and said to his eldest son:

"You shall inherit the Crown when I die."

"What happened to Bernard?" people asked the brothers.

The second brother said they had no news of him; he had not turned up at the cross-roads on the day they had agreed.

Then the eldest replied, as if his mouth were full of peas:

"Don't speak of him. he did not appear; he abandoned us, so we could very well abandon him. Anyway, who made me my brother's keeper?"

This scoundrel was quite sure his brother was dead and would never come out from under the sand. But Bernard had long, long, hair; and his brother, when burying him, unknowingly left one hair showing a little above the surface of the sand.

What do you think? That hair began to get thicker and thicker, and it became a cane-plant with good long joints and bright green leaves, very shiny and pointed; and as the wind played among them they made a whistling sound, very sweet and gentle. It spoke straight to your heart.

One day a shepherd boy came by and saw the cane.

"Well!" he exclaimed. "Here is a cane growing all by itself! What a beauty! And what long joints it has! And here am I badly wanting a flute; this cane is just what I need."

He cut the cane down and made a flute from it; then he tried it for its sound, and it was very good. So off the lad went blowing for all he was worth, with the flute sounding and sounding away as if it would split with so much playing.

If you will believe it, the flute as it sounded began speaking:

O shepherd, good shepherd!
You play me and do me no hurt.
In sand was I buried
For the Rosemarian Flower.

The shepherd boy was amazed, astonished. He tried playing the flute again, and he tried it ten, twenty, a hundred times; and every time he played it the flute said:

O shepherd, good shepherd!
You play me and do me no hurt.
In sand was I buried
For the Rosemarian Flower.

This shepherd one day went past the King's house, playing away on his flute. The King was looking out of a window, and he noticed that the shepherd's flute, as well as playing a tune, was speaking:

O shepherd, good shepherd!
You play me and do me no hurt.
In sand was I buried
For the Rosemarian Flower.

This struck the King as very strange, so he called the shepherd and said:

"What is this? How comes it this flute speaks?"

"I cannot tell you," the boy replied. "I just blow it and this voice comes out of it."

"Let me see if the same thing happens when I blow it."

The King put the flute to his mouth and began to play it. He played away and the flute kept saying:

O Father, my father!
You play me and do me no hurt.
In sand was I buried
For the Rosemarian Flower.

Then the King called the Queen and said: "Come, you play this flute."

What for?"

"Play it, I say, and don't argue."

The Queen took the flute and she had hardly played the first notes on it when it began saying:

O Mother, my mother
You play me and do me no hurt.
In sand was I buried
For the Rosemarian Flower.

What the devil can be the meaning of this?" said the King, quite astonished. "Who has ever heard of a flute speaking?" A terrible idea came into the King's head and he called his two sons. "Play this flute!" he ordered them. The elder was not willing. The second son did not argue; he put the flute to his mouth and played it. The flute said:

O brother, good brother!
You play me and do me no hurt.
In sand was 1 buried
For the Rosemarian Flower.

"Now you must play it," the King said to his eldest son.

"I am not in the mood," he replied with bad grace.

"Then you had better get into it."

"Put the idea out of your head; I will not play it."

Then the King became really angry and said:

"You shall play it or go to the Devil. Play it now, at once."

The scoundrel had no choice but to put the flute to his lips. As soon as he blew into it the flute said:

O brother, bad brother!
You play me and you do me hurt.
In sand you buried me
For the Rosemarian Flower.

The King wasted no words; he went with the whole Court and the shepherd boy to the sand-quarry where the cane had been growing. They dug down and they found Bernard under the sand, alive and well.

He had shown his brother only one of the flowers, and only that one had been taken from him; he still had the other flower, and so long as he had it on him no evil could kill him. Even if he had remained under the sand for a thousand years he would still have been alive at the end of that time.

He recounted everything that had happened to him, and he begged his father, for the love of God and of the Blessed Virgin, not to put his brother to death. His father agreed to lock up the culprit in the dungeon of a castle for the rest of his life. And then and there his father gave the Crown to Bernard, who became one of the best Kings there have ever been.

The tale is finished; and if we do not see each other again here, may we all meet in Glory. Amen.

The Well of the Moon

THERE WAS ONCE a King who had three daughters; the eldest was called Anne, the second Mary, and the youngest Catherine. They suffered from a certain weakness that troubles nearly all women; they wanted to be better-looking than they actually were. All three were pretty enough in the face and handsome in all parts of the body; but they wanted to be even more so.

Searching and searching around for some way of becoming more handsome, they one day met a fairy and at once surrounded her asking what they should do to become more beautiful.

The fairy looked at them closely.

"Are you not the King's daughters?" she said.

"Yes, we are."

"Alright," said the fairy; "go to The Well of the Moon, pull up a bucket of water, pour the water all over yourselves from head to foot, and you will see what a lot of good it does you."

So the three girls, as if their shoes were on fire, went straight off to The Well of the Moon; they pulled up a bucket of water and poured it over themselves. But instead of becoming more beautiful they turned into three stones.

The fairy had followed in their footsteps and arrived soon after them at The Well of the Moon; she picked up the three stones and threw them into the well. Then she fled like a flash of lightning.

She had a grudge against the King because he showed great ill-will towards fairies; he was in fear that they might do some harm to him or his family.

And so it happened, poor man. You can imagine how worried he was when his three daughters failed to appear. A day passed, and two days, and three; and a week passed, and another week, and a month; and still the King's daughters did not appear.

The King and the Queen were in despair, naturally enough; they tore their hair; they hit their heads on the walls; they thought they were going mad.

At length the King issued edicts saying that any single man who should find the three princesses could marry one of them and would be heir to the Crown.

I cannot tell you how many young bachelors got busy and went off searching for the King's famous daughters, hoping to marry the prettiest and become king. It is not surprising that so many went off full of spirit and furiously eager. Indeed, all the young men in the kingdom went searching here and searching there for the King's three daughters, but could not find them – not even a trace nor a clue.

Among those in the search there were three brothers belonging to one of the poorest families; one was called Peter, the second Paul, and the youngest Bernard.

Peter was the first to raise his head, and he said to his father:

"Father, I am thinking of going to search for the three daughters of the King. Imagine what luck for us if I should find them; I could marry one of them, and when the King died I should be King."

"Quite true," said his father, "but is it certain you will find them?"

"Well, certain, not quite," said Peter, "but it could be. Anyway, if I don't find them I shall have lost no more than my footsteps."

"Alright," said his father; "for my part you may go and satisfy your urge, and may God help you to find these three blessed daughters of the King!"

"Amen," said Peter, and away he went.

Walking and walking along, first in one direction and then in another, because he did not know which way to go, he came on an old woman shuffling along, bent double, with her face nearly touching the ground.

When she saw Peter she came up to him and said:

"Oh, young man, spare me some little thing, for the love of God!"

"This is no time for little things or big things," said Peter. "How can I give you anything? I am not for giving but rather for receiving!"

"And have you no compassion for a poor old woman?" she said. "I don't think you will fare very well."

The old woman went on her way, and Peter too, but he had no luck; and although he tramped to the east, to the west, to the north, and to the south, he could find no trace of any of the King's daughters, nor even word of them.

After some time Paul made the same kind of noise to his father.

"Father, do you know what I have been thinking?"

"Who is able," said his father, "to know other people's thoughts?"

"Well," Paul said, "I have thought of going to see if I can find the King's three daughters who are lost. There is a big prize for whoever finds them."

"Do you know what will happen to you?" his father said. "It will be like Peter who went in search of them, and must have found them about as much as the Man in the Moon."

"Alright," Paul replied, "but if I don't find them, what have I lost besides my footsteps?"

"That's true," said his father.

"Well, then," Paul went on, "if you don't mind too much, I will go; and if I don't succeed, too bad!"

"Alright! Go along then!"

And Paul went off to search the world, to see if he could find any news or word of the King's lost daughters, who had disappeared without trace.

Walking and walking about, to the east, to the west, to the north, to the south, and asking, asking everywhere about those three girls, he could not find anybody who had seen them or knew anything about them.

Would you believe it? One day Paul came on the same old woman shuffling along, bent double, with her face nearly touching the ground. And what do you think? She stood in front of Paul saying:

"Oh, young man, spare me some little thing, for the love of God!"

"Is this the time for little things, or big things?" said Paul. "I am more for receiving than for giving! Perhaps you will do better with somebody else."

And he left the old woman standing there. She looked at him for a while and said:

"I shall be surprised if you have much success."

The old woman was right; Paul nearly dropped dead searching for the King's daughters, but nowhere could he find them, or even news of them.

Then Bernard was stung by the same fly as were Peter and Paul, so he faced his father and said:

"Father, do you know the idea that I have had?"

"To search for the King's daughters, like your two brothers?"

"You have guessed it!" said the lad. "I have the courage to go and find those famous daughters of the King."

"Peter and Paul had courage too," said his father, "and you see what has happened to them."

"You are quite right," Bernard replied, "but what can I say? I believe I shall have better luck than they did. So, if you don't forbid me, I shall go."

"No, my boy," said his father; "I will not deprive you of that pleasure. As I have allowed your brothers to go, I may as well let you go too. God give you more success, my son, than the others have had!"

"Amen!" said Bernard, and off he went.

Walking and walking along, first in one direction and then in another, searching and searching for the King's daughters, he one day came on that same old woman shuffling along, bent double, with her face nearly touching the ground.

When she saw Bernard she went up to him and said:

"Oh, young man, spare me some little thing, for the love of God!"

"For the love of God," said Bernard, "one cannot refuse anything. I can give you only a little, because I am penniless, but we can share what I have."

He had a loaf of bread, a red sausage, and three shillings in his purse; he gave the old woman half the loaf, half the sausage, and one of the shillings. He insisted on tossing for the odd shilling with the old woman; they tossed and it fell to him.

"Oh, young man," the old woman said, "you don't know how much good you have done yourself with what you have given me out of your poverty. You look to me as if you were searching for the King's three daughters who got lost and cannot be found."

"You are quite right, mother," Bernard replied. "How did you know?"

"Ah!" she said. "If I were to tell you that, you would know as much as I do."

"And you, now," said Bernard; "can you tell me where the King's daughters are?"

"I certainly can!"

"Oh, what a great favour you would be doing if you were to tell me!" Bernard exclaimed.

"For the kind heart you have shown towards me, I will tell you. The three daughters of the King were sent by a fairy to douse themselves with water from The Well of the Moon, to become more beautiful; but instead they turned into three stones, which that same fairy then threw into the well. Inside the well is a great cave with no water in it, and the three stones are in there. They are guarded by a serpent, a lion, and a malignant devil; these creatures will devour anybody who approaches them, unless he can throw in their faces a jet of water from the seven wells that surround The Well of the Moon at a distance of about an hour's walk. What is good is that the serpent is coiled up like a length of rope on top of the stone that it guards, and never moves so long as nobody approaches it. And the lion is the same; it lies on the stone that it guards and it never moves so long as nobody approaches. And the devil does much the same; he squats on the stone with his tail wound round his body and never moves unless somebody approaches.

"Now what you have to do is to get a flask and fill it with water from the seven wells that I have told you about; then you bring the flask, carefully hidden, and you go down into The Well of the Moon. When you are there you throw a jet of water at the serpent, which will whistle and then explode with a bang; at that the stone will turn into the King's eldest daughter Anne. Then you throw another jet of water at the lion, which will give a roar and explode with a bang; and at that the stone will turn into the King's second daughter Mary. Then you throw another jet of water at the malignant devil, who will give a squawk and a bang and will start dancing about on the stone. You must at once go for the devil's left ear with your teeth and bite off half of it; you must carefully put away the piece of ear in your pocket. The devil will fall backwards crying: 'Curses on the one who gave you that advice!'

"At the same time the stone will turn into the King's daughter Catherine. The devil will ask you to give him back the piece of his ear; but you must take care not to do so until he gets you all out of The Well of the Moon and takes you to the King's house."

Imagine how wide open were Bernard's eyes when he heard all this rigmarole from the old woman. He knelt before her and kissed her hands, but she suddenly disappeared into thin air.

As you may imagine, Bernard at once set off for The Well of the Moon, which the old woman had said was among some very rugged mountains, in the middle of a deep valley. The well had no posts, nor roller, nor rope, to draw water because that wicked fairy who threw the King's daughters into the well also threw in the bucket, the rope, the roller, and the posts; she left only the well-head because it was built of stones too big and heavy for her to move.

Bernard listened in case he might hear some noise or voices of people inside the well, but he heard nothing – nothing at all. He thought it must be The Well of the Moon, going by the old woman's directions, but he still had some doubts.

He sat down to think for a while what he would do or not do, when – *snap!* – along came a shepherd boy driving a flock of ewes before him while he followed along behind playing his flute – *peepity-poop! poopity-peep!*

Bernard hailed him, saying:

"Can you tell me, good shepherd, what this well is called?"

"It is The Well of the Moon," said the shepherd boy, leaving off playing his flute; and he had hardly finished saying it when he began to play again – *peepity-poop! poopity-peep!* – and went off with his sheep as cheerful as you please.

So what did Bernard do? He made for the King's house to ask for a flask and some rope to be able to bring back the King's three daughters, since he knew where they were.

He presented himself before the King and said:

"My Lord King, is it true Your Royal Majesty has made an edict stating that if a single man finds Your Royal Majesty's three daughters he may marry one of them and, with her, will become heir to the Crown?"

"Yes, it is true," the King replied.

"Well then," said Bernard, "I have come to tell you that I know where your three daughters are."

"What's that?" exclaimed the King.

"Just what you heard, my Lord King!"

"Look, young man," the King said. "Don't deceive me, for goodness' sake, for if you did we would make a leather bag out of your hide."

"Never fear, my Lord King," said Bernard. "Would I be so stupid as to come here to lie to you? I admit I should deserve any punishment you like if I were to deceive Your Royal Majesty."

"Tell me, then," said the King, "if you need any help in finding these three mirrors of my soul, these three girls of mine."

"I need a flask and a good length of hemp rope, brand new."

The King arranged for him to have what he wanted, and Bernard, with the flask and with the length of rope over one shoulder and under the other arm, set off for The Well of the Moon.

Bernard's audience with the King and what they had said to each other became known, and a group of young men – those who were most anxious to be son-in-law to the King and heir to the Crown – sniffed each other out and said among themselves:

"Can you see this country yokel finding the three girls when we were not able to? But suppose he did find them; it would be terrible to have as King a lump of a bumpkin who cannot be worth the straw he lies on."

When they had done talking about it, they decided to follow Bernard at a prudent distance and to prevent him, by fair means or foul, from taking the three princesses to the King; they were resolved to kill him rather than allow such a thing to happen.

No sooner said than done. A party of these young men went off following Bernard at a good distance but without losing sight of him.

And what did Bernard do? When he was once more at The Well of the Moon he again listened for any noise in the well. He heard none at all, so he went in search of the seven wells that the old woman had told him about, so as to fill his flask with their water.

These wells were scattered about among the mountains; Bernard found one today, tomorrow another, and the day after yet another. He let the flask down with the rope, and from each well he drew enough to have the flask full of water from all the seven wells; and when he had it – having found all seven – he went back to The Well of the Moon.

The party of young men were observing him from afar, and they were saying to each other:

"Let's see what this bird gets up to! We must watch him carefully."

And they watched him closely. They saw how he unwound the length of rope, how he tied one end to the rocks at the mouth of the well, and how he went down with his flask, hanging onto the rope.

The young men came nearer and nearer, so that when Bernard should come out with the King's three daughters they could surround him and take the princesses from him, by force if not with his consent.

Bernard meanwhile was going down and down. The rope was very long, but he was getting near the end of it and still he could not see the bottom.

The well widened out so much all round that he could not see the sides; it was a terrifying great cavern. He came to the end of the rope but still his feet did not touch the bottom. He looked hard and saw something; then he let go of the rope and landed on his feet on the floor.

He looked and looked all round; his eyes were beginning to make things out, and he found he was standing among three very large stones. On one of them there was a serpent coiled up like a length of rope; on another there was a lion; and on the third a malignant devil.

The first thing Bernard noticed about these three creatures was their eyes, which glowed like coals.

Then Bernard commended himself to God and to all the saints and lady saints of his prayers, summoned up his courage and said:

"Now for the bang!"

He took the stopper out of the flask and threw a jet of water from the seven wells onto the serpent's head. Then – *splash!* – another generous jet onto the head of the lion; and then – *splash!* – he threw all the water left in the flask at the head of the malignant devil.

When the water from the seven wells touched the serpent and the lion, these two creatures exploded with bangs like thunder, and at the same time the two stones stood upright and turned into Anne and Mary, the elder daughters of the King.

The devil, as soon as he felt the water from the seven wells on his face, made a *bang* and jumped at Bernard, but Bernard was just as ready to attack and take a bite at the creature's ear, and he had bitten the top off before the devil was aware of it.

That devil, when Bernard had taken a piece of his ear, was like Samson after his hair had been cut: he did not have the strength to lift three bushels of rye. The devil was lying on the ground howling and roaring till the whole place resounded, but it was clear he no longer had any power against Bernard; he was not even looking at him.

What Bernard was looking at very closely was the stone where the devil had been sitting. As soon as the creature jumped at Bernard the stone stood upright, as the other two had done, and turned into Catherine, the most graceful and most beautiful of the King's daughters.

Then the three princesses fell on their knees before Bernard, crying out:

"Oh, young man, you have saved us! May God reward you as fully as we are grateful to you. Tell us what you want of us."

"What do I want?" said Bernard. "I want to get you out of here and take you back to your father the King."

"Do you mean you knew we were the King's daughters?"

"It is because I knew it that I came to get you out, at the risk of my own life," Bernard replied.

While they were talking like this the devil, still lying on the ground, kept on saying:

"Bernard, give me back the piece of my ear that you have bitten off! Give it back to me, Bernard. It is of no use to you, and I need it badly. Give it back to me, I say! Don't be cruel! Give it back!"

"We will see about that later," said Bernard. "I will give you back the piece of your ear if you will get me, with these three girls, to the King's house."

"Do you give me your word that if I get you to the King's house you will give me back the piece of my ear?"

"Word of honour!"

"Alright then," said the devil, "You shall be taken at once." He whistled with all his remaining strength, and suddenly there was a great noise of approaching wings.

It was a crowd, such as you have never seen, of crows, kites, vultures, and eagles, which came flocking to The Well of the Moon, made their way into it and surrounded the devil, all crying out:

"You have not yet told us what you want of us."

"I will tell you straight away," the devil said, and then to Bernard: "Do you see that canvas sheet hanging in the corner?"

Bernard went over to it and found it was indeed a canvas.

"Bring it over here. Open it out in the centre; then all four of you get onto it, all hold hands and be careful not to let go."

Bernard and the three princesses did this, and the devil said:

"Are you ready?"

"Yes," all four replied.

"Right, then!" he said to the swarm of crows, kites, vultures, and eagles. "Bear this canvas in your beaks and carry it at once to the front of the King's house!"

Believe it or not, all those birds seized the canvas in their beaks, spread their wings, and up and up they went, making for the King's house like ten thousand streaks of lightning.

You can imagine what a shock this was for the party of young men waiting at the well-head for Bernard to come out with the

King's three daughters, whom they were going to seize. When they saw the huge swarm of crows, kites, vultures, and eagles going down into the well, and soon afterwards coming out again bearing Bernard and the King's daughters through the air, they were dumbfounded, stunned. What do you think? The swarm of crows, kites, vultures, and eagles made such good speed that they were soon in front of the King's house. They came down to earth slowly, and the King's daughters and Bernard stepped off the canvas. He threw the piece of the devil's ear into the canvas, saying:

"Take this; it belongs to your master. Please give it to him."

"Do you want anything more from us?" the birds asked.

"Nothing more!" Bernard replied.

And the birds all flew off to The Well of the Moon, taking back to the devil the canvas and the piece of his ear, which joined up at once. Then the crows, kites, vultures and eagles all flew off, each its own way.

Now you can imagine what was bound to happen at the King's house. Everybody was bursting with happiness and joy, most especially the three princesses and the King and Queen.

The King took Bernard aside and said:

"Have you any brothers?"

"Yes, two," Bernard replied.

"Single or married?"

"Single."

"Then go and fetch them here!"

Bernard dashed off and came back with his two brothers, and the King said:

"My three daughters are for you three, one each. But Bernard must have first choice, and he will be heir to the Crown."

So Bernard chose Catherine, Peter took Anne, and Paul had Mary. They were duly married and there was a wonderful wedding feast and a lively ball, and festivities and merrymaking galore.

And they are still at it if they have not stopped.

And I came along with a morsel of cheese, and the cats along the road – *miaow! miaow!* – left me not a bite.

Two Carriers
or
Is it better to set off early than to go to Mass?

FRANK AND NICK were two carriers of Manacor, in the days when there were very few carts, and those few had solid wheels. These two fellows used to go to the City and to Sineu with pack-saddled mules.

Frank so much liked going to Mass that he went even on weekdays, no matter how little time he had to spare. Nick, on the other hand, only just managed to go on Sundays, always in a hurry and hardly ever on time.

They were old friends. One Tuesday evening they happened to meet, and Frank said:

"Shall we go to Sineu tomorrow?"

"Yes, let's."

"Very well, after dawn Mass."

"After dawn Mass, did you say? By that time I shall be past Petra."

"No, Nick; to Mass first, and then we set off with God's blessing."

"Don't bother me with your blessings. It's *better to set off early than to go to Mass*."

"You're wrong, you know."

"No I'm not. Never mind; if you want to come along with me, I am setting off an hour before dawn. And if you don't, I'll see you in Sineu. Good night for now."

Nick kept to his word; he was up an hour before dawn, he loaded three sacks of wheat onto his mule and set off.

Near a farmhouse a little way out of Manacor he came on a man wrapped up in a blanket sleeping by the roadside. It was still dark, and the mule took fright and jumped backwards; with the jolt two of the sacks of wheat fell off, and burst open as they hit the ground. There was wheat all over the road, and to make it worse the road was inches deep in dust. Nick flew into a rage, and there he was shouting and cursing and stamping on his hat in his fury.

If the sleeping man had not been lucky enough to wake up at once, and if he had not been a hefty fellow of forbidding appearance, Nick would have laid into him and killed him. He did not actually attack the man, but there was not an ugly word that he did not shout at him. But the man was a cool customer and went off as if nothing had happened.

Nick at last saw that cursing was getting him nowhere, and the best thing he could do was to gather up the wheat as quickly as possible. But it was all mixed up with dust and gravel, and cleaning it was going to be a tremendous job.

Then Frank appeared. He had been to Mass and was coming along with his mule and its load, as happy as could be and singing like a nightingale.

"Good heavens!" he said when he saw Nick in this pass. "I thought you would have been in Petra by now. What the devil happened?"

Nick told him, and he said: "Never mind. You may thank God it was the least that could have happened; may he spare us from anything worse. Now what we must do is go and borrow a sieve from this farmhouse and clean the wheat; and with God's help we shall still be in time for the market."

They did that, and by the time they had the wheat cleaned and bagged, and were moving on, the sun had been up an hour.

As they went along Frank came out with:

"And do you still say, Nick, that it's *better to set off early than to go to Mass*?"

"Of course I do! Look where I should be now if I had not come across that devil of a man sleeping."

"Ah, but you did come across him, didn't you?"

"Don't tell me I came across him just because I didn't go to Mass. Anyway, I'll lay a bet with you that I'm right."

What shall we stake?"

"Our loads."

"Alright – agreed."

"And the first man we meet shall say who is right."

"Very well; the first man shall say."

Now it so happened there was an unoccupied devil just there, flicking the flies away with his tail. He heard what they said, so he took on the appearance of a very respectable man and casually came towards them.

"Friend," they said, "would you mind if we had a word with you?"

"Not at all; even two words if you like. What is it?"

"Well, we are two carriers from Manacor on our way to the market at Sineu, and we have been arguing about the best time to set out – whether it's *better to set off early than to go to Mass*."

"To Mass?" exclaimed the devil, gesticulating and grimacing as if someone had thrown strong vinegar in his face. "Go to Mass, did you say? Any fool can see that having to wait for Mass is a waste of time; that way a man could be on the road when the sun was hot enough to fry his brains."

The rascal went on his way without another word, and there was Nick shouting and nearly bursting with glee and throwing his hat in the air.

"There you are, Frank! Did you hear that chap? Both the loads are mine now! I've earned good money today – and without going to Mass!"

Frank was furiously angry and burst out:

"Who do you think you are? What does it matter if someone says you are right, when actually you are quite wrong!"

"Oh, I'm wrong, am I? Want another bet on it?"

"Yes. What shall we stake?"

"Well then, our mules."

"Alright – done."

"And do you agree that the first man we meet shall say who is right?"

"Yes, I agree."

They were near Petra; the same devil took on the appearance of a man a little different from the one before, and came towards them.

"Look, friend," they said as they came up, "you seem to be a respectable man... "

"As to that, I consider myself the equal of anyone."

"Well then, we are two carriers from Manacor on our way to the market at Sineu, and we have been arguing about the best time to set out – whether it's *better to set off early than to go to Mass*. What do you think?"

"What should I think?" he replied, his eyes flashing. "I think going to Mass is a mistake, and no small one. To work! To work without delay, and away with sloth! Don't you think there are enough idle hands and lazy backs in the world already?"

Then the devil left them and seemed to go on his way. Nick once more made a shocking noise, shouting and jumping up and down and throwing his hat in the air, and saying over and over again:

"Well, Frank, did you hear what this other man said? Both the mules are mine now. Today I have earned really good money, and all at your expense, Frank. You know, you should join those who don't go to Mass."

When they were in Petra he restrained his taunts a little, so as not to attract people's attention, but as soon as they were out of the village he went on even more than before.

Frank lost his patience altogether, and said at length:

"Can't you shut up? I'm sick of it. You are just as stupid as those two men who said you were right; and you are no more right than the Man in the Moon."

"What is quite certain is you no longer own your load nor your mule."

"But it is even more certain that I am utterly right."

"But, old cock, even now you don't seem to understand."

"I still say it's better to go to Mass."

"And I say it isn't. I'll have another bet with you."

"What shall we stake?"

"All the money we have with us."

"Very well – done."

"And the first man we meet shall say who is right."

"Yes, agreed."

Of course that devil was quick to take on an appearance something like the other times, and he looked as if, when it came to advice, he would be as wise as Solomon.

"Look, friend," they said when they came up to him; "you seem to be a respectable man."

"You may be sure there's none like me under the sun."

"Well, then, we must tell you that we are two carriers from Manacor, and we have been arguing about the best time to set out: whether it's *better to set off early than to go to Mass.*"

"Go to Mass, did you say?" exclaimed the devil in disgust. "You can put your Mass in the pot and stew it. Why not try and sell some to the farmers where you got your wheat... Go to Mass? No, no! Set off early! Set off early! That's what really matters!"

When he had said this the devil pretended to go on his way, and he was quickly out of sight.

Nick was beside himself with joy; he hardly knew what he was doing jumping about and shouting and throwing his hat in the air. Frank kept hitting himself on the head; he could not understand how three respectable-looking men could seriously have said it was *better to set off early than to go to Mass.*

He pulled out his purse and handed it over to Nick. And he went no farther; there was nothing left for him to do in Sineu.

He walked for quite a time aimlessly, without thinking where he was going. Late in the evening he came on a cave; he went into it. and there he saw a great bell on the ground, all chipped and with a couple of cracks that you could easily have put your hand through.

"Well," said Frank, "I might as well spend the night here; and the best thing will be to lie down under the bell, where I shall be safe."

He found a plough-beam lying about; using it as a lever, he

raised the bell on one side and got underneath it. What with having been so angry and being so tired, he went straight off to sleep. But around midnight he had rumblings in his belly and woke up hungry.

While he was wondering what he could do about it, he heard footsteps. He looked out through one of the cracks in the bell and saw a troop of devils marching into the cave. The leader was as tall as a belfry, with horns seven yards long, and a powerful tail that coiled seven times round his body; as for his talons, they were beyond description: he could have carried a man impaled on each of them, like so much fluff.

He sat himself on top of the bell, and four small devils fanned him with empty panniers to cool him off a bit. He was breathing heavily, and it was clear that he was flaming angry. All the other devils were trembling, but not with cold.

More and more devils appeared, from the four quarters of the world, and they all gave account of what they had fouled up during the day, of the souls they had tempted and those they had led astray, of the families they had embittered, the marriages they had upset, the sisters-in-law and daughters-in-law and mothers-in-law whom they had set to squabbling, the nets and traps they had laid, and the hooks they had baited to catch big fish.

Suddenly one came marching in with his tail erect; instead of hanging down at all it was pointing straight upwards.

"Good evening, Lord Satan," he said from a short way off.

"Hello, old cock! Have you any good news?"

"Yes, plenty. On the road from Manacor to Sineu I came on a couple of carriers who were arguing about whether it was *better to set off early than to go to Mass*. One said *Yes* and the other said *No*; three times they laid bets on it, to be decided by the first man they should meet. I heard all this, took the form of a man, and each time came to meet them; and each time I gave the verdict against the one who said it was better to go to Mass. The one who was against it is now firmer than ever in not going, and the other is furiously angry; it will not take much to turn him against the Mass, and against him who established it."

"Nice work! Nice work!" they all shouted, waving their arms and jumping up and down in a general uproar.

"Shut up, you filthy beasts! You are giving me a headache." shouted the boss devil. Then he snapped at the one with the tail:

"Very well. You have earned your keep for today; but look here: you had better see to it that these two birds don't escape us. If they get away, that tail you are holding up so proudly will pay the bill; we'll chop it off with an axe, a little bit at a time, till you haven't even a stump left."

He had hardly finished giving this warning when another devil turned up. He was a lively spark with a nose that, at a rough guess, must have been a foot long, and from his nostrils sprouted two tufts of hair like the bristles on a wild boar. From some way off he called out:

"Good evening, Lord Satan!"

"Hello, old cock," replied the boss, looking very serious, "have you anything good to report?"

"I have netted a whole lot of souls, and no mistake."

"Explain that a bit more."

"Well, last night I blocked up Saint Margaret's spring in Felanitx, which is used by everybody in the town. This morning, when they realized what had happened, there was a great to-do. They tried to unblock the spring; they went at it first from one side and then from the other; they brought in blacksmiths and stone-masons and all the most skilled men in the town. None of them was able to move the blockage. Then I went among the people to stir it up; I made them suspect each other – without reason – and soon they were accusing each other face to face rather than bottling it up; then people got excited and in every street you could have seen quarrels and arguments galore, curses by the cartload, and a spate of ugly words, split lips, scratched faces, caps knocked off, shawls dirtied, skirts spoiled, chunks of hair pulled out, broken heads, arms and feet dislocated, lumps on the head, split ears, and noses that will never be the same again. You could have seen a great outburst of slaps, blows, punches, boxes, fisticuffs, and brawling of every kind. It was terrific. This blocking of the spring, with all its consequences, will be good business for us. Who knows what we could gain or the souls that we could trap with a bit of care."

"That's true! He's right! Hoorah! Hoorah!" they all yelled with screams and shrieks loud enough to wake the dead, until the boss devil shouted at them:

"Shut up, you filthy beasts! You are giving me a headache!"

"And will they not know how to unblock the spring?" asked a small devil.

"How could they know?" said the one with the nose. "Unless they rinse the mouth of the spring with a tuft of black wool it cannot be unblocked; and how should the people of Felanitx think of that?"

"Very well," said the boss. "You have earned your keep for today, but you had better look to it that this nicely baited fish-pond is not lost to us – and that someone else does not catch the fish. Because if that were to happen it would be those bristles in your nose that would pay for it, and then your great nose itself. The bristles we would pull out one by one, and your nose we would wrench with pincers until it came right off."

He had hardly given these warnings when another devil appeared, very jaunty, barely touching the ground with his feet. He bore a tremendous array of horns; he had two main horns like plough-frames with lots of smaller horns branching out, like a fig-tree without leaves. From some distance away he shouted out:

"Good evening, Lord Satan'"

"Hello, old cock! Do you bring any good news?"

"I certainly do. You know the King's daughter?"

"Do you mean that big girl of twenty who, for all our trying, won't let go of her mother's apron strings?"

"Yes, that same silly girl. She likes a bit of fun, but she never does anything to annoy our enemy. Imagine what fun! As exciting as cold boiled beans. We try hard but we get no more profit out of her than Mrs Fried-Fishy who used to sell fried fish at the same price as raw, even though she had bought the cooking-oil. Well then, for this bright girl I managed to get some poisonous herbs into a pot of jam that she ate this evening. She hardly had it inside her when she began to feel griping pains. The doctors came with their prescriptions and medicines, but none of them gave her any relief or comfort. And so, if all goes well, she has not long to live; she will soon turn up her toes. The King and Queen have no other children, and they are now fairly old; they too will be dead within about four days, and nobody will remember this rotten family, who have brought us nothing but losses. There will be a new king, and with luck he will not keep us out in the cold, us and our friends."

"Good news! Good for us! Hoorah! Hoorah!" they all yelled, and they made such a din that you could not have heard yourself speak, until the boss devil shouted:

"Shut up, you filthy beasts! You make my head spin."

"And will they not be able to cure the King's daughter?" said a small devil.

"They cannot possibly cure her," answered the one with the horns. "The doctors will never guess the right medicine. She will not recover unless she drinks a cup of lioness's milk."

"And would they have to go abroad to find a lioness?"

"There would be no need. There is a suckling lioness in a cage in the King's garden."

"Very well," said the boss to the horned devil. "You have earned your keep for today, but I warn you: if the King's daughter should recover we shall saw off all your horns with a log-saw, until there is nothing left thicker than my fingernail; you'll be lucky if we don't get down to your brains."

After this warning he turned to the others and said:

"Come on, it's time to begin the day's work. Out you all go! No idling, no going to sleep! To work and look out!"

The devils all made off, and soon there was not even the dust to be seen.

Frank had not missed a word of what they had said. As best he could he got out from under the bell and set off for Felanitx.

He found the people there in an uproar; you could not have heard yourself speak. Everybody was clamouring for water; children were crying for it, women were screaming for it; men were shouting for it, cats were miaowing, pigs were grunting, dogs were madly growling and donkeys and mules were braying loud enough to split your head open.

The Mayor and all the Officers of the Law were there

standing before the spring discussing the matter; and the less each one knew about it, the more he talked.

Then suddenly Frank turned up and said:

"What will you give me if I unblock the spring?"

"Are you being serious?" they all cried together.

"I am so serious that you may hang me if I don't clear it – provided you bring me what I need."

"Tell us, friend" they all said. "Whatever you say shall be yours for the asking."

"Very well; to begin with bring me a tuft of black wool and a small bowl of water."

They brought them. He thoroughly soaked the tuft of wool in the water and then began rinsing the mouth of the spring with it; and he went hard at it, soaking the tuft and rinsing away. After a while the mouth of the spring began to ooze water; soon there was a trickle like a piece of spaghetti; then it was as big as your finger, then like your arm, and then the size of a man's leg. The spring was fully cleared; indeed, it had never given so much water.

The townsfolk nearly went mad with joy. They almost squashed Frank as they surrounded him, all wanting to hug him. They carried him shoulder-high round the town. They gave him more money than he wanted; they filled his pockets and his shirt-front with gold and silver coins.

They wanted him to stay with them for a week, but Frank said he had a job to do in the City. He went off as quickly as he could, on horseback, and kept going full tilt all the way. He got there an hour after sunset and made straight for the King's house, where the Princess was breathing her last. He went to the Queen and said:

"I know what medicine will cure your daughter."

"Do you really mean that?" exclaimed the Queen, with her eyes as wide as saucers.

"It shall be my head on the block if I am deceiving you."

"Well, then, where is this medicine? Quick!"

"Send someone to milk the lioness that you have in a cage in your garden, and bring a cup of the milk."

They brought it. Frank gave it to the Princess; she drank it, and she went straight off to sleep, breathing quite naturally.

Would you believe it? The next day she was as fit and well as could be. Her father, her mother, all her ladies-in-waiting, the pages, the menservants, the maidservants, the whole City, nearly went mad with joy when they knew of it, shouting and jumping, throwing their hats in the air and dancing round.

They all hugged Frank and almost ate him with kisses and caresses. They carried him in triumph all over the City. Then the King took him to the Treasury and stood him before a mound of gold coins piled up high and covering the space of a bed-sheet.

"Take all the money you can carry," said the King.

Frank filled a large bag and went home, as happy as a bride.

His wife at first could not believe his story. She could not understand how he had managed to clear the spring at Felanitx, and to cure the Princess, or that the tremendous amount of money was honestly come by; but in the end she was convinced. I cannot tell you what happiness there was in Frank's house.

There was very little happiness at Nick's. He had been so thrilled at having won the three wagers that he got to the market puffed up like a toad; he sold both the loads of wheat and then started back towards home, without taking any notice of the great heat of the sun. He wanted to get back to Manacor in daylight, so that everyone might see he had two mules. He got them there, but they were white with froth. One of his boys, without thinking in all the excitement, gave them water; they got such a colic that the vet, with all his medicines, could do no good. The next day before dawn the mules were dead; the knacker had to take them away to the slaughterhouse.

Nick was wild; he kept bashing his head against the wall, and he thought he would go mad. Then he heard that Frank had come home loaded with money, so he went off at once to see him.

"How the devil did you manage to come by this huge amount of money?"

"I'll tell you," said Frank, and he told him the whole story of what had happened.

"I will go there too!" exclaimed the silly fellow. "I'll hide under the bell in the cave, and perhaps it will go as well for me as it did for you. I'll go straight away."

So he went, as quickly as he could. When he reached the cave it was beginning to get dark; he went in and hid under the bell, and there he waited and waited.

About midnight he heard footsteps; it was the boss devil arriving with the group of smaller devils who were his courtiers. He sat on top of the bell and the others fanned him with their grass panniers. More and more devils began to appear from the four quarters of the world to give account of their misdeeds.

The one with the long tail, the other with the great nose, and the third with the tremendous horns, arrived hanging their heads and looking crestfallen. You could see from a distance they would rather have had a thrashing than have had to appear there.

"Hey, you rascals!" shouted the boss in a flaming temper. "You're pretty slow! By the time you move one foot the other has taken root. Come on now, you shall each give me an account of your doings. You: a few nights ago you had your tail in the air, and now it's trailing on the ground. You stirred up the argument between those two carriers; tell me how it is going."

"What can I say?" replied the poor devil. "It's going very badly; I don't know what has happened. The one who said it was *better to set off early than to go to Mass* has quite lost his courage, because both his mules have died; and the one who said it was better to go to Mass came home with his pockets, and a large bag, full of gold and silver. He is no longer angry, while the other is envious, and furious at having made those wagers against going to Mass. Now he seems even more likely to go than his friend."

"Is that how it is?" said the boss devil, and then he shouted at the others: "Haven't you got the axe and the block ready?"

"Lord Satan, I swear it wasn't my fault that it went wrong. As I am a devil, I couldn't help it!" cried the long-tailed one.

"Don't bother me with arguments!" snapped the boss. "Come on, the axe. Come on, the block!"

And they brought them along. Then one group of devils took hold of the wretched culprit; another lot held his tail on the block; and another devil took up the axe, which was all chipped, and he hacked and hacked away. Each chop took off a chunk of tail, and the poor devil was shrieking loud enough to be heard a couple of miles away. But the more he screamed the more noise the others made. And they chopped away at his tail till there was not even a bit of stump left.

Then the boss devil turned to the one with the nose, who was looking far from happy, and said:

"Now, you miserable-looking creature, tell me how things are going at Felanitx."

"What can I say?" he answered. "Badly. Someone has cleared the spring, and the town is once more as quiet as a bowl of oil."

"Good! Very good!" cried the boss. "You have won your prize and we simply must give it to you." Then he turned to the others spewing fire between his teeth, and said:

"Haven't you pulled out those bristles growing in his nostrils? Haven't you got the pincers on his nose yet?"

"Lord Satan!" cried the poor devil, "I swear it's not my fault that someone has unblocked the spring."

"I've heard that one before! Come on there, onto those bristles! And you others, onto his nose!" shouted the boss to the two gangs that had lined up.

One gang seized the culprit while another lot attacked the bristles in his nostrils, and they pulled and pulled, sometimes pulling out four or five at a go; the poor devil was screaming and braying, and all the others were making a shocking noise. When there were no more bristles left, a couple of devils came up with the pincers, and they pinched and they pulled and they tugged mercilessly. The wretched devil let go curses and screams by the cartload, and still they could not pull his nose right off, try as they would. At length seven of them piled onto the pincers and pulled with all their might; then at last the great nose came out by its roots, and the devils took it in the pincers and paraded it round the whole gathering, all making a terrible hullabaloo.

Only the devil with the horns was left, and he was trembling like a poplar-leaf, as terrified as a rabbit.

"And you, you rascal?" cried the boss, with sparks coming out of his eyes. "Did you think you were going to get out of having to account for your doings? Come on, now; how is the King's daughter?"

The horned devil's teeth were chattering so much that he could not utter a word.

"Have you gone deaf or have you lost your voice, you great oaf?" yelled the boss. "I said: How is the King's daughter?"

"She is... quite... well," said the horned devil trembling like a linnet caught in the talons of a hawk.

"Didn't you say she could not be cured?" exclaimed the boss in a fury.

"Yes – I don't know what the devil has happened."

"Your horns shall know it! Come on there, bring the saw, and be quick about it!"

"Lord Satan, I swear I did all I could."

"Yes, go and reserve a niche and we'll put this saint in it. Well, go on – go and do it! But never mind now; we'll have the saw first."

They brought the log-saw; its teeth were an inch long and well cross-set. One gang of devils took hold of the culprit by the head, so he could not move, and others took the two ends of the log-saw and began sawing off the smaller horns, one by one. And I can assure you they did not bother about whether they hurt him. The saw was very blunt, and it was not so much a matter of sawing off horns as of hacking them off in bits. When there were no more branches to cut off they started on the main horns, and there they had a tough job. They cut off bits only three or four inches long, and if the saw did not cut much on the branches, it cut even less on the big horns. But they went on hacking off bits until there was not a stump to be seen. The poor devil cursed and swore and roared, and he struggled and squirmed; but the others, far from being sorry for him, kept up a tremendous hullabaloo and thoroughly enjoyed it all.

When the noise had died down, one of them exclaimed:

"All the same, when you think of it, it's a bit too much that in so short a time the two carriers should come to agree, that there should have been someone to clear the spring, and someone to cure the King's daughter."

"Yes, it's too much!" they all cried. "And did you tell anyone?" they asked the three who had lost tail, nose, and horns.

"Do you think I did not like my tail and was ready to risk losing it?" replied the first of them, cursing.

"Was I so anxious to lose my great nose?" said the second, spitting gall.

"Do you need to ask?" said the third, swearing at them.

Then they all cried out. "Well then, how is it we have had this set-back? How can it have happened? What the devil went wrong?"

At length one of them, with the meanest face you can imagine, said:

"Could it be there was someone hidden here who heard us the other night?"

"Search everywhere, double quick!" shouted Satan in a flaming rage.

"Oh, horrors!" said Nick when he heard this. "There's no escape – I'm done for! It's all up with me! And I deserve it for being an ass!" The poor fool did not know what to do.

Meanwhile the devils were searching all the holes and corners in the cave, all the piles of stones and bushes and thickets near-by. They almost killed themselves searching, but they never found a trace of anybody.

At length one of them said: "He might be under the bell."

A group of them went and raised it off the ground. They had hardly got it up when Nick dived out between their legs and shot off like a streak of lightning down the hill, with the devils after him full tilt. He ran on, with his heels kicking his buttocks; the devils following him managed to scratch his thighs and his bottom with their nails and they tore away pieces of his shirt and strips of his trousers, and some bits of skin. But they could not catch him because he was running for his life, as hard as he possibly could, while they were many and got in each other's way, getting their horns hooked together and hitting each other in the eye with the lashing of their tails.

At length Nick saw a row of beehives; he jumped into one that happened to be empty, and once inside he pulled the cover on again. The devils swarmed up to the hive shouting:

"Now we've got him! Now we've got him!" But they came up against the cross on the cover of the hive, and I need hardly tell you that when they saw it they fled like lightning in all directions, cursing Nick and everything to do with him. In a flash they had all vanished.

After a while a group of young fellows came by on their way home from a ball, all as greedy as pigs. They saw the row of hives, and one of them said:

"Shall we take one of those hives? We could have our fill of lovely honey."

"That's a good idea" said the others. "And let's make sure we take the heaviest, so as to have plenty of honey!"

No sooner said than done. They went up to the row of hives and began feeling their weight, one after the other, until they got to the hive with Nick inside.

"This is a good one!" they all exclaimed. "This is the heaviest; the honeycombs must be well filled."

Would you believe it? They loaded the hive on their backs and went off with it.

"Oh goodness!" said Nick. "I'm in trouble again! What will they do to me when they open up the hive? It will be terrible!"

With the fright of all those devils, Nick had *done it* in his trousers, and with this new shock he did more. With the jolting of the hive it began to run out. The fellows carrying the hive felt something wet on their backs, and they saw that the hive was dripping everywhere.

"This is no mean load of honey! Look, it's running out of the combs."

Here the greediest of the lads saw a trickle beginning to drop; he caught it in his hand and eagerly put it to his mouth. He had hardly done so when he spat it out, and he went on spitting and saying "Uugh! Hell! Uugh!"

"How can you say *Uugh* at honey" cried the others.

"That's a fine sort of honey" he cried. "That's not honey – it's shit!" The others sniffed it and tasted it, and they all agreed that it was.

They wasted no more words. There was a huge bramble thicket near-by; they tossed the hive into it with all their strength and took to their heels – because by now it was daylight and they were afraid of being late at the farm where they worked.

The bramble thicket concealed a deep ravine. The hive went down the slope and rolled on down over crags, rocks, brambles, gorse and thorn bushes. Soon it was not the hive that was rolling, because it broke up; what was rolling was Nick, and he rolled right down to the bottom of the ravine. By the time he stopped rolling he hardly looked like a man: lumps on his head, wounds on his face, huge scratches down his back, on his belly and on his legs, both arms injured, his knee-caps and his feet dislocated, bruises and thorns all over his body, and blood everywhere.

Somehow he managed to pick himself up. Limping and staggering, he eventually got home and had to go to bed. He sent a message to Frank asking him to come, and he said to him:

"Look where it has got me, not going to Mass! I am a fool and I deserve a worse fate."

He recovered fully, but he was a changed man. He set off early, certainly, but he also went to Mass, like Frank; and from then on he prospered.

And Nick and Frank and Frank and Nick lived happy and contented until they died.

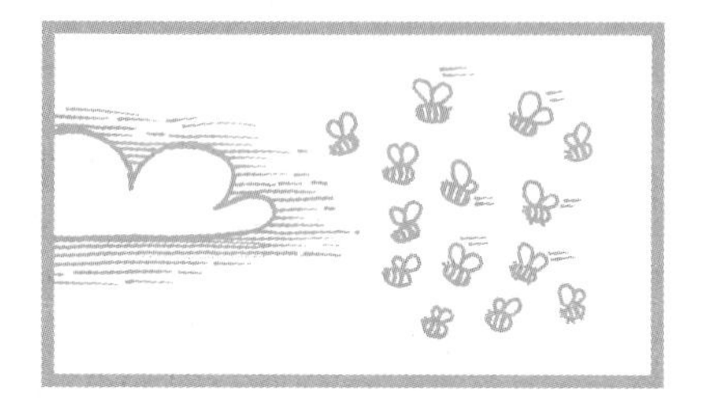

Gus the Robber

THERE WAS A COUPLE in Artá who had only one child: a boy called Augustine. Before he was seven years old his father died, stating in his will that Gus should be given a start in any career that he chose.

When he was a little older his mother put him into school; but he did not care for it at all; he often played truant or arrived late. He was never still and was like a spark from the fire; he incited the other boys and upset them; and if one of them stood up to him he would land a few blows on the fellow's mouth or nose, and there would be blood and tears everywhere. Then the schoolmaster would intervene and make Gus pull up his shirt-tail, and with some raw-hide straps would whack away at those buttocks until they were good and red. Then Gus would come home, and his mother – who knew about it because the other boys had come to tell her – would lay into him again with some cord that she kept for the purpose, since using her hand would have hurt her too much.

What a dreadful boy he was! He had a devil in every hair of his head, and she did not know where to strike him; she and the schoolmaster punished him on his cheeks, on his buttocks, and on his ribs; but the more beatings they gave him the more rebellious he became and the worse he behaved. His mother had many headaches about him; she did not know which way to turn because she had tried everything; if she treated him kindly he took advantage of her, and if she treated him harshly he became more rebellious.

When he was twelve years old she took him aside one day and said:

"My boy, it is time you showed some common sense; we have had enough mad pranks and bad behaviour. You must learn the ways of the world; if you don't behave sensibly – and I am telling you in advance – if you don't change radically, you must not be surprised if I break your shoulder with a club; though I think you are more mad than bad. Your father left it in his will that I was to give you a start in whatever career you might choose. Now, what profession do you want? Would you like to be a priest?"

"No," he replied. "You have to study too much."

"But look how well off you would be if you were a priest! You could be eating *chocolate*."

"I don't like priests or preachers. I am not drawn towards that idea."

"Well, would you like to be a lawyer?"

"What are lawyers?"

"They are gentlemen with beards who dirty a lot of paper and tangle up a lot of tape, and earn a lot of money."

"And what do they have to do to become lawyers?"

"Ah, my boy, they have to go and study first in the City, and then away from Mallorca."

"And to tangle tape and spoil paper, all that studying? I could do that as well as anybody without moving from Artá."

"And are you thinking of tangling tape and spoiling paper as the lawyers do?"

"Shall I tell you? Between two cats there can be nothing but claws. Anyway, I don't want to be a lawyer."

"Then how about being a doctor?"

"Even less. What sort of people you bring up! Doctors are only good for making you take castor oil, senna, salts, and such things, all of them bad! You only have to look at a doctor for your stomach to be turned."

"But they do it to cure sick people."

"A fine cure! The sick people end up in the cemetery. Mother, don't speak to me of doctors or quacks."

"Then we must make you a carpenter, or a blacksmith or a miller..."

"I don't at all like those trades; there is too much work to be done."

"And so I should think! As far as you are concerned all work could be forbidden and there would be no danger of your breaking the law. What you would like is the life of a gentleman: eating and drinking and doing nothing... other than mad pranks and escapades. Come on, now: what is the career you would like best? What are we going to make of you?"

"What will you make of me? A robber."

"What's that you say, you rascal?"

"I want to be a robber. That's a profession worth having. It costs you no more than the effort of taking! A good, quick, profitable career."

When his mother heard this she could bear it no longer; she attacked him and *bing-bang! bing-bang!* she made his cheeks scarlet and his buttocks blue; but the devil of a boy, kicking away, kept on saying: "I want to be a robber! I will be a robber! A robber! A robber! A robber!"

Tired of beating him, his mother left him still crying out:

"I want to be a robber! I will be a robber!"

After a while his mother tackled him again, saying:

"Gus, you still have not said what you want to be, joking apart."

"I will say it again quite clearly," he replied. "A robber."

"What do you mean by *a robber*?"

"I mean that a robber is what I want to be, and there's an end of it."

"But who has ever seen anybody become a robber?"

"Who has not seen it? It is easier to see robbers than not to see them; there are no other people about in the world. What other profession yields such quick results? And it is so simple; it needs no more than the effort of taking."

"But robbers are caught and put in prison."

"Only the stupid ones are caught – those who steal too little. Steal a lot and you will not be caught."

"But could you not be a priest?"

"Don't talk to me of priests! So much work for so little money."

"Well then, a lawyer?"

"I don't want to be a feathered animal. And to pluck anybody who comes along I don't need to go to the City or away from Mallorca to empty my head with studying. Do you think me so stupid? Anyway, a robber is what I want to be, and no more argument. You have an obligation to make me a robber; my father left it in his will that you had to start me in the career that I should choose. If you don't do it you cannot inherit; and take heed of what I say."

All this weighed heavily on the poor woman; she felt the wings of her heart drooping, and she could say no more. She burst into tears and was inconsolable. At her wits' end, she went to tell her brother-in-law about Gus, and he said:

"Send the boy along to me one of these days and I will see if I can knock some sense into his head."

After a couple of days she sent Gus along on the pretext of returning a basket. His uncle gave him a friendly welcome, and then brought up the subject in this way:

"And you, Gus, have you thought at all about what profession you might follow? Because, you know, you cannot go on leading the lazy life you have led until now. Come on, tell me which way you feel drawn."

"I am tired of telling my mother," the rascal replied "that I feel drawn to be a robber."

"Have you been secretly at the brandy bottle? Are you drunk? What is the point of wanting to be a robber?"

"Have you and my mother both been bitten by the same bug? She too comes out with such objections whenever she hears this profession mentioned. And it is the career with the quickest progress, the lowest cost, and the biggest rewards!"

When his uncle heard this string of nonsense he desperately wanted to let loose with slaps, punches, and kicks, but he held back so as not to quarrel too soon and spoil it all.

"But, Gus," he said as calmly as he could, "Don't you see you are on the wrong track?"

"I am very much on the right track."

"But don't you see you will be caught?"

"Me, caught? Not likely! Only the stupid robbers get caught – those who steal only a little! What I say is: keep your eyes skinned, and once you are in, watch out."

"But why do you utter these heresies?"

"I don't utter any heresies. I am going to be a robber, even if the sky should kiss the earth. And please tell my mother so, if you wish her well. She has an obligation to start me in my chosen profession, and if she does not do so she will not go unpunished; I will report her to the judge and she will not inherit; she will have no excuse."

His uncle could bear it no longer; he completely lost his temper and went for Gus with kicks, slaps, punches and blows. And this devil of a boy, defending himself as best he could, kept on crying out:

"I will be a robber! I will! I will!"

Time went by and the lad reached the age of sixteen; he tackled his mother, saying:

"Mother, I have had enough of this. Your obligation is to start me in the career that I want. You know quite well what it is. I hear there is a cave full of robbers at the Bec de Ferrutx, where I can learn the trade very well. Take me there and I shall be satisfied. And listen to me: I give you a week. If in that time you have not taken me there I shall report you for failing to carry out what my father laid down in his will."

The poor woman, when she had done weeping about it, turned again to her brother-in-law for help over what she should do.

"So he has asked to go to the Bec de Ferrutx", he said. "Then it still might work out alright. I know the captain of this band of robbers, and I am sure he would do me a favour that he would not do for anybody else. Look: I will give you a letter for him telling him what the trouble is; that this crazy lad, my nephew, is the son of a poor widow; and I will ask him to see if at the start he can give the boy such a roasting as to make him hate the life of a robber. I see no other way of getting this obsession out of the lad's head."

That is what they did. The brother-in-law wrote the letter as he had said; and one day before dawn mother and son set off for the mountains and the Bec de Ferrutx.

They passed Son Fortesa and went down through Morell. Sunrise saw them at the foot of the mountain, where it was all bushes, coarse grass, and palm trees, seeming to be wrapped round that enormous rock, shaped like a gigantic beak, which rises terrifyingly above all the neighbouring peaks and overlooks the whole central plain and the mountain range of Mallorca. It is reddish, full of crevices and ravines, with hardly any foot-hill, leaning forward and threatening the valley and the houses below.

Gus was thrilled to find himself in these wild fearsome places so far from any help.

"Hurrah! Hurrah!" cried the crazy boy, jumping about and playing the fool. "I shall have a great time here with the gang of robbers! Here I shall be satisfied! We shall have plenty of adventures among these valleys and hills and ravines! Everybody who comes this way with a full purse, or with baggage worth anything, will find out what's what!"

His mother, as you can imagine, was in floods of tears when she heard him carrying on like this.

"Oh, my son!" the poor woman kept saying. "You will be the death of me with all these heresies that you are uttering. I have never heard so many! You must have gone completely mad, and there is no sense at all left in you. You should be locked up! I wish I could lock you up; you would not take another step."

Gus hardly paid attention to what she was saying; he was wondering why he had not yet seen the robbers' cave, and his eyes were nearly jumping out of his head looking for it.

All at once he saw three men running down the slope towards them, each with a blunderbuss over his shoulder, shouting:

"Hey you! Stop or you die! Not another step!"

The three men were soon on them, shouting all the time:

"Your money or your life! Your money or your life!"

"Hallo, comrades! Hallo, mates!" Gus kept saying to them. "I am coming to join you I want to be one of you! I want to become a robber!"

"Your money or your life!" said the robbers, thinking Gus was saying all this only to be rid of them.

"We have no money," said his mother, in tears. "I am a poor

widow; this is my only son and I am bringing him to you. This is gospel truth. I wish it were not so."

"You can believe her," said Gus. "What she says is true. I have come to be a robber along with you."

The bandits searched them and felt in their pockets and, finding no money on them, decided to take them to the captain.

When the captain had seen them and had read the letter he was convinced they were speaking the truth.

"Alright, the lad can stay from now on," the captain said to the widow; "and don't you worry about him. I will take care of him. You can go home at ease."

The poor woman, as you may well imagine, was in floods of tears and kept on saying:

"Oh, my son, that I should have to see you here! That you should have made me come here! Oh, if only your father were alive – such a good man he was! Who could have foretold this about the little angel he knew when he died! I cannot bear it, having to leave you here, my son! I shall never get home alive – I shall drop dead on the way."

"You will get home alright," said the callous boy. "Do you know how happy I am? I have got where I wanted to be! Come, you can go home, and everything that was my father's is now yours; I want no part nor share. This career that I am starting will give me enough, and more than enough, to live on. Oh, what a great and delightful profession!"

"Gus," said the captain after a little, "don't be so brutish; don't turn the knife in your mother's wounds; they are painful enough as it is. And, for your guidance, you must understand here and now: I am not given to saying anything twice. The men whom I command may be robbers, they may be scoundrels, or what you will, but disobedient I can assure you they are not – not at all. They obey me or they go to Hell."

Gus saw the captain was in earnest, so he kept his mouth shut and said no more. The captain gave orders that the lad's mother should have something to eat, and that two of the robbers should accompany her as far as Morell. The robbers did just as they were told, and the poor woman returned to her home in floods of tears.

The captain, to oblige the friend who had written him the letter, spent a couple of days thinking and thinking how he could give a roasting to this mad-cap boy who believed that just by being a robber he could make a fortune at once.

The robbers' cave was a fissure in the rock; it was reached only by a goat-track with any number of twists and turns; nobody other than the robbers could possibly find the way. From the mouth of the cave they commanded an immense view. They could see almost the whole of the Roqueta. In the distance on the left they had the black peak and the peaks of Calicant at Sant Llorenç des Cardessar and of Mount Randa. To the right was the sea with Cape Victoria and Cape Formentor; and in front was the whole range of the Mountains of the Snow as far as Mount Teix near Sóller and the peak of Galatzó. They could clearly see the torrent bed of Sa Vall, the plain of Petra, Sineu, Llubí, Santa Margalida, Muro, Sa Pobla, Alcudia, Inca, and beyond Binisalem.

Those robbers could survey the distance to their hearts' content, and they could easily see if anybody was coming with something to say from the Police.

One morning, about an hour after sunrise, the captain was at the mouth of the cave scanning the view when he saw a man coming up from the direction of Betlem, walking along below the houses at Sa Devesa. He looked carefully and saw it was an Artá man named Massot, who was carrying a lamb across his shoulders.

The captain called Gus and said:

"Do you see that fellow coming up the road with a lamb across his shoulders?"

"Yes, I see him."

"Then you can make a start by stealing the lamb from him; and don't come back without it."

Gus thought for a moment and then he said:

"Alright. I shall need a sword with a scabbard; better if the sword is fairly shiny."

They brought him an old sword. He rubbed it up a little and made it good and bright, put it in the scabbard, and went off down the mountain-side as fast as he could.

"He will do well with the sword and the scabbard!" said the

robbers when they saw Gus running off so eagerly. "Can you see Massot letting Gus take the lamb from him? There is not a tougher man in Artá, nor one more heavy-handed! Gus will soon find out! Massot will squash him, and no mistake!"

Meanwhile Gus had reached the bridle road that comes up skirting the mountain through the bushes towards Son Fortesa, where Massot was bound to pass. Gus dropped the scabbard in the middle of the road and went on up the hill; then, farther on, he dropped the sword and went and hid in the bushes.

Massot, with the lamb across his shoulders, came to where the scabbard was lying in the road; he saw it and picked it up.

"Oh, it's a scabbard," he said. "Somebody must have dropped it. But it was not worth bending down to pick up such a thing. I have no sword, nor do I want one, even if it cost me nothing; so what should I do with a scabbard alone?"

He threw it down and went on up the hill, striding along. A son of his was to be married the next day, and the lamb was for the wedding feast.

Some four hundred yards ahead he saw something shining in the middle of the road; he walked faster, to see what it was. It was the sword left by Gus, looking brand new and shining brightly.

"Well!" said Massot. "A sword! It must be the sword belonging to that scabbard. I will go and get it and then I shall have both. It would save time if I were to leave the lamb on the ground here. Its four legs are tied, so it cannot escape."

Massot left the lamb there and went back for the scabbard. Gus, who was watching him as a cat watches a mouse, came out of his hiding-place, made a dash for the lamb, picked it up, and was away up to the robbers' cave.

He was soon there; the captain and the other robbers were amazed when they saw him.

"So you have got it!" they said in astonishment.

"Didn't I tell you I would get it?"

"And Massot didn't make mincemeat of you?"

"He never touched me; he did not know I was there."

"You are the very devil!" they all said, and not one of them could understand how he had done it.

When Massot had picked up the scabbard he went straight back to the sword. He got there but he could not see the lamb or any trace of it. He stood as if stunned.

"This is too much!" he said. "What sort of trick is this?, What can have happened?"

He looked all round the place for some time; he searched several bushes and clumps of reed-grass in case the lamb, by kicking and wriggling, had managed to get caught in one; but he looked and searched in vain. The lamb was not there, and that was that.

He did not give another thought to the sword or the scabbard. At length he said:

"It can only be that the lamb's legs came untied and it has run back to the flock. I am sure to find it there."

He turned back and kept going until he came up to the shepherd.

"Has the lamb come back?" he asked straight away.

"What lamb?"

"The one I took earlier."

"The one you took? Don't you remember you tied its legs and put it across your shoulders?"

Then Massot told him exactly what had happened.

"Well, friend," said the shepherd, "I cannot tell you where the lamb is because I don't know; what I can tell you, and swear to, is that it has not come back here, so far as I know. To make sure, we can look."

They looked; but how could the lamb be there? What a chance! It was actually in the robbers' cave, dead and half flayed.

Massot went to see the farmer and told him what had happened.

"Alright," the farmer said; "if you need a lamb for tomorrow take another. The first one will turn up."

"It is very kind of you," Massot replied. "And if the first lamb does not appear I will pay you for it."

He took another lamb, tied its four legs very carefully with seven knots, so that it should not play the same trick as the first lamb. Then he slung it across his shoulders and set off for Artá on the same road.

It so happened that the captain of the robbers was again looking out from the mouth of the cave, and he spied Massot with the lamb on his shoulders.

"Here we have Massot coming once more with another lamb. Come on, Gus; go and get it from him. I want to see you back here with it!"

"Wait a little and you shall see me!" said Gus, and off he went trotting down the slope, and he did not stop until he reached the road. He hid in a bush and waited. Soon he heard Massot's footsteps, and he started bleating: *Mé-é-é! Mé-é-é!*

"There!" said Massot. "That's a surprise! And what luck! There is the other lamb. It must have got lost and not been able to find the flock. I must catch it; then I can return one of them and shall not have to pay for two. I know what: I will put this one down, and then I can move quicker."

While Massot was putting the lamb down on the ground Gus moved to another bush, farther in, and kept on bleating *Mé-é-é! Mé-é-é!*

"The devil is running away!" said Massot. "I must get moving. I will try doing the ewe: *Bah-ah-ah! Bah-ah-ah!* And he bleated away for all he was worth, making for where he heard the other bleating.

Sometimes he heard it near, sometimes farther away; at times it seemed as if the lamb would burst itself bleating; then for a while he did not hear it at all. This was because Gus was moving quickly from one bush to another, crouching down, so that Massot should not spot the trick.

"*Mé-é-é!*" bleated the trickster, very lifelike.

"*Bah-ah-ah!*" replied Massot making in that direction. "This lamb is the very devil," said the poor man, finding he could not catch up with it. "He will stay among the bushes. I can hear him bleating clear enough, but I have not yet seen a single strand of his wool. But the bleat is his alright; I know it well. I wish I could be as sure of going to Heaven."

Massot did not notice what a long way he had gone into the thicket of bushes. With so many twists and turns he no longer knew where he was; he was dead tired and sweating so much you could have wrung out his clothes.

Gus then stopped bleating and dashed back to the road. He found the second lamb on the ground with its legs tied; he at once seized it, slung it across his shoulders, and made for the cave as fast as he could.

The robbers reckoned that this time Massot would have finished Gus off, and they would never see him again. When they did see him, with the second lamb across his shoulders, they began crossing themselves in amazement; they could not understand how he had done it.

"The Devil take me!" said the captain to himself. "What sort of a rascal is this? He has turned out to be a pretty smart recruit. Will he be teaching us all? Two such feats in one day! We can give him his degree right away and let him loose on his own!"

Massot, after bleating away *Bah-ah-ah*! for some time till he was completely hoarse, realized that for a while he had not heard a bleat nor seen a sign of the lamb anywhere.

"Well, this is too much!" he exclaimed. "The wretched creature has made me kill myself running about and bleating, and has now disappeared. I might as well chase it to put salt on its tail. Anyway, if it does not return to the flock I shall have to pay for two lambs, and that will be the end of it. So now I had better go back to the road, pick up the other lamb and think no more about it!"

He went back to the road, but how could he find the lamb if Gus had already taken it to the cave?

Massot stood as if stunned; he was aghast, and then he began reciting verses – that is to say swearing.

"But what the Hell makes these lambs disappear like this? Are they bewitched? No doubt about it; they must be. But here I am once more high and dry, and I cannot appear at home like this. There is nothing for it; I shall have to go back to Betlem and see if the two lambs have turned up there; and if they have not I will bring another. I cannot have a wedding party at home without a lamb to cook. I shall find some way of paying."

He went back crestfallen to the field where the Betlem flock was grazing; when the shepherd saw him coming back empty-handed for the second time he called out from a distance:

"Ten thousand devils! Did the second lamb escape too?"

"Don't speak of it," the poor fellow replied. "I feel quite ill with the business. Has either of the two returned?"

"I have not seen them; I don't think they have come back, and I have been watching carefully to see if the first one should turn up."

Massot told him everything, and they went and told the farmer, who said:

"Never mind; take another lamb and we will say no more about it. A wedding party without any meat would be too meagre."

"Look," said Massot, deeply grateful, "what I said before I say again now: if the other two lambs do not appear, here am I to pay for them to the last penny."

"Take the lamb, and God bless you," the farmer replied.

Massot asked for a couple of yards of hemp rope, which they gave him; he went and chose a lamb, tied its four legs very firmly and made extra twists and knots till he came to the end of the rope, and said:

"You will be the very devil if you too get loose!"

When he had the lamb all roped up, he put it across his shoulders, took to the road, and went off.

There was hardly an hour left till sunset; the captain of the robbers was again at the mouth of the cave, looking and looking around. He soon spotted Massot with the lamb across his shoulders.

"Once more! Blow me down!" he exclaimed, bursting with laughter. "Here we have Massot again coming up with another lamb!"

"Come on, Gus," said the captain. "It would be a pity if we missed this one. Run as quick as you can and take it from him. Hurry up! You should be back here by now! Go like a bullet!"

"Let me have two pieces of cork of about a hand's breadth," Gus said excitedly.

They gave him the pieces of cork and off he dashed down the mountain-side so fast that he was bouncing along.

He reached the road and hid in a bush, waiting for Massot. When he heard him coming, *tramp-tramp*, he took a piece of cork in each hand and began making a noise like *tutup-tutup-tutup*. The noise reached Massot.

"What the devil is that?" he said, stopping. Meanwhile Gus went on making *tutup-tutup* behind the bush with the two pieces of cork.

"Hell's bells!" exclaimed Massot. "I know what that dry dull sound is; it must be the two lambs that escaped; they have found each other and now they are larking about together. It's as clear as can be. This time I will catch them!"

So what do you suppose he did? He put down the lamb he was carrying and went quickly towards where he heard the *tutup*. Gus then began to dodge from one bush to another, and to yet another, with *tutup-tutup* all the time; now he would do it loud and clear, and then very softly, softly; and he was going in twists and turns and dashes to and fro; and for a while he would make no noise, and then he would go at it harder than ever.

And there was Massot chasing him and flaming away, and cursing and swearing fit to burst as those two errant lambs proved so hard to catch.

He was furious and he never noticed when the sun set, nor was he aware it was getting dark, until he could not see any distance in front of his nose; and there he was all tangled up among the bushes and the palm trees, with nothing gained and a long way from the road where he had left the third lamb.

Much closer to the lamb was Gus; when he saw his chance he dropped the pieces of cork and made straight for the lamb, which he slung across his shoulders and took up towards the cave.

Meanwhile Massot was kicking about among the bushes and the reed-grass half a mile away, now stumbling along, now falling over, and swearing to left and to right.

In a few bounds Gus was at the cave, and he found the captain and the other robbers sitting round a basin of rice with pieces of meat as big as your fist; and I can tell you they worked their spoons hard and were not at all put off by its being rather hot. What mouthfuls! How they stoked up!

Even so, when they saw Gus arriving with another lamb they paused for a moment and made all kinds of exclamations; they found it incredible and they could not understand how the devil the lad was so cunning and so diabolically clever at stealing lambs from a man as strong and tough as Massot.

"So you are having supper?" said Gus. "Some of that rice would suit me very well, and I am really hungry. I mean it when I say God alone knows the effort and the running about that I have had to put in today. So when I say I can make a good meal, you may believe me. There will not be a lick left in that great basin."

He picked up a spoon and moved into the circle. But just as he was stretching out his hand towards the basin the captain spoke, saying:

"Hey! Just a moment, young fellow. Don't you dare take any unless you want to know what's what here." And then he turned to the one who acted as cook and said: "Have you got those beans we left yesterday?"

"Those beans," said the cook. "Yes, I think they are still there; but don't you recall they were such poor stuff that they would not cook properly; and there were other reasons for not eating them."

"Never mind that," said the captain, "and don't meddle where you are not asked. Put the beans on the fire; Gus will have them for supper."

When Gus heard this he was stunned, speechless; then his blood boiled, he ground his teeth with rage, and his whole body was trembling with fury and the urge to fight back.

He could not contain himself.

"What is this, then?" he said, flaming angry. "Do I get only a handful of ill-cooked beans?"

"Yes, my boy," the captain replied, "and be grateful for them too."

"Do you mean that I who have sweated all day to steal three lambs from Massot, I who have brought you food for a couple of weeks, no matter how much you eat, I have to be content with your left-overs from yesterday?"

"Yes, my boy, and you will not get anything else, however much you may kick and stamp."

"And what law is this," said Gus, "which allows you to spend the day scratching your bellies and sitting on your bottoms and then to fill yourselves with rice and tasty fresh meat, while I must be content with a mouthful of air if I don't want to touch a handful of badly cooked beans? I have nearly dropped dead up and down this hill, and on the flat down there, and have brought you three lambs good enough to set before the King. For you, who have done nothing, the meat and the rice, and for me, who have done everything, a handful of ill-cooked beans heated up. What sort of law is this?"

"Are you expecting to find laws about here?" said the captain. "Is this the place to talk of laws? Don't you know where you are? Do you come here looking for laws? Do you want to know what the law is? I will tell you. Just as you stole the lambs from Massot, we have stolen them from you. Here everybody steals as he can, and the more you steal the less you have. Do you like the dish? If you don't, mind your step and you will have nothing to complain of; if you are angry put your head in the water-butt or go to Mass – whichever you like."

"So that's how it is?" said Gus. "You say everybody steals for himself, and the more you steal the less you have."

"That's it, exactly."

"Then I have chosen a bad career. I have seen quite enough; now I understand about the profession of robber, and I want no more of it. I am satisfied. Thank you for the lesson you have given me; you have made me see at first hand what my mother and my uncle kept telling me, but I did not believe them. Anyhow, you go your way and I will go mine. I hope you keep well and strong; and if there is anything you want from Artá, be quick and tell me now, because I am going there straight away. Good-bye! God be with you!"

No sooner said than done; he went off down the mountain-side like a bullet, leaving the captain and the other robbers cut short.

At Son Fortesa he came on poor Massot, who at last had been able to reach the road and was going along as best he could, more dead than alive and cursing away at the three fearful mishaps he had suffered. He could not refrain from telling Gus all about it, without suspecting anything. Gus played the part of the listener very well and managed to cheer Massot and give him courage, saying the lambs must surely have gone back to Betlem, and he should not worry about it.

On entering Artá they parted, and Gus went and knocked on his mother's door. She was in bed, but he made her get up and he told her he had come back disillusioned about the profession of robber, and was now resolved to be a good man for the rest of his life.

And he was – abundantly so.

He began working in the fields as hard as he could; he was able to improve the land, and he soon had a corner of his own; he repaid Massot for the three lambs. He married a first-rate girl; he never neglected his mother, and he gave his own children an upbringing such as few parents give. He was the most peaceable and satisfied man in the world, following the light at all times and making everybody under him follow it too. He lived... until he died.

And if you don't believe it, go and find out for yourself.

The Two Thieves

THERE WAS ONCE a lad who had the idea of becoming a thief. He ran away from home – and they were very good people – and he went to see the man known to be the biggest thief in Mallorca. He came straight to the point:

" I am here because I want to be a thief like you."

"Have you thought about it carefully?" the thief asked.

"Have I thought about it? I have, and so much that if you will not have me as a disciple I will find somebody else who will."

"Very well; but before I take you on you must pass the test."

"I will do it here and now."

The older man led him into a wood, and to the foot of a very tall pine-tree, and said:

"Do you see that bunch of twigs up there? It is a crow's nest, and the female crow is sitting on the eggs. Your test is to take the eggs without her noticing.

"Then wait a little," said the lad.

He climbed up the trunk of the pine-tree, and up he went so quickly and quietly that a spider running up its web would have made more noise and disturbance. He reached the branch and the nest, and then he began taking away twigs from the bottom, which he did very gently.

Would you believe it? The female crow noticed nothing. He made a hole in the nest and filched all the eggs; as he took them he put them in his pockets.

Then he came down, and the older man said:

"Did you manage to steal them all?"

"Yes, and quite quickly."

"Let me see them."

The young lad put his hands in his pockets but found no eggs; and his pockets had holes in them.

"Ten thousand devils!" He exclaimed. "How amazing! And who the devil has cut holes in my pockets? I know very well they had no holes before."

"You are right," said the old thief. "I did it; I climbed up after you, and while you were taking twigs out of the nest I cut holes in you pockets with scissors; and as you put the eggs in your pockets they came straight into my hand, which I was holding just beneath. And to show you that I am telling the truth, here are all the eggs."

He showed them, and not one was missing.

"Alright," said the old thief, "you have passed the test and I will accept you as a pupil. You can come home with me."

And they went home.

A couple of days later the older man's wife said:

"We have no more sausages, and no oil, which we cannot do without. Could you not take a walk?"

Her husband then said to the lad:

"Let's go to St Anthony's Gate and see if we can find a piglet."

They went there and found a merchant with a good herd of pigs. They looked at the pigs, made a deal on one, and then the married thief began feeling in his pockets, saying:

"How annoying! I have left my purse at home."

"Where do you keep it?" said the other. "I could run and fetch it for you."

"My wife knows, and she will give it to you. Go, quick! You should be back here by now."

Just as the lad was leaving the older thief said to the merchant:

"Perhaps he could take the piglet now, and we could save ourselves an extra journey, because after this we have several jobs to do."

"Yes, let him take it," said the merchant in all good faith.

The younger thief took the piglet, and off he went as fast as he could.

The married thief waited there, and when he saw the merchant busy over a deal, he put a very smooth silver coin into one eye, he took off a sash that he was wearing, rolled it into a bundle and thrust it under his jacket between his shoulder-blades; he twisted his neck and his whole body so that he seemed to be another man, one-eyed and hunchbacked.

The merchant turned to him and said:

"That fellow is a long time coming. Is your house far from here?"

"I think you have mistaken me," said the married thief in a different voice. "I am sure you have mistaken me."

The merchant looked him up and down carefully, and was quite taken aback.

"Are you not the man who bought a piglet from me?"

"You have mistaken me, I tell you," said the thief.

"There is nothing for it," said the merchant at last. "The man who bought the piglet had two good eyes and a straight back. Adios, piglet!"

The thief hobbled off with a crooked walk. As soon as he was out of the merchant's sight he took the silver coin out of his eye, put the sash round his waist, and made for home intending to plunge his knife into the piglet; but he was too late. He found the piglet flayed and cut up, and soon the red sausages were hanging up, the black puddings cooked, and the rest in brine.

The next day the older thief said to the younger:

"Today we must provide ourselves with oil. Come on!"

He took a length of cloth that his wife was going to use to make skirts for herself, and off they went looking for an oil merchant.

They found one leading a mule carrying two panniers with a skin of oil in each. He had stopped and was about to unload.

"Wait a moment, friend," said the two rascals. "We will help you."

"That's kind of you," said the oil merchant, and he took up one of the skins.

The married thief grabbed the other and with the bachelor made off with it as fast as he could go.

The oil merchant did not hear any footsteps following him; he turned round and saw the two helpers running away as fast as bullets and disappearing round a street corner. He put his skin of oil on the ground and ran after them. By the time he went round the street corner the young thief was hidden in a doorway, and the older thief had put the skin on the ground, all wrapped up in the length of cloth, and was whipping it with a length of rope.

"You cursed woman!" he was saying, pretending to be madly angry.

"I will kill you! You will never do it again, as I am your husband. I will not spare a single one of your ribs... Cursed woman!" And lashes and more lashes as if he would drive the object into the ground.

"There now!" said the oil merchant. "There is a man beating up his wife."

"I am going to kill her! Saint Peter will not be any help to her."

"And would you have seen a man running away with a skin of oil on his back?" the oil merchant asked.

"Yes, I think one did go by a little while ago. Hurry, and perhaps you will catch him."

The oil merchant went off down the street as fast as he could.

The older thief picked up the skin of oil; the younger thief went to where the oil merchant had left the other skin, and picked it up too, and then they both made for home like hares.

When they got in they emptied the two skins and filled their oil-jar to the brim.

So they were provided with sausages and with oil.

After some time the married thief had his wife make four canvas bags. Then one evening after supper he said to the bachelor:

"Tonight let's go and fill these four bags at the King's treasury."

They went there; they succeeded in climbing onto the roof, they removed several tiles, they raised a section of the ceiling, and they let down a length of rope inside. The older thief said to the young thief:

"Lower yourself down; fill the bags; and when you have them full tie them to the rope and give me a signal; I will pull the bags up; then you will come up. We will put back the ceiling and the tiles in their proper places, leaving no traces, and away we go."

Just as he had said, so they did, and they were devilish quick to return home with the bags full of gold coins.

The next day the King learned of the break-in perpetrated in the night, and he was furiously angry.

In the dungeon of his castle the King was holding a sixty-year-old thief whose eyes they had had to put out to keep him captive. He was a wily rat who had made plenty of trouble when he was at liberty; the devil surpassed him only by having horns.

The King sent two of his men to tell the old thief what had happened, and to get him to say how the thieves could be discovered and caught.

When the blind thief heard the tale he said:

"Was there a door broken down or a hole made in a wall?"

"No," they replied.

"Then they got in by the roof. Shut all the doors and windows tight and make a fire inside. If they did not plaster the boarding properly the smoke will come out there. If it comes out anywhere, you must put below that spot a big cauldron full of bird-lime. Those who broke in will be greedy for more, and they will come again. They will break in at the same place, and they will be caught in the bird-lime. That way you will get them."

The two men recounted all this to the King. The King had a fire lit in the treasury, which was tightly closed everywhere.

The two thieves had not plastered the boarding, and soon the King's men saw a wisp of smoke rising from the tiles. They removed the tiles where the smoke was coming out, and they found the loose boarding; then they replaced the tiles.

Below this spot they arranged a large cauldron full to the brim with bird-lime; then they closed the treasury and went off.

After a couple of days the married thief one evening said to the bachelor thief:

"Let's go and fill those bags again at the King's treasury."

They went there, they climbed onto the roof, they removed the same tiles, pulled up the same boarding, and let down a length of rope inside.

"Who is to go down tonight?" said the older thief.

"It is your turn," said the younger.

So the older thief let himself down, and down he went. He was so confident that as soon as his toe touched the bird-lime, which had a little crust on it, he was sure it was the floor and he let go of the rope. He fell into the bird-lime and was stuck in it up to the neck.

"What the devil is this?" he said in amazement. And he began to struggle, but the more he struggled the more deeply trapped he became. He made violent efforts, but it was in vain.

Seeing it was all up with him and he was sure to be found there, and blind with rage, he said:

"They may find me here but – the Devil take me! – the executioner will be too late." And he sank down into the bird-lime and there he remained, drowned.

The young thief had heard the noise and commotion made by his companion down below, but he could not catch any words.

When he heard nothing more at all he became impatient, and to find out what was happening he lowered himself by the rope.

With his toe he touched the bird-lime and felt his foot sinking in; so he went no farther down the rope. Then he looped his sash under his buttocks and tied it to the rope so that it held him up; he brought out his steel, flint, tinder and tow; he got a flame and lit a resin stick.

Beneath him he saw the cauldron of bird-lime and his companion inside it. By making the rope swing he managed to jump down outside the cauldron; he cut off his companion's head and put it in one of the bags, which he slung over his shoulder; then, leaving the body in the bird-lime, he climbed back up the rope and made for home.

He told the dead man's widow what had happened; and he said: "So long as they don't find out who he was, we shall be alright."

The following day the King's men found the headless body in the cauldron; the King sent his men to tell the thief in the castle dungeon, who said:

"There were two of them; one went in first and got stuck in the bird-lime, and the other cut his head off so he should not be identified and nothing should be found out about him. He certainly is clever, that fellow. Oh, if I had eyes to see I'd want him to work with me! But let's see how we can catch him."

"That will be pretty difficult."

"One way or another we will get him!" The blind thief thought about it for a while, and then he said: "Here is something you could try; it might work, but I cannot be certain."

"Tell us."

"You could put the body on a bier, with a collecting bowl on it, accompanied by a crier with a trumpet who should call out: 'Charity, to give this man decent burial.' He should do that, while you are there watching carefully to see who puts most in the bowl. That will be the other thief."

They did that, and it happened that the man who gave the most was a common soldier, a thoroughly good man and very well thought of by the officers. They all went and presented themselves before the King in defence of the man.

"Lord King, this soldier is innocent; we answer for him."

The King saw they were telling the truth, so he released the soldier. Then he sent his men to tell the old thief in the castle, who when he had heard the story exclaimed: "He certainly is clever, that fellow! Oh, if I had eyes to see I'd want him to work with me. Never mind. Now you could try wheeling the dead man all through the city; where you hear weeping, that will be his house."

They went off and wheeled the dead man all through the city, and as they were passing the thief's house his widow broke down and burst into tears.

The King's men went up to the door and *knock-knock!*

"Who is it?"

"Open up, in the King's name."

The young thief kicked over the oil jar, and there was oil all over the house. Then he opened the door.

"What's all this weeping?" said the King's men.

"What do you think? We have had an accident with the oil jar and the wife is inconsolable.'"

"Fair enough," said the men, and they went on their way.

They went all through the city, but they heard no more weeping. They went and told the King, and he sent them to the thief in the castle, who heard the story and said: "He certainly is clever, that fellow! Oh, if I had eyes to see I'd want him to work with me! Where you heard weeping was the dead man's house; the man who opened the door was the man we want; the woman weeping was the dead man's widow."

"If that is so, then we have got him," said the King's men. "We remember which house it was; we can go there and arrest him."

"Don't you see that by now he will have moved house?" said the old thief. "What you could do now is to wheel the dead man once more all through the city; where you hear weeping again, don't stop but make a mark in red-lead on the door-jamb; then go early in the morning and catch him. If you don't get him then, let him go."

When it was quite dark they set off to wheel the dead man through the streets and alleys. When they were outside the house where they had heard weeping before, they stopped to listen but heard nothing.

They carried on, going through street after street. At length they reached the thief's new home, and the dead man's widow broke down and burst into tears.

The King's men heard her; they marked the jamb of the door with red-lead and went on their way.

The young thief noticed this and after a while, when there was nobody in the streets, he took a pot of red-lead and a paint brush and made the same mark on the jambs of all the doors in that street and in the four neighbouring streets.

The King's men came along early in the morning and they found no end of door jambs with the same mark.

"This is the very devil!" they said. "How can we possibly know which is the rascal's house?"

They went and told the thief in the castle, who exclaimed: "He certainly is clever, that fellow! Oh, if I had eyes to see I'd want him to work with me. Where you heard the weeping was his house; but he noticed the mark, and so that you should not find him out he marked all the houses round there. Never mind; try something else. Put the dead man on a wooden platform near the cemetery, with seven or eight soldiers hidden underneath, watching all night. The fellow will go with the aim of taking the dead man and burying him in hallowed ground, and then you have got him."

The men went and told the King, and the King arranged for the dead man to be placed on a platform near the cemetery, with seven or eight soldiers hidden underneath, watching.

What do you suppose?

The young thief borrowed a donkey with a pack-saddle, and he bought nine friars' habits. He put one of them on and packed the others in one of the two panniers; in the other pannier he put three strings of red sausages, some fresh bread and a small barrel of wine.

He whacked the donkey and off he went. In the dead of night he passed by the platform. The soldiers saw him and called out:

"Brother, why are you still about at this time of night? You will hardly find the friary open."

"Good soldiers, I have lost my way!"

Here the soldiers noticed a couple of sausages peeping out of the pannier; so of course they came up close to him at once.

"What's this, brother?" they cried. "Sausages and all?"

"Yes, it is a gift that has been made to our Community."

"There is a good community right here. Anyway, we must have a taste."

"But you must promise not to tell on me," said the friar, who wanted nothing more than that they should taste the sausages.

"The devil may take us if anybody gets to know about it!" said the soldiers.

And there they were gathering twigs and getting a fire going. They soon had a good fire blazing away, and before long a great pile of embers; then they threw the sausages on, and there was *sizzle-sizzle* and smoke everywhere.

Half cooked, half raw, each man grabbed a sausage; then the friar said:

"Wait a moment, I will bring you some fresh bread; sausage alone might make you ill."

"Fresh bread?" they cried. "Have you got some?"

"A little."

He brought the bread out and with pleasure watched them stoking up. They were not in the least shy about it, I can assure you.

"Is it a bit salt, boys?" the friar asked.

"Salt?" they said. "Who cares if it is?"

"I asked because I have here a small barrel with a little wine in it, and I thought you could each take a drop, unless you are water-drinkers."

When those oafs heard about wine they began jumping up and down and throwing their caps in the air, shouting:

"Come on, brother friar! Bring it out at once before it goes off! Bring it out even if it is vinegar!"

"But boys, let's be serious! You must not tell on me for the love of God."

"Don't worry, brother friar! The wine! The wine, quick!"

The friar brought out the barrel, which was good and full. The first soldier in line had his turn and went at it.

What do you think? When they had all had a go the barrel was empty and they were all dead drunk. They did not move; they collapsed where they stood, and they did not notice the cold night air, I can assure you.

What do you think the friar did? He took off their soldiers' uniforms and put a friar's habit on each of them. Then he took the dead man into the cemetery and buried him. And he returned home as cool as you please.

The next morning, when the soldiers had recovered from their hangover and found themselves dressed in friars' habits, and the dead man missing from the platform, they had the most dreadful shock; they stopped laughing altogether.

"It's all up with us!" they groaned crying like little children. "The King will kill us! And we fully deserve it!"

When the King heard what had happened he was about to pass the sentence of *Off with their heads*, but then he took pity on them and said:

"Very well; this time they can run the gauntlet of a thrashing."

And that was done.

The King then sent his two men to tell the thief in the castle; when he heard the story he exclaimed: "Ah, if I had eyes to see, I'd want him to work with me! It was our fellow who dressed the soldiers as friars and took away the dead man; by now he will have buried him. Tell the King to let him go, because you will never catch him."

Look what a clever idea the King had in the light of this advice. He issued an edict through all his kingdom: Whoever it was that had broken into his treasury and had taken such a lot of money, and had succeeded so many times in escaping and laughing at Authority, should now come forward; and if he promised to give up for ever the life of a thief, he would have the King's word that he would be pardoned.

The young thief learned about this edict and he thought inwardly:

"Until now I have had success in the trade; but who can guarantee that it will always be like this? Up to now I have been lucky, but who can tell me if I shall always be so? You know, it would suit me best, now the King is offering me a pardon, to give myself up and ask for it. Once pardoned, I could take up another trade, a better and a quieter one, and I could still be a man of substance."

No sooner said than done. He presented himself before the King, saying:

"My Lord King, here I am – the subject you are looking for."

He promised never to go stealing again, and the King pardoned him.

The dead thief's widow was still young and good-looking, so the young man married her. They returned to their village, they devoted themselves to farming, and they never again left the straight and narrow path. They followed the light truly. And whether you believe me or don't believe me, they must still be alive if they are not dead.

Old Mother Cricket

SHE WAS AN OLD WOMAN of the year dot, scrawny, loose-lipped, for ever on the run, as wily as a vixen, and given to laughing at other people's expense and scoring off the unwary. She was a widow and had one daughter, Catherine, who did not resemble her in the least, neither in appearance nor in character; she was the most good-looking and well-behaved girl.

Catherine was being courted by a young man, a really good fellow, who proposed marriage.

"Alright," said Old Mother Cricket; "we must begin making preparations: furniture for the house and Catherine's trousseau."

"You may begin when you like," said the young man. "At home we shall be doing the same."

"The trouble is," said the old woman, "I have no money, and no way of making any. But never mind; I will contrive something one way or another. If I cannot find means, nobody else is likely to."

She heard that a local Farmer and a neighbouring Market-Gardener intended to go to the City with two mules loaded with runner beans to sell there; and she thought: "Very well, I will follow along behind them and we shall see who profits from this trip to the City. I shall be surprised if I cannot teach them a good lesson; they are so dim-witted I can surely play a trick or two on them." It is true that the Farmer and the Gardener both suffered a little from Saint Peter's trouble and did not quite have the wits needed to go about this world. It is certain Old Mother Cricket could run circles round them; even asleep she saw more than they did when awake.

She watched for them; when she saw the Farmer leaving his farm with a mule carrying a load of beans, and joining the Gardener with his mule, she set off after them, but without getting near, so they should not see she was following them. They went through the town of Manacor and took the road to the City, and the cunning Old Mother Cricket followed and followed some way behind, without catching them up nor letting them get too far ahead. Then some way farther on she began to walk faster; she soon came up with them and greeted them cheerfully: "Praised be the Lord! Fancy meeting you!"

"Praised be the Lord for ever," they replied. "So it's you! You are Old Mother Cricket, aren't you?"

"The very same."

"We had noticed you, but as you were some way off we were not sure it was you. And are you going to the City, if it's not asking too much?"

"Yes, I am going to the City to see to some business that I have there. And I suppose you are too."

"We are going in the hope of getting a good price for these two loads of beans," said the Gardener. "After all, a man must be wide awake and make the most of his opportunities, and profit from every chance. These beans are tender and delicious, and since the City has so many gluttons and people with refined taste and more money than they need, it is the place to go for a good sale."

"I think you are quite right," said the old woman. "So you are going to the City just to sell these beans at a good price?"

"Yes, just for that," replied the Farmer.

And they walked and walked and talked and talked about whatever came to the tips of their tongues, until they came to an inn.

"We might stop here and have a drop to drink, and give the mules a bit of feed," the Gardener suggested.

"A very good idea," said the Farmer.

At the inn they took the mules to a manger and gave them half a bag of mixed feed, and the animals went at it hungrily. Meanwhile the Farmer, the Gardener, and Old Mother Cricket went into the inn and, each with a good glass of white wine, sat in front of the fire chatting and chatting away.

The Farmer and the Gardener were clearly going to stay there for some time. The old woman got the measure of them, and after a while she stood up, saying: "Well I cannot stay here any longer; it suits me to be getting ahead. Would you like me to untie your mules and start walking on with them?"

"Yes, do," said the Farmer and the Gardener, without suspecting anything amiss.

Little did they think...!

Old Mother Cricket untied the mules and gave them each a lash, and off they went; she followed close behind them with her stick, and whenever she was within reach – *whack!* – she laid it on. Those mules were so belaboured that they were bounding along.

The Farmer and the Gardener went on sitting by the fire at the inn, warming themselves very comfortably and chatting away, without noticing the time. At length, after more than an hour, the Farmer suddenly said: "Good Heavens! God knows where Old Mother Cricket is by now."

"You are right!" said the Gardener.

They stood up, paid what they owed, and went off towards the City at a good pace; and they pressed on and on, all the time looking ahead to see if in the distance they could descry the old woman with their two mules. How could they descry anything? By then the old woman was well ahead.

As luck would have it, she met some merchants, who at once offered to do a deal with her. She did not play the unwilling seller but said she would sell the loads of beans and the mules too.

The merchants were eager buyers, and they made her a good price for the beans, and for the mules. The old woman accepted their offers and said: "The beans are yours. The mules are yours." Then the merchants brought out their money-bags and – *ding-dong!* – counted out the cash on the nail. The old woman gathered up all this money and put it in a handkerchief, which she tied under her skirts; then she went on towards the City, walking as fast as she could. The merchants took another road with the mules and the beans, and they were soon out of sight.

The Farmer and the Gardener nearly burst walking as fast as they could; they were quite bewildered and mystified by not seeing the devilish Old Mother Cricket and their two mules. They were not worried on the old woman's account, but they certainly were about the mules – very worried indeed.

"But what the devil can have happened?"they said to each other. "How can the old woman have made such speed? Never mind; we are sure to find her at St Anthony's Gate."

That was the only hope left. They pressed on as fast as they could, and eventually they reached St Anthony's Gate. They looked and looked everywhere in the hope of catching sight of Old Mother Cricket and the two mules waiting for them. But all their looking was in vain; nowhere could they see a trace of her, neither with nor without the mules. They went from one inn to another asking if such an old woman with two mules had stopped there; but nowhere could anybody give them any news or even a clue.

The two men, as you may imagine, were furious.They cursed and they swore at Old Mother Cricket and the mules, and at the mules and Old Mother Cricket. When they realized that all this cursing was hurting nobody but themselves, they at length said:

"There is nothing for it but to go into the City and walk about there to see if we can catch sight of this old devil; and if she does not hand over the mules double-quick we will beat them out of her. We will flay her alive! There will be no escape for her."

Well, if you will believe it, the first thing Old Mother Cricket did when she was in the City was to go to a good clothing outfitter and to a furniture shop, and she bought her daughter's trousseau and furnishings for the house, so Catherine might be married whenever she wished, because, said the old woman, *Strike while the iron is hot.*

As she had the money from the two mules and the two loads of beans, she paid cash down and asked the shop people to keep what she had bought until the next day, when she would come with a carter to take it all away.

Then she went off to an out-of-the-way inn where the two men missing their mules and their beans would not easily find her; she had supper there and went promptly to bed. The next day, good and early, she got up, paid the inn, and went off searching the streets to find a carter to take the things she had bought. She found one and did a deal with him, and then went with him and his cart to the outfitter's and the furniture shop. They quickly loaded up at the two places, and the carter said:

"Good! To gain time it would suit me to set off at once and go steadily, so as not to tire the animals too much."

"It suits me too if we go right away," said the old woman. "I have no more business to see to in the City."

But she had hardly said it when – *snap!* – she spotted at the other end of the street two men coming along slowly, looking all about them, as if they were dazed. They were none other than the Farmer and the Gardener searching for her, dead tired with looking for her in the City, and saying to each other every now and then:

"We shall never find the old devil. Would she might get cramp in both legs, wherever she is, and stay rooted there for us to catch her!"

When the old woman caught sight of these two she said to herself: "This looks serious. I must be ready for a real show-down." To the carter she said: "You see those two coming towards us? They are acquaintances of mine, and I had quite forgotten that I have some business to do with them. So it will be best if you set off, and I will catch you up, or if I don't I will get a ride from somebody. When you reach my village, if I have not caught you up, ask for the house of Old Mother Cricket, leave the load there, and then go your way." The carter agreed, and he set off for the village.

Then the Farmer and the Gardener spotted Old Mother Cricket and they came up to her flaming angry, as if they would have made mincemeat of her.

"Ah, you old rascal!" they said. "Now we have got you! Where are the mules and the beans, you old thief? If you don't produce them at once we will take you by your scrawny old neck and we will twist it, like killing a hen, you double-dyed scoundrel!"

"Hey!" said Old Mother Cricket. "Be more careful how you talk, if you don't want things to end badly. That's no way to speak to a respectable lady such as me."

"Well, let us have the mules and the loads of beans. Where the devil have you put them? What have you done with them?"

"Don't shout so," she said. "There is no need to disturb the street and create an uproar. What will the passers-by think, all these citizens who look like important people?"

"Do you think you can cheat us again?" said those two simpletons. "We are only demanding what is ours, and it is we who are disturbed. We want the mules and the loads of beans, and the point is that you should hand them over double-quick!"

"Alright," said the old woman, "let's talk about the mules and the beans. You must remember that at the inn where we stopped you told me I could start walking with the animals and you would catch me up. I did as you said, and I walked on and on; every so often I looked back, but I kept going, and you took care not to show up. Anyway, I reached St Anthony's Gate, and there I waited and waited for you to come, but you failed to appear. So at length I said: 'These men must have got lost or had some mishap. The best thing I can do is to sell their loads of beans for them; and then when they arrive they will have nothing to do but pick up the money, turn round, and go home again."

"And did you sell the beans?" they asked.

"Yes, and very quickly."

"You old thief!" they cried. "And who gave you orders to do that?"

"Well, you should have bestirred yourselves and not been idle so long at the inn.What is more, I did another much bigger deal. After I had sold the beans a merchant came by; he spotted the two mules and he exclaimed: 'Oh, what fine well-kept mules! Are they for sale, ma'am? Yes, if you pay enough for them."

"This is really terrible!" said the Farmer and the Gardener. "And did you sell the mules?"

"Yes, as quick as two and two make four."

"Oh, you old devil, you!" they cried. "This is too much!"

"Some saint must be protecting you, since we have not smashed you to bits here and now. If we did not have to settle our reckoning with God, we would flay you right here."

"Why don't you let me finish speaking?" she said. "When both parties have been heard, only then is sentence passed, my good men. And, what do you suppose they gave us for the two mules? Two hundred pounds."

"Is that true?" said the Farmer.

"Absolutely true. Anyway, to prove it to you, let's go to the house where they are keeping the money from the mules and the beans, which also fetched a good price: ten pounds a load. And you can see for yourselves and collect all this money; you will each have enough to buy another mule, and look at the money you will have to spare. I don't think you will still be angry with me."

The two men, hearing all this, were amazed and did not know what to think; they could hardly believe it was all true, nor did they want to dismiss it as all lies, especially as the old woman was pulling them by the arm towards the house where she said the money was being kept.

So they went off behind Old Mother Cricket, along street after street and round one corner after another, and it was as hard as they could go, because the devil of an old woman went whipping along without slowing down or slackening her pace; she kept going like a hare.

At length they came to a very grand house, and she said: "This is where they are keeping the money for me. You stay here; wait just a moment while I go in and warn them – one should never take anybody by surprise – then I will call you, you will come in, and *ding-dong* you will collect all your money on the nail."

The two men, thinking nothing wrong – *who does no evil expects no evil,* as the saying is – waited while the old woman went into the house. This house belonged to a dentist, the top dentist in the City, where many people went to have their teeth put right; he employed two servants to look after the house and to attend to his parishioners.

If you will believe it, the devilish old woman went up the steps into the house and said to the dentist: "Sir, down there I have left two sons of mine who are being driven mad with toothache. If you could pull out all the teeth that are hurting them, you would be doing us a great favour."

"By all means," said the dentist. "This is just what I need – work in my profession. Good! Why don't they come up? Let them come up."

"Just a moment, sir," said the old woman. "I must explain something.The toothache has been so severe that it has affected their brains, and the poor fellows are out of their minds, crazy. Imagine: they have got the idea that somebody will pay each of them for a load of beans and a mule, and there is no way of making them see sense. And then, when they don't get what they want, if I am present, they turn against me, which makes it worse. Therefore, if you will tell me what the extraction will cost, I will pay for it now and leave, to see to some other business that I have."

"Madam," said the dentist, "I charge a pound for each tooth extracted. How many am I to extract?"

"Never mind," she replied. "Here are ten pounds to cover all costs." And she took out ten pounds and gave them to the dentist; and away she went down the steps to the street. She found the two innocents waiting for her there.

"Look," she said to them, "you can go up when you like, and they will pay you at once. I cannot stay any longer because I have a lot of jobs still to do. Good-bye!" And she dashed off at great speed.

The two men went up to the dentist's. They asked for the master of the house, and the servant at the door, who had been warned, showed them into the surgery. They were taken aback at being shown in there and at seeing so many strange-looking tools, and at the gentleman wearing a white apron from his chest down to his feet. So they stood there tongue-tied.

"Good morning, and a good year!" said the dentist. "Are you having a lot of pain with those teeth?"

"What teeth?" they said.

"Come on," said the tooth man. "Don't pretend not to understand. I know all about it, and you may speak in confidence."

"But what do you know all about?"

"That's a good one! I know you have come for me to pull those teeth that are giving you so much pain."

"Sir," they said "no more joking, please, because we have had quite enough of it. For Heaven's sake, please be so kind as to hand over the money left here yesterday by the old woman who has just gone out, because the money is ours, from two mules and two loads of beans that she sold for us."

"Forget it, my good fellows, all that about mules and beans and money, because I know nothing about it and I am not the least bit interested. I am a man who earns his living by pulling out teeth, and I have nothing to do with anything else. So sit down in this chair, and you will see how quickly I can pull out all the teeth that are giving you pain."

"Alright, but who told you we came here for anything to do with teeth?"

"Who else," said the dentist, "but your very own mother, who went down the steps just now and told you to come up."

"And the old rascal told you this story about teeth, and said we were her sons?"

"Certainly she did." replied the dentist. "Come on now, my good fellows; let's get on with the job. Let's not waste any more time. One of you sit in this chair right away, and we will get on with it. What's more, I can tell you that your mother has paid me in advance; so I am quite easy about it and sure of not losing anything over the business."

"Sir," said the Farmer and the Gardener, "if she has paid you, it is her teeth you should be pulling out, not ours – which until now have never given us any pain at all, thank God. And we are not such idiots that we should have them pulled out now, for no good reason. You may pull out the old woman's teeth – the very reverend demon incarnate she is! This is the second time she has tricked us, the old devil!"

"I don't reckon to chase her for her teeth," said the dentist.

"But we most certainly do reckon to chase her! And wherever we find her we will flay her. She shall not get away with it! She cheated each of us of a mule and a load of beans, the old demon, and then she brought us here telling us you were looking after the money for her, and that you would give it to us at once."

"Well, she certainly is a fast mover, this old woman," said the dentist. "You must try and catch her because she has played a really dirty trick on you, which she should never have done."

The Farmer and the Gardener came away from the dentist's furious with Old Mother Cricket, breathing fire and raging. They set off to search for her in the City, asking people if they had seen such an old woman; but nobody could give them any news of her. They were hitting themselves on the head and pulling their hair out; their anger knew no bounds when they saw how they had been left, with no mules, no beans, and no money. If they had chanced to find her then, she would not have been spared; they would have beaten her up mercilessly.

After all, she had tricked them a bit too cruelly.

"And where are we going to find the old devil now?" they said. "We must not waste time. Where will she be making for? Back to her village? Or might she have gone off in another direction that we should never think of? This is no old woman; this is a real devil! Only the Devil himself has bigger horns than she has. May she be struck by lightning!"

Up and down street after street, without knowing where they were going, they found themselves coming out of the City at St Anthony's Gate. Looking around, they noticed a cart loaded

with furniture; they went up to it, without knowing why and without suspecting anything. They stood there for a while looking at the furniture, all brand new and of good quality: a mulberry-wood chest, an olive-wood bed with turned posts and a fine big head-board, two dozen cherry-wood chairs, and other bits and pieces, all nicely varnished and shining like silver, and with a smell of newness given off by the chest, the bed, and the chairs. The two men little thought all this furniture was anything to do with them.

The cart was standing still while the mule drawing it was flicking its tail and trying to drive away the flies; it was clearly getting impatient. The mule took a step forward, and a woman's voice from inside the cart cried out: *Whoa!* And the mule halted.

The two men were so confused and out of their minds that they did not recognize the voice – the voice of Old Mother Cricket. The old devil, as soon as she had told the Farmer and the Gardener to go up to the dentist's to collect their money from the beans and the mules, made straight for St Anthony's Gate so as to be on the road to Manacor as quickly as possible, in the hope of catching up with the carter who was taking the furniture to her village. She found him at St Anthony's Gate talking with a man. When he saw her he said: "You have arrived at the right moment, ma'am. It is quite a time since I have needed to see this fellow, and I have found him here. You will be doing me a great favour if you will get into the cart and keep an eye on the mule while I have my talk."

Old Mother Cricket would have been better pleased if they had set off at once, but it was not to be; and there she was waiting and waiting for the carter, who seemed never to be coming to the end of his conversation with that man. She was thinking:

"It would be terrible if those two oafs came this way! It would be a disaster and a half if they came now."

Well, what do you think? When the Farmer and the Gardener had done looking at the cart-load of furniture at the back and on both sides, they walked on, and when they were ahead of the mule they turned and looked into the front of the cart. And there they caught sight of Old Mother Cricket.

Oh, when they saw her in there! They began shouting like madmen, cursing and swearing without pause, uttering a stream of bad words, both saying:

"Ah, you rascal, you scoundrel! Now we have got you! This time we will kill you! This time you shall not get away with it! You will not live to trick us again! You can begin saying your prayers! We will make a leather bag with your skin! Now you are going to pay for all the tricks you have played on us!"

But do you suppose Old Mother Cricket was at all taken aback by this flood of oaths, curses, insults and swearings that the two men poured over her in their rage? Not a bit; she was not in the least put out, but came back at them as fresh as you please.

"Why all these curses you are hurling at me? Why are you so angry? This is no way to address a respectable woman like me, with insults. Moreover, it costs nothing to speak politely."

"So you will answer us back! After having stolen our beans and our mules, you still come back at us like this? Come on, get down from that cart double-quick and hand over the money from the beans and the mules."

"And did they not give you the money at the house where I told you to go?"

"Do you still have the face to speak of that house, you old devil? It was a dentist's you took us to, and you played the trick of telling him we had toothache and were there for him to pull out the teeth that were hurting us."

"How is this?" said the old woman. "The people at the house, did they not hand over the money from the beans and the mules? Didn't they give you the cash that I left with them to keep safely for me, so you could collect it all without losing a penny?"

"At that house," replied the two simpletons, "they said they were dentists and did not know, or want to know, anything about beans and mules."

"Is that how it is?" she said. "They had the face to play such a dirty trick on us? They shall know all about it, I assure you. They will cough up the money one way or another, even if the Devil is mixed up in it. Let's go straight away to the Law Court! At once! This is no way to deal with proper people!"

Saying this, Old Mother Cricket jumped down from the cart; she went over to the carter, who was still talking away with the other fellow, and said:

"Everything is getting tangled up today, my friend. I have to go to the Law Court now with these two men; someone has done us a dirty trick, trying to cheat us of a big sum of money."

"Never mind," said the carter. "I will finish my talk here and then I will start off at once. If you come back you can get into the cart and we will travel together; and if you don't I will just carry on and we shall meet at your village."

"Very good," she said. "Agreed."

Then she turned to the other two, who were quite astonished at this new act of hers and did not know whether to believe her this time or whether they should wade in and make mincemeat of her.

"Come on," she said. "We have a job to do at the Court. We shall have to tell the whole story to the Judge. Come on, step out a bit more! Make a bit of speed! And don't be afraid; you must not be tongue-tied before the Judge. You will have to speak out strongly, loud and clear!"

What do you think? The Farmer and the Gardener came to believe the old woman was telling the truth, so they followed her through the streets and alleys of the City; she was ahead all the time, and they followed on behind as fast as they could. Strangely enough they quite forgot about the rage they had been in, and about the threats and oaths they had sworn to beat her up wherever they found her. They were quite convinced they were really going to the Law Court to make a statement about the people in the big house having pocketed the money from the beans and the mules, and that the Court would make those people pay, even if the Devil were mixed up in it.

And where do you think Old Mother Cricket took those two innocents? She took them to the recruiting office at the Town Hall to sell them as soldiers for Havana, no less.*

*The Cuban revolt against Spanish colonial rule led to the Ten Years' War of 1868-78 and, with the later intervention of the USA to the Spanish-American War of 1898.

When they reached the Town Hall, which those two bumpkins had never seen before, Old Mother Cricket told them it was the highest Law Tribunal in all Mallorca, and that she was friends with the highest Judge of all. She told them to wait for her a moment while she went upstairs to have a word with him, telling them it was better if she first went in to see him alone, so he should be able to speak more freely and in confidence. The two men waited for her in the entrance of the Town Hall, looking at everything and awe-struck seeing so many gentlemen passing by, some going up and others coming down; and they both said "Good morning, sir" to all of them.

Meanwhile Old Mother Cricket went to where volunteers signed on to sell themselves as soldiers for Havana, and she spoke to the official in charge.

"Good morning, sir."

"And good morning to you too."

"If I don't tell you why I have come here you will never guess."

"You are absolutely right!" said the official.

"Well," she said, "I have two sons, not quite so young as they were, who are determined to volunteer as soldiers for Havana. To tell you the whole truth, they have turned out to be rather dim-witted and much too timid; but as good boys and hard workers I put them above anybody."

"Very good," said the official. "Are we not to have a look at them? Otherwise it would be like marrying without seeing. Don't you know the song:

> I wed without seeing her – my mistake!
> One could hardly do worse, I think.
> She cannot sew and will not bake,
> And she's too much addicted to drink.

And what would my superiors say if I took on two men without seeing their faces or their general appearance?"

"You are quite right, of course," said the old woman. "But I must warn you: if they are made to present themselves all of a sudden we shall get nowhere. If it were enough for you to see them without their being aware of you, then I think we might succeed."

It so happened that at this time volunteers for Havana were very scarce, and the official found it suited him to take on the two men offered to him in this way. Old Mother Cricket showed him the Farmer and the Gardener from a window; the official thought their appearance was good, and he struck a deal with the old woman at two hundred pounds for each of them.

She said she would take the money, and they handed it to her on condition that the two volunteers should be in agreement with all that their mother had said and done. And what do you think she did? She called the two over to her and said to them secretly:

"Right; the Judge is willing to go at once to that house and make them pay up the whole amount, willy-nilly. But this Judge is a Do-it-and-shut-up man who does not like a lot of talk. Now I will present you to him, and you have only to tell him you entirely agree with everything I have recounted, and that it is all the perfect truth. The important thing is not to waste time. The Tribunal should be at the house by now."

The Farmer and the Gardener, quite convinced all this was true and that they had to be quick, presented themselves with Old Mother Cricket before the Havana recruiting official who said:

"Very good! Are you in agreement with everything that this lady has done on your behalf?"

"Yes, sir," they said. "And let's get it done quickly."

"Alright," said the official. "Sit down for a moment and you will soon be attended to."

The two sat down on a bench, looking to right and to left with frightened eyes. And what did Old Mother Cricket do? She saw their attention wandering a little, so she darted out of there and down the steps, took to the street and made like lightning for St Anthony's Gate and the road to Manacor, bounding along at tremendous speed.

Meanwhile a sergeant appeared, summoned by the recruiting official, to take charge of the two volunteers. The sergeant asked the official: "Where are the two volunteers you spoke of?"

"Here they are," said the official

"So it is you two?" the sergeant said, turning to the Farmer and the Gardener.

"That's right," they both replied, supposing that the sergeant had come to fetch them to go and collect the money from the beans and the mules.

"Come on then," said the sergeant. "You go ahead."

And the Farmer and the Gardener, in good spirits and all eager, went off ahead of the sergeant, who said no more than was needed to tell them which streets to take and which corners to turn. Eventually they had the courage to ask him:

"Do you think they will actually hand over the full amount?"

"What amount?" said the sergeant, perplexed by the question.

"What amount! The money from selling the beans and the mules, of course!"

"Beans? Mules? I don't know what you are talking about."

"What is this?" they both exclaimed. "Are we not going to the house where they are keeping the money from the beans and the mules that Old Mother Cricket sold for us, without any order from us to do so?"

"No, mates," said the sergeant. "I don't know anything of these beans and mules and old women that you are burbling about, and I don't want to know. Where we are going is to the Barracks."

"What do you mean *to the Barracks*? What business have we got at the Barracks?"

"That's a good one!" the sergeant exclaimed. "You come and enlist as volunteers for Havana, and you ask what business you have at the Barracks! Or did you enlist just to have a night out in the City?"

"What is it you say?" cried the Farmer and the Gardener. "That we enlisted as volunteers for Havana? Are you joking?"

"Is this a time for joking?" replied the sergeant. "From the Town Hall they sent word that they had two volunteers for Havana, enlisted and paid, and we were to fetch them. So they sent me and, as you saw yourselves, the recruiting official told me you were the volunteers. I told you to go ahead of me, and you did, and off we went."

"Yes, but," said the Farmer and the Gardener, "there, where you found us, was it not the High Court of all Mallorca?"

"A fine kind of High Court! Would the High Court enlist you as volunteers for Havana?"

"But who says we wanted to enlist as volunteers for Havana?"

"Who says? Didn't you hear the gentleman at the Town Hall when he said you were the volunteers?"

"Do you mean that place was the Town Hall?" said the Farmer.

"Do you mean that place was not the High Court?" said the Gardener.

"That place is just the Town Hall," replied the sergeant.

Then the Farmer and the Gardener burst out, with a torrent of oaths:

"It's the devil of an old woman who has tricked us again. Let's face it, we are a couple of four-footed asses, only lacking a halter!" And they went on swearing and cursing at Old Mother Cricket and at themselves.

The sergeant, as you may imagine, was taken aback by all this; he was sorry for these two simpletons, good honest men as they were, so he turned them round and took them back to the Town Hall. He found the official who had enlisted them, and said to the two of them: "Now explain everything to this gentleman, and make a proper confession of it!"

The Farmer and the Gardener explained what had happened with Old Mother Cricket, about the beans and the mules, and the dentist's house; and how finally, with the pretence of going to the law court to recover the money, she had taken them to what she said was the High Court of Mallorca, but that there – according to the sergeant – she had sold them as volunteers for Havana.

When the official at the Town Hall and the sergeant heard all this rigmarole they exclaimed:

"What a devil of an old woman, and no mistake! She is much too sharp for these two simple fellows. It is clear she has amused herself playing ball with them, and expects to get away with it."

Then the official turned to the Farmer and the Gardener and said: "Let's get it straight. This woman said you were her sons."

"She is a liar from head to foot," they both said. "We have no connection with her whatever. She said the same thing at the dentist's, the old rascal."

"What is more," said the official, "I now see she hoodwinked me too. With the pretence that you were very shy, she persuaded me to be satisfied by seeing you from a window. Who would have thought she was so sharp as to deceive me in this way. We made a deal over you two, and she got me to give her the money; and with the money, it seems, she has made off. So the best thing would be for you both to set off at once for your village, and when you catch her you must make her hand over the sum that I gave her – four hundred pounds – and bring it back to me at once; and we shall just be in time to delete you from the register."

"Yes, and more than that," said the Farmer and the Gardener, "we will make her give back not only the four hundred pounds belonging to you, but the money from the beans and the mules as well."

"I wonder," said the official, "whether she will play another trick and cheat you again."

"Never fear." they both said.

Well, what do you think? They asked their way to St Anthony's Gate and from there they set off on the road to Manacor, as fast as they could go. They left off walking only to run. They worked their feet so hard and made such good speed that they caught up with Old Mother Cricket near the pine wood at St John's.

They were on her before she knew it, and she saw that this time it was all up with her and they would finish her off.

"You double-dyed scoundrel!" they cried. "This time we have got you! You will never cheat us again! We are going to carve you up without remorse! You have been laughing at our expense a little too much, and we never gave you any cause. If you don't want to die here and now, hand over at once the four hundred pounds you collected at the Town Hall, and the money you got for the beans and the mules. What matters is the money, the money!"

Old Mother Cricket could do nothing but bring out the handkerchief bulging with gold from under her skirts, saying:

"Here it is – all of it! Take it, but don't kill me!"

The Farmer and the Gardener counted it, and it was all there except for what the old woman had spent on the furniture and the trousseau for her daughter.

The Farmer and the Gardener each heaved a great sigh of relief, I can assure you, and they said:

"As only that amount is missing, then let it be for your daughter, and we will go short as punishment for our stupidity; another time we shall be more on our guard and shall not let ourselves be fleeced by an old woman like you. But for now, to be quite sure, we will tie you to the trunk of a pine-tree, and there you shall stay until we come back from the City after returning the four hundred pounds to the Town Hall. We shall leave you tied up so that you cannot play another of your tricks on us. When we come back from the City we will free you, and you can go off wherever you like."

The old woman protested and said that since she had given them all the money they should let her go in peace; and she gave her word she would have nothing more to do with them. But they would not listen to any argument; they tied her to the trunk of a pine-tree and made off for the City.

They reached the Town Hall and returned the four hundred pounds to the Havana recruiting official. As it was by then quite dark they waited until the next day to return to Manacor.

Then in the early morning they set off for their village, jumping for joy at having escaped so well from the wiles of Old Mother Cricket.

They reached the pine-wood at St John's, but they did not find Old Mother Cricket tied to the pine-tree. Instead of the old woman they found the local hunchback tied up there.

How was that? I will tell you. It happened that soon after the Farmer and the Gardener had left, the hunchback came by on his way to the City. He saw the old woman tied to the trunk of the pine-tree, so he went up to her and said:

"Who tied you up like this, my friend?"

Who tied me up?" she replied. "Never mind who it was; they have made me very happy by tying me up!"

"Oh!" said the hunchback. "Do you mean it was not against your will?"

"No indeed! It was to my great pleasure. Imagine; I was more hunchbacked than you are, and when they tied me up to this tree my hump disappeared at once. As you can see, I have none at all."

The hunchback went up close and looked at her back, and of course he saw no sign of a hump.

"It is true you have none," he said. "There is nothing to show that you ever had. Anyway, my friend, would you be willing to let me untie you, and then to tie me up, and perhaps I could be rid of this devil of a hunchback of mine, which is such an encumbrance."

"Indeed you may untie me," said Old Mother Cricket, "and don't worry I will tie you up as well as I can, so you may be cured in a twinkling."

You can imagine! The hunchback untied the old woman, and then she tied him up, with his hump pressed hard against the tree-trunk.

"Ow! You are hurting me!" the hunchback cried.

"If I don't tie you up tight your hump will not go." And when she had him firmly tied to the trunk of the pine-tree she left him there and made off for her village as quickly as she could.

She walked all night, and by the next morning she was in her village; at her house she found the furniture and her daughter's trousseau, none of which had cost her a penny. Her daughter was duly married, and Old Mother Cricket never again moved out of her village, nor did she ever again see the Farmer or the Gardener.

Well, the Farmer and the Gardener found the hunchback tied to the trunk of the pine-tree, and they made him explain. When they had heard his story they untied him and told him never again to trust old women, because there were some about who were as bad as the Devil himself and only lacked his horns.

The hunchback went off cursing the wicked old woman who had tricked him so badly. The Farmer and the Gardener went on towards home, and I can assure you that for the rest of their lives they were cautious of old women and never again trusted one – just in case...

And Old Mother Cricket, and the Farmer, and the Gardener, lived for years and years, until they died.

And may we all meet in Heaven.

Amen.

The Old Man of the Hut

ONCE UPON A TIME, a long while ago, there was a little old man who was always called the Old Man of the Hut, because he lived in one, on top of a hill. He was so short-tempered and tetchy that nobody would talk to him, and women used to say to their children when they cried:

"If you don't stop crying I'll take you to the Old Man of the Hut; he makes lard out of fat children and broth out of thin ones." And the children would shut up, because they would rather have gone on living than have fallen into the clutches of the Old Man.

In those days the Good Jesus and Saint Peter were walking about the world. One evening dusk caught them near the Old Man's hut, and they saw him gathering a handful of twigs to cook his supper. They exchanged greetings with him:

"Praised be the Lord."

"For ever."

"God give us a good evening."

"It will be good if God wills it so."

"Could you give us shelter for the night?"

"Yes, if you don't mind sleeping on the floor."

"That will be fine."

"Very well, that's settled."

The Good Jesus and Saint Peter went into the hut. The Old Man heated up some soup that he had left over from mid-day, he set the table, and he brought out a crust of bread as hard as a roof-tile.

"Aren't we going to have some slices of bread with our soup?" the Good Jesus asked.

"But this is all the bread there is."

"Cut some, all the same," said the Good Jesus. And the Old Man began to slice the old bit of rye bread; and the more he cut at it, the more slices came. Every now and then he said:

"The Good Jesus is giving us plenty!"

The next day, as the sun was appearing in the east, the Good Jesus and Saint Peter were ready to leave. The Good Jesus called the Old Man and said:

"Well, grandpa, you have treated us very kindly; what would you like as a gift?"

"Ask for Glory," said Saint Peter under his breath.

"I don't care for glories," the Old Man replied. "I'll tell you what gift I would have. That anyone who climbs this pear tree shall not be able to come down until I say."

"It is granted. What other gift would you like?"

"Well, I should like..."

"Ask for Glory!" Saint Peter said again, getting annoyed.

"Let me be, will you!" replied the Old Man, also pretty cross. "Well, the other gift I would have is that with these cards I may never lose." And he produced a pack of cards thick with grime.

"It is granted. Would you like another gift?"

"Ask for Glory, you dolt!" exclaimed Saint Peter, by now beside himself.

"If you had said that when I was in my prime, I would have bashed your face in," said the Old Man, his eyes flashing. Then he picked up a bag that he had just outside and, turning to the Good Jesus, he said:

"The gift I would have is that anyone who gets into this bag shall not be able to get out until I say so."

"It is granted," said the Good Jesus. Then he and Saint Peter went on their way.

The Old Man of the Hut had been kicking about the world for eighty years but he was very much alive. One morning, all of a sudden, Death appeared and without ceremony said to him:

"Hello, Old Man! Come along with me."

The Old Man looked her up and down and then said:

"Very well, I'll come, so long as it's nowhere bad."

"Come on then! Be quick about it! Be quick!"

"What's the hurry?" he said. "It will go on being today till midnight. And by the way, do you like pears?"

"Indeed I do!" Death replied.

"Well, climb into this pear tree and eat as many as you like. I will go and pack my bag."

"Be quick about it, and then we'll get going."

Death climbed into the pear tree and began eating pears, and she went on until she was full to the teeth. But when she tried to come down she found she could not, because the Old Man did not want to go away with her; he wanted rather to go on kicking about the world. And there was poor Death cursing and swearing as if she would set the place on fire.

The Old Man got it into his head to keep her there for a long time. Years and years went by with Death up the pear tree, unable to take anybody away. If any grave-diggers had known about it they would have had something to say to the Old Man, because nobody was dying and they were not earning any money.

Finally there came a day when Death could no longer bear it in the pear tree, and she said to the Old Man:

"Let me go, and I won't bother you any more."

"Do you really mean that?"

"On the word of an honest man."

"But you're not a man."

"Then may I be hanged if I touch you."

"Very well, you may go. If you'd like more pears, do come again."

"I don't care for pears," Death replied; and as soon as she was able to escape she went hot-foot to tell the Devil, who was all ablaze like a penn'orth of matches, because nobody had died and so no damned people had gone to Hell.

When Satan heard Death's story he swished his tail, saying:

"Leave that old rascal to me."

One winter's evening, when it had been raining all day and the Old Man was warming himself in his hut, the Devil turned up, wet to the skin, carrying a couple of souls.

"Hello, Old Nick, what news?" said the Old Man.

"Well, would you believe it? I was coming along the fallow just below here, with these two chaps – one was a publican and the other a smuggler – when we were caught in this downpour; so I came in here for shelter."

"Good, good. Glad to see you. Come near the fire and warm up, since that is something you always need to do."

The Devil came up near the fire. "How about a game of cards?" he said. "It would help to pass the time."

"That's a good idea!" the Old Man said. "And I have some cards... What shall we play for?"

"One of these souls against yours."

"It seems you deal only in souls."

"Everyone lives by the trade he learns."

"Very well, we will play for souls," replied the Old Man, because he knew he could not lose. And, as you may imagine, he won from the Devil both those souls, one after the other – and they, of course, were jumping for joy.

Then the Devil said it would not be Christian of the Old Man not to buy him a drink. The crafty fellow reasoned like this: "To reach the tavern we shall have to cross the torrent, which is running high. If I am lucky enough to push this old chap into the water as we cross over, I may yet win. He is the very reverend Devil. He beat even me at cards, and I thought I was pretty smart."

The Old Man agreed to go and have a drop to drink; and he had the foresight to slip the bag under his jacket. When they got to the torrent the Devil tried to make him go first, but the Old Man saw his ruse and said to himself: "You won't catch me with that trick!" Aloud he said: "No, no, my friend; you're wrong! It would suit you better to get into this bag and let me carry you across; then you won't wet so much as a hair. You are used to living with fire, and with today's drenching and now having to cross this torrent with water up to your waist, you might catch

your death. And think what the world – and especially Hell – would be without you?"

With all this talk the Devil, though he cursed like a trooper, had to get into the bag. I think he must have been at the publican's bottles when he went for the man's soul.

As soon as the Old Man had the Devil in the bag he said: "Now I've got you!" and he went along to see a blacksmith who was a good friend of his.

"Give this bag a good hammering for me," he said to the master blacksmith. So they put it on the anvil and four or five apprentices took a sledgehammer each and bashed away at it – *bang, bang-ti, bang, bang!* – till they were out of breath.

Then the Old Man opened the bag and the Devil, without stopping to see what had hit him, went off to Hell like a hundred thousand streaks of lightning. The men in the forge nearly burst with laughing, and they called out:

"Come back if you'd like some more!"

Then the Old Man went back to his hut, saying: "This is what you might call tremendous; neither Death nor the Devil will come near me now, so perhaps I can go on kicking about the world for a good few years yet."

Many years went by – very many. When the Old Man had turned a hundred he began to be tired of living.

"I can't bear this much longer," he said. "What am I doing messing about in the world for so long? I'll go to Heaven and see if they will have me."

He set off, and he walked and walked through deserts and forests, over mountains and peaks, and between crags and rocks, until he reached Heaven. He found the gates open, so he went in, as cool as you please. He saw the Good Jesus there and went and greeted him.

"You may stay," said the King of Heaven and Earth.

"I came with the idea of staying," said the Old Man, and he went and sat down. But he was soon upsetting things and making everybody laugh, and there was so much noise that you could not have heard yourself speak.

When the Good Jesus heard this turmoil he exclaimed:

"Peter, throw out this mad fellow. Heaven is no place for brawling." And Saint Peter took the Old Man by the neck and sent him packing.

"Heaven rejects me, so Hell protect me." he said as the gates were shut in his face; "so to Hell I will go."

He walked and walked through hills, thickets and ravines till he saw in a deep valley the mouth of a great cave, with a lot of smoke belching out of it.

"This must be hell," he said as he approached. He went into the cave and came to a great gate. He knocked, and a hoarse voice inside said: "Who's there?"

"The Old Man of the Hut."

"Bar the gate! Don't let him in!"

"If you don't open up I'll knock the gate down."

As soon as the gate was open crowds of big and little devils were on him with firebrands.

"Be careful! You might burn a person!" said the Old Man very crossly. "And where is your boss?"

When the devils heard him they dropped their firebrands, muttering between their teeth: "This customer is not like others... What can he be doing here? All the others come from the world with their tails between their legs."

A week went by and the Old Man came out of Hell. He did not like the place and decided to go up to Heaven again. As he was leaving, the devils shut the gate so quickly that they caught a piece of his trousers.

"Only the Devil can live with the likes of you!" he said angrily. "Can't you be a bit more careful? What a bunch of fools, good Lord!"

When the Old Man reached Heaven, Saint Peter was looking out of a window, and from some distance he said:

"Ah, you rascal! You won't trick me again this time. You should have asked for Glory when I told you to, and then I could have let you come in."

"And if I brought you two souls, what then?"

"Well, Paul did say that anyone who saved a soul also saved his own, but... Very well, I'll go and ask the Good Jesus and see what he has to say."

Then, as he was to be granted what he asked, the Old Man of the Hut went and fetched the two souls – the publican and the smuggler. When he came back with them Saint Peter opened the gates to him and he went in. And he is still there if he has not come out.

The tale is ended and if you don't believe it, go and find out for yourself.

Doctor Wink

ONCE UPON A TIME, if you will believe it, there was a man called Mister Wink; he was married but had no children, and he was as poor as a church mouse; most days he suffered the dreadful fate of finding the bread was finished before his hunger was. The poor fellow's stomach was all wrinkles and he felt as if he had rats running round inside him. Eventually he could bear it no longer, so one day he said to his wife:

"Do you know what I have thought of doing?"

"What is that?"

"To buy a doctor's gown and go away somewhere, posing as a new doctor; perhaps in one way or another I could have a little luck and get us out of this miserable state we are in."

His wife thought this was an entirely crazy idea; they did not have the money to buy a doctor's gown, and moreover he would risk killing a patient instead of curing him, and at the same time his own life would be in danger.

Just then Wink happened to hear that in a neighbouring village a doctor had died; so off he went and begged the family, for the love of God and his blessed Mother, to give him as charity a gown belonging to the doctor who had gone to see Saint Peter. The family were such good people that they gave poor Wink a cap and gown, which he put on at once, and went straight off to act the doctor.

Walking along, he came to an inn. He asked if he could stay the night there; they said *Yes* and he stayed there for several days, with plenty to eat and drink. He never said a word about paying, nor about leaving.

The inn-keeper was wide awake, and nobody had ever swindled him; that is to say, nobody had ever left without paying, because he kept his sights on the bull's-eye. One day when Wink had finished his dinner, the inn-keeper approached him.

"Sir, forgive me for troubling you, but you have been here some days and so far you have not offered us any money. We, as you can see, are just poor people making our living from the inn, and the amount of credit we can give is hardly... You understand me, no doubt."

"For Heaven's sake!" Wink exclaimed at this point. "Have you not looked at me? How can you bring up such a matter with a doctor such as I am."

"Do you mean you are a doctor?" said the inn-keeper, surprised and impressed.

"Of course I am a doctor! Or do you have your eyes at the back of your head? Would I wear this gown otherwise?"

"Oh, good sir, forgive my stupidity. I noticed you were not dressed like other gentlemen, and that your clothes were as a doctor's are, but as you never said anything... But look, Doctor, what a lucky chance! We have an only daughter, and for almost a year she has been very poorly. We have taken her to all the doctors we know of, and they have ordered all sorts of remedies and scribbled prescriptions galore, but it has been like hitting your head on the wall; we have seen no improvement. If you would do us the kindness of having a look at her..."

"And where is the girl?" said Wink.

"I will go and fetch her."

He went off and soon came back with the girl. Wink felt her pulse and asked her all sorts of questions about what made her feel ill, and where did it hurt and where did it not hurt, and in the end he got it clear that she felt as if she had a loaf of bread in her stomach, that food nauseated her, and that she had a constant pain in her belly.

"Right," said Wink at length to the inn-keeper. "She has a grave illness, which could go well, or could go badly. She might be cured by certain herbs, which I myself will go and find and pick carefully, one at a time; and then we will apply them, inside and outside."

He took his cap and his walking stick and went off to look for the herbs. Racking his brains over which herbs would be good for the poor girl, he remembered the old saying: *If you have a belly-ache look for mallows.*

"There is no question, mallows will do her no harm, and it is just possible that mallows could cure her." And there was Wink searching and searching away for mallows; and whenever he saw one – *snap!* – he picked it. You can imagine: he soon had a good handful, and made his way back to the inn.

When he got there he had a pot half-full of water placed on the fire, and then he put in his mallows, and there they were cooking away. When the pot boiled he had it taken off the fire, and he said to the inn-keeper's wife:

"If you want your daughter to recover, if you want her to throw off this illness, you must do everything I say and do it just as I tell you. Alright?"

"You tell us, Doctor, what we must do, and we will do it without fail," said the inn-keeper's wife.

"Very well," Wink went on "you must strain these herbs, and the patient must drink the juice as hot as she can bear it, and at the same time you must make a poultice of the herbs and place it on her belly."

The inn-keeper's wife did just that; she began by making the girl drink the juice, and at the same time she made a poultice of the herbs and placed it on the girl's belly, and she tied it on tight so it should not slip off.

And there was the poor girl gulping and gulping away at the hot potion, that mallow-broth! And what do you think? The broth and the poultice caused such a revolution in her guts that there was no stopping it; it broke out upwards and downwards, and the loaf of bread that the poor girl said she felt in her belly disappeared entirely; everything came out double-quick.

The girl was naturally exhausted by the upheaval, which got rid of everything lodged in her belly, but she came out of it sound and well.

The inn-keeper and his wife were amazed and kept crossing themselves; then they could not contain their happiness and delight, and were jumping for joy, as you may imagine. The inn-keeper took Wink aside and said: "Doctor, you have cured our daughter; tell me your fee and I will agree to anything you say."

"Oh, no," said Wink. "If you are satisfied with the cure, give me whatever you think right."

"If I am satisfied? I am so satisfied that I could not possibly be more so." And the inn-keeper went into his bedroom and came out with a bag of money. He opened it and counted out three hundred pounds in full. He put the money in Wink's hand, and Wink put it in his pocket. Then he took his leave of the family and went *tramp-tramp* home.

When his wife saw him dressed up as he was, and with so much money, she could not believe that he had come by it honestly in so short a time.

"You cannot have earned so much honestly! You must have done something wrong. This money must be stolen. Now I see it! I suppose the police will be coming to take you off to prison!"

Wink let her cluck away as long as she wanted, and at length she calmed down; and I need not tell you that with those three hundred pounds they were quite comfortably off.

About this time it happened that the Queen, being very partial to fish, ate some rather too fast; she was careless and a fish-bone got lodged across her gullet. She tried hard either to swallow it or to pull it out, but she had no luck and could not move it; the more she tried the more deeply the bone became embedded. At length the Queen lost her spirits altogether and began to decline. The King summoned the doctors, and there they were poking about in the poor Queen's throat, and to no effect; the bone became all the more firmly lodged. Other doctors were called, and if the first lot had no success, even less had the second lot, and the third, and the fourth ...

Then the inn-keeper, whose daughter Wink had cured, attended on the King and said: "My Lord King, I have come to tell you, in case it should be useful, that I had a sick daughter whom no doctor had been able to put right until we consulted one called Doctor Wink. With his first prescription he made her sound and well. Perhaps this same doctor would be able to cure my Lady the Queen, God willing."

What the inn-keeper said was welcome news to the King, and he at once asked for details of this Wink. Then he had a coach harnessed with four mules and sent it off to find Doctor Wink, double-quick.

The coach set off *clankety-clank. clankety-clank*, with the coachman whipping up the mules, and they went like rockets. Believe it or not, they made such good speed that in a twinkling they were in Wink's village. The coachman halted the mules and asked a woman who was passing with a pitcher of water on her head:

"Excuse me, ma'am; would you tell me, if you will, if you can, and if you don't mind, where Doctor Wink lives?"

"Doctor Wink?" said the woman in surprise. "I don't know of any doctor of that name here. I do know a Mister Wink; he is as well known to everybody as is bad weather, but I don't know if he is a doctor of any sort."

The coachman and the King's men accompanying him, on hearing this, conferred together on what they should do. They decided to call at this Mister Wink's house and see if he was a doctor or what. They asked the woman where the house was, and when she told them they made for it in the coach. They got there and pulled up right in front of the house; one of the men got down and went and knocked on the door with the knocker. A woman came and said sharply: "Who is it?"

"It is God and us," said the man. "Would this be Doctor Wink's house?"

"Doctor Wink?" said the woman. "What have we to do with doctors? Who has turned my husband into a doctor?"

"Do you mean your husband is called Wink?"

"Yes, at your service in any way, so long as it is good."

"Well, by order of the King, he must without fail come with us."

"Oh, blessed Jesus!" cried the woman. "We are lost! It will kill me! I knew he had done something wrong, the rascal, the double-dyed scoundrel! It's to do with all the money that he brought! Rascal! Villain!"

There she was in floods of tears, carrying on, while the King's man was so confused by the whole business that he did not know what to say or what to do. At that moment Wink arrived from taking a walk to stretch his legs a bit; as you can imagine he was mightily surprised to see the coach and four mules, and the coachman and the other men, all very smart and polished.

Wink's wife saw him coming and she went for him like a lioness, weeping and shouting: "Rascal! Scoundrel! Now you will have to pay for your misdeeds! They have come from the King to take you away!"

Then the King's man turned to Wink, saying: "Are you Doctor Wink?"

"The very same," he replied.

"Well then, from my Lord the King, will you please get into the coach and come with us, to see if you can cure the Queen, who has been given up by all the doctors because of a fish-bone lodged across her throat. They have not been able to pull it out nor to make it go on down. Quick, Doctor! We must not fail to arrive in time!"

Wink did not argue about it. He got into the coach, and off it went like a rocket to the King's house; those mules were not running so much as flying. They were soon there; the coach drew up, Doctor Wink got out very smartly; a group of important gentlemen came out to receive him, and they all made for the Queen's bedchamber. The crowd of lords, doctors, servants, and hangers-on greeted the new doctor most respectfully, and he was all the time looking as serious as our Vicar. He came to the bed-chamber and the King came out with tears in his eyes, very upset.

"Good morning, my Lord King!" said Wink. "What the devil is all this about the Queen? How the deuce did she get like this?"

The Queen was stretched out on her bed at her last gasp. She looked as if she were about to surrender her soul to God.

"Doctor," said the King, half weeping and with a big sob, "Doctor, the trouble is this devil of a fish-bone. Doctor, there will be a big prize for you if you can restore her to health, my poor wife. Would you like to consult the other doctors?"

"What do I want with consultations or conferences?" said Wink. "Is not the trouble a fish-bone stuck across her gullet?"

"Yes," said the King.

"Then what need have I for consultations? Does Your Majesty want to see her cured quickly?"

"I most certainly do."

"Then let us have a handful of pine resin," Wink ordered. "Your Royal Majesty can stay and look after my Lady the Queen, and I will go to the kitchen to prepare the medicine."

"Doctor," said the King, "we have here the house pharmacist who will prepare whatever you may order."

"The pharmacist? Does Your Royal Majesty think I would rely on any pharmacist, however smart he may be? I am my own pharmacist."

Wink went to the kitchen, and the King instructed the cooks and kitchen boys all to take their orders from the Doctor. Then Wink placed a pot on the fire and in it he put the handful of pine resin; he told the cook to keep stirring it constantly so that it should melt smoothly. Then he had them bring him a rabbit-skin, and he cut off the skin of the legs, the head, and the tail. Then he said to the cook:

"Good. When the resin is melted and is a good natural pitch, bring it to me, in the pot, in the Queen's bedchamber; I am now going there to make preparations, and I will expect you there."

He went to the bedchamber with the rabbit-skin. All the lords and ladies and young gentry, and all the men and maids and assistants, were watching closely the strange things the new doctor was doing. They whispered among themselves: "But what the devil is this fellow going to do with the pitch and the rabbit-skin? What good is a pot of pitch and a rabbit-skin to move a fish-bone, either up or down? We shall see how this clever man resolves it."

Wink went into the Queen's bedchamber and said to the King: "My Lord King, now comes the crucial stage; I can assure you it will last only a moment."

"What are you saying, Doctor?" asked the King, very upset.

"What you hear," Wink replied. "Anyhow, lay the Queen on her stomach, and when I say *Now!* I want four men to hold her, because a sudden twist could spoil everything."

"Will it hurt her a lot, Doctor?" the King asked.

"Not a lot, my Lord King. Don't worry; it will be nothing much."

So they put the Queen lying on her stomach and four men stood ready to hold her down so she could not move when the Doctor said *Now!*

At that moment the cook arrived, saying: "Doctor, it's boiling."

"Then bring it," said Wink.

The cook went off and came back with the pot of boiling pitch.

Wink emptied it onto the rabbit-skin and cried *Now!* The four men held the Queen very firmly while Wink planted that horrible pitch poultice right on her bottom, on the bare skin. Imagine what a burn it made – terrible.

"OW!!!" cried the Queen. And it was such a sudden, violent, powerful, deep-down cry that with the effort of her whole body, and above all her throat, the fish-bone in her gullet jumped out onto the bed, covered in blood.

The King saw it, picked it up, and looked at it, saying:

"But what is this? Is it the fish-bone?"

"Yes it is," exclaimed the Queen, and a good thing too! I don't feel it now. I am saved, thank God. But how it hurts on my behind! What was it you put on me?"

"It was what brought out the fish-bone," said Wink. "It is not important; your doctors here will soon cure it. It is no more than a scalding on a place where there are no nerves or tendons; it is all flesh there."

The King did not know where he was, for sheer joy. He embraced Doctor Wink, and then he took him to the Treasury and loaded him with golden guineas – as many as he could carry; and I can tell you he managed to carry a good few.

Everybody was astonished at Doctor Wink's success, and amazed at his idea for getting the fish-bone out of the Queen's gullet; and they all congratulated the Queen a thousand times.

"That's a proper doctor," they all said. "What a lively mind! There is nobody like him!"

Meanwhile the other doctors set about curing the Queen's burn. The King caught Wink before he went home, saying: "Doctor, we have a hospital full of sick people, and nobody seems to be able to make them recover and throw off their illnesses. Can we go there now, and will you look at them? Perhaps you could cure them as you did the Queen."

"Alright, let's go!" Wink replied.

They went to the hospital, and there were crowds of sick people; they occupied a whole row of wards. The King and Wink began at the first ward and, going from bed to bed, went through all the wards. Every now and then Wink said in the King's ear, but loud enough for the nearest patients to hear:

"Those in the poorest state of health could be made into broth to strengthen those who are more likely to survive. Those in the poorest state of health could be made into broth to strengthen those who are more likely to survive."

When they had seen all the wards in the hospital, the King and Wink went away. And – would you believe it? – what Wink had said now and then in the King's ear, as they were going the rounds of the wards, was echoed from bed to bed, each patient saying: "Is this how it is? Is it true that those in the poorest state of health will be made into broth to strengthen those who are more likely to survive? Well, they are not going to make broth out of me!" And each one jumped out of bed, got dressed as quickly as he could, and took to his heels as fast as he was able, so that the new doctor should not catch him to make broth.

And what do you think? The next morning, when the King went again with Wink to decide which patients should be made into broth and which should have to drink it, they met one who had just come down the stairs, dragging himself along.

Now, what is this?" said the King

"What do you think?" the sick man replied. "I am quite well now, and I don't need to stay here any longer."

"And what about the others?"

"They have all gone," said the man. "They are all well, like me." And the poor fellow went on his way homewards, creeping along.

"You see, my Lord King," said Wink, "they are all well again!"

The King was astonished, and so were all the people of the Court, and of the city, when they heard about it; and they again loaded Wink with all the gold he wanted. And what do you think he did? He went home double-quick. He caught up his wife, and the two of them left the Kingdom for a place where nobody would know them, so he should not be pressed into curing sick people. He feared that by bad luck something might go wrong and bring unhappy consequences.

And those two bodies, rich and comfortable, enjoyed all their wealth in peace and concord for years and years, and they are still alive if they are not dead.

And may we all meet together in Heaven.

Amen.

Solly and the Mayor

THERE WAS ONCE A MAN called Solly, who was as poor as a mouse and was blessed with more children than you will find flies on a donkey; but he was a bright spark, and as quick as a flash.

One day, when there was not even a mouthful of bread in the house, and nothing to make bread with, Solly went to see the Mayor of the town.

"Mister Mayor," he said, "could you please spare me something in charity? For three days we have been sitting with our mouths open, but nothing has come in, except perhaps a stray mosquito."

"A man like you, with shoulders a yard wide," said the Mayor, "how can you have the face to come begging?"

"Well, what am I to do?"

"Go and steal – you're old enough," said the Mayor.

Solly thought for a moment, and then he said:

"Very well, Mister Mayor, I will go and steal."

It so happened the Mayor had just sent off a ploughman with a yoke of oxen to plough a piece of land that he owned. Near this field there was a very large and thick pine-wood. Solly went and hid in this wood. He was a very good flute-player, and he began to play away *peepity-poop, peepity-poop*, and the more he played the better it got, and the more cheerful and lively the sound became. When the ploughman heard these pretty notes he stopped and listened, so as to enjoy them the more.

"Who the devil can that be playing the flute?" he exclaimed in astonishment. "I must find out."

He left the oxen standing there and went into the pine-wood. Solly saw him and played on as hard as he could; then he began to move away into the wood, with the ploughman following. He went first one way and then another; at one moment he played fit to burst, and at another very softly; and then he was silent for a while, only to begin again. He soon had the ploughman dead tired and utterly lost among all those pine-trees and saplings.

"To hell with the flute, and whoever is playing it!" the fool exclaimed at last. Then he flung himself down on the ground, running with sweat and panting loud enough to be heard three hundred yards away, and cursing the idea of looking for the flute-player.

Meanwhile Solly went in a flash to the pair of oxen; he unyoked them and, with the ploughman's own whip, drove them off to the town as fast as he could go.

When the ploughman had cooled off a bit he said:

"Goodness! I left the oxen there, and if the Mayor should come and not find me at work he will cut my ears off." He got up and made his way back to the field. There he found only the plough and the yoke.

"Oh, horrors!" he cried. "The oxen – the oxen – where are they?" He was as white as a sheet. He ran off to see if he could find them. He asked everybody, but nobody had seen them at all. At length he came on a little old man, who said:

"Yes, I saw Solly taking a pair of oxen along."

The ploughman went to Solly's house and found him flaying one of the oxen.

"You villain!" he cried. "You thief. You double thief."

"You might use more polite language," said Solly.

"You thief – worse than thief. You have stolen the oxen from me, and they belong to the Mayor."

"Well then, they don't belong to the King, do they?"

"You shall pay dearly for it! You shall learn what it means to steal from the Mayor!" the ploughman cried.

"I had his orders to do so," said Solly cheerfully.

"To steal?" asked the ploughman in surprise.

"Yes, to steal. I went to ask him for a little charity, because we had had nothing to eat for three days, and he said: 'Go and steal

– you're old enough.' So I went stealing, and the first thing I came on was his pair of oxen. You may tell him that."

The ploughman had not a word to say.

"'What's more," said Solly, "this ox is going to be very good, you know. What lovely meat! We shall have enough for more than a week. And if you are not in a great hurry don't go; stay and taste it. The wife and children are already frying up a tremendous dish."

The ploughman went and told it all to the Mayor.

"What a dreadful man!" cried the Mayor when he heard the story; and he let go a string of scorching oaths. He went to Solly's house and found him at table, filling himself and all his brood with beef.

"Good morning, Mister Mayor," said Solly. "Fancy seeing you here! If you would care to join us, pull up a chair. This beef is really delicious!"

`How can you be such an ass?" cried the Mayor, furiously angry.

"There's a lot of asses about, you know," Solly replied. "And the worst of it is that the biggest and stupidest of them go about without halter or bridle."

"But have you no shame?" said the Mayor.

"I have shame enough. There are others who don't have any, or don't appear to have any. Have you something to say to me?"

"How can you ask that when you are gobbling up one of my oxen, and have the other hidden somewhere."

"And what has that got to do with it?"

"Do you mean to say your having robbed me of a pair of oxen has nothing to do with it?" exclaimed the Mayor, beside himself with rage.

"For someone else it might have, but not for you," said Solly. "Don't you remember what you said when I came and asked you for charity?" You said 'Go and steal', so I went. I have done no more than you told me to do."

"I see one can't make a joke with you," said the Mayor.

"Is this a time for jokes?" Solly replied.

"Well, anyway," said the Mayor, after going on for some time, "hand over the other ox without any more talk."

"It is being dealt with," replied Solly. "You won't see it again. I have sent it to a place that I know of, and it will not come back until it is flayed and cut up; that will be when we are down to the bones of this one that we began today."

"You wouldn't do that to me!" cried the Mayor, cursing.

"Wouldn't I just!"

"I'll put you in prison."

"You cannot do that. People who obey the Mayor don't get put in prison; and you know very well I have done no more than obey you."

"Alright," the Mayor said at length. "You win; but I tell you that you will remember me."

"Of course I shall remember you," said Solly. "What a lesson you have taught me! I will take all your money, even out of your very hands."

"What's that you say?"

"That just as I took your oxen I will take your money bag. And I am telling you now, in advance."

When the Mayor heard that he was furious.

"I will give you four gold doubloons," he said, "if you can take my money-bag."

"It's a deal," said Solly. "A week hence be ready for me to strike."

The Mayor went home, but he could not get Solly out of his mind. "This man is driving me frantic!" he said. "But he will have to be the Devil himself to get my money-bag." He went and bought two really large bulldogs; he prepared a lot of long thick wooden cudgels; and he drew up his plan of action like this:

"If Solly is unwise enough to come, he will not get away alive. When the dogs have got a firm hold of him I will break every one of these cudgels across his back. That will teach him to play the fool and to throw it in my face if I tell him to go and steal. To make the most of it I will sit in the middle of the house, with a bulldog on each side of me and my money-bag between my legs, with the doors of the house wide open. He will be able to walk

straight in, and his confidence and daring will be his undoing. When he thinks he is going to get his hands on the money-bag he will have the bulldogs on him, and then all these cudgels will rain blows on him. It will be terrific!"

Came the day that made the week. In the evening the Mayor arranged everything as he had said.

Meanwhile Solly took the horns of the ox and fried them in lard; they smelled delicious. As the town clock was striking twelve he set off for the Mayor's house, taking the horns. He saw the house all wide open, with the Mayor sitting in the middle. He walked round a bit and then came up on tip-toe. He saw the Mayor nodding at his post, and when he saw him fast asleep he went in; he threw the horns to the bulldogs, he made for the money-bag between the Mayor's legs, grabbed it, and went off with it like a streak of lightning.

The bulldogs were famished.; the Mayor had not fed them all day so that they should attack Solly as soon as they saw him. Of course, when they got those horns smelling so good they jumped on them and gnawed and gnawed away at them. One of the dogs got tired of gnawing and not getting any meat; he thought the other dog must have more, so he tried to get the other's horn; and there they were in a tussle, snapping away at each other.

With all this noise the Mayor woke up. He supposed Solly had come in and the bulldogs had him on the floor, so he began shouting: "At him, boy!! Get him!! Come on, boy, let him have it!!" And he picked up a couple of his cudgels and went laying about between the dogs yelling:

"Ah, villain! You won't do this again! Now I have you!"

The dogs thought this meant they should be after someone running away, so they bounded out of the house as fast as they could, barking as if possessed by devils. The Mayor looked about but he could not see anybody, neither lying on the floor nor running away.

"And my money-bag " he cried, looking all round where he had been sitting. He looked and looked and searched and searched, but all in vain.

How could he possibly have found it? Solly already had it locked in his chest at home, with the key in his pocket.

The Mayor began to shout like a madman, he woke the whole street, he threw himself on the ground, he foamed at the mouth, he gnashed his teeth.

"What has happened? What has happened?" asked some of the neighbours.

"Would you believe it?" said others."Solly has taken the Mayor's money-bag!"

"He's the very Devil "' exclaimed those who heard the news.

The next day Solly contrived to meet the Mayor, and he said:

"Well, Mister Mayor? Did I get it, or didn't I?"

"Solly," said the Mayor, "let's not be childish about this, or it will end badly."

"For you it certainly will," Solly replied, "but for me it will be different. Your advice to me will cost you dearly. Or do you think that all you have to do is to give advice? You have asked for it. You should never have said 'Go and steal'."

"Solly, don't try this silly business on me. Give me back my money-bag, and that shall be the end of it."

"Give it back? Not on your life! And what's more, I have yet to steal something even more important to you."

"'What's that?"

"I will steal your wife," said Solly.

"My wife? You must be the Devil himself at stealing!"

"You should never have sent me to do it."

"To Hell with you and your stealing!" cried the Mayor in a rage. "What's more, you will not steal my wife."

"I will do it no more than a week from today, and I am telling. you now, in advance."

"Very well, I shall be expecting you, and as Mayor I say that if you come you will not get away alive."

"We shall see about that," Solly replied. "All I need is for you to open the window that looks out over the well where your servants draw water."

"It shall be open," said the Mayor, "and it will suit me nicely because, if that is to be your way in, you will not come in. I myself will grab you by the neck, and even in the very teeth of the Devil I will throw you face downwards into the mud at the bottom of the well."

"Alright, we shall see about that," said Solly.

He went off home. He stuffed an old pair of trousers and a shirt with straw and made a dummy. On the day that made the week, just as the town clock was striking twelve, he was on his way to the Mayor's house.

He saw the window open. The Mayor was inside with two of his men, each armed with a hatchet, one on each side of the window-frame. As soon as Solly should appear in the window they were to let him have it with their hatchets.

Solly came up very quietly, on tip-toe, holding the dummy by its legs; he slowly pushed its head in at the window.

"There he is!" cried the Mayor, and the two men struck hard with their hatchets. They only shaved the dummy a little, because Solly was pretty quick to pull it back.

"Whew, Solly!" the men exclaimed. "We almost cut off your eyebrows!"

"Quiet." said the Mayor. "He may come back."

After a while Solly again pushed the dummy in at the window, and the two men struck again with their hatchets. They were pretty quick to strike, but Solly was even quicker in pulling the dummy back. He did this six or seven times; and the last time, as soon as he had pulled the dummy back, he threw it down the well and then went and hid a little way off.

The dummy made a tremendous splash as it hit the water, and the noise resounded everywhere. The Mayor and his men came running out of the house, shouting like lunatics, and they went and leaned over the well-head.

"We've got him this time!" they cried, jumping up and down. "He can have a nice cool drink! Is it good, Solly? Drink, man, while you are there; drink away – don't be afraid! Weren't you going to steal the Mayoress? Well go on, take her! Hurry up! Don't waste time scratching yourself."

The Mayor and his men went on like this with such stupidities until they had had their say; then they went and fetched ropes and hooks to pull out what they thought was Solly; and there they were fishing away. After a lot of trying they managed to find him. Several times they got him hooked and began to pull him up, but the clothes were far from new, and with the weight of the wet straw they split, and he splashed in again.

"Goodness, Solly!" they cried. "You'll be well soaked by this time! You must be pretty clean by now. No need to go and bathe in the sea next summer!"

Those three men fishing away for Solly had no thought for anything else. All three were glued to the well-head, all leaning over. You might have carried away the house and they would never have noticed.

When Solly saw them so busy, and found the front door of the house wide open, he walked in and went to the Mayor's bedroom.

The Mayoress was there, sound asleep. Solly wrapped the counterpane round her, slung her over his shoulder, and made off with her.

How could the Mayor and his two men possibly be aware of what was happening? They were much too busy trying to get Solly out of the well. At last they succeeded in hooking him properly; they pulled him up and out of the well and saw... It was not Solly but a dummy.

All three of them stood there as if turned to stone; they looked at each other but could not utter a word.

"This Solly is the Devil himself" said the Mayor at last. "How can this be? He must have magic powers."

"Of course, he must have" said the two men together, aghast.

"Because," the Mayor went on, "didn't we all three hear him fall into the well? And wasn't he swimming about in the water? And now it turns out to be a dummy!"

"But of course, Mister Mayor, he's the Devil incarnate, and he's got magic!" said the men again, terrified out of their wits.

In the middle of all this a dreadful idea came to the Mayor.

"Do you know what?" he cried. "The villain has used his devilish arts, and while we were here fishing he has probably stolen away my wife." He ran to his bedroom, and of course he found the bed empty – empty.

The Mayor and his men looked everywhere, but they found no trace of the Mayoress. The Mayor was so incensed that you could have lit a taper at his face.

He went off at once to Solly's and found him at his door, as cheerful and smiling as you please.

"Solly," he said, "You have gone too far this time. That was no trick to play."

"Nor were your words when you told me to go and steal."

"To hell with you and your words!"

"Another time you'll be more careful what you say."

"No more arguing now! I want my wife."

"Your wife? It will be hard for me to let you have her."

"Why?"

"Because I haven't got her."

"What have you done with her?"

"I have sold her."

"You have sold her?"

"Well, what else should I have done with her?"

"Who have you sold her to?"

"Well, as I was carrying her off," said Solly "I met the Devil, and he said: 'who are you carrying there?' 'The Mayor's wife,' I said. 'I will buy her,' he said. 'Alright,' I said, 'I will sell her.' And so we made a deal."

The Mayor nearly burst. When he had done shouting and swearing, he said:

"Solly, have a little pity. If not for my sake, then for God's sake, go and ask the Devil to call the deal off."

"Do you suppose the Devil would call off any deal?"

"It costs nothing to try," said the Mayor. "How much did he give you for her?"

"Three hundred pounds."

"Here's six hundred. Go at once, and for God's sake bring her back – dear Solly."

"Very well; because it's you, I will go."

And Solly went off to the cavern where the Devil usually appeared. When he got there he began shouting out:

"Satan! Satan!"

"What the devil is all this shouting?" shouted the Devil from deep down, below.

"Come up quick!" cried Solly.

"Wait till I lay on some fire-brands."

"Alright, but be quick about it."

Soon there appeared out of the cavern first the Devil's horns, then his head, then the rest of him; and he said:

"Hello, Solly! So it's you! What news?"

"We must call off the deal."

"You mean the Mayoress?"

"Yes," said Solly. "The Mayor is too upset."

"All the better if he is," replied the Devil. "And is that what you came for? What a wasted journey! Call off a deal – me? Don't you know me? I never buy to sell again. Whoever falls into my clutches never escapes."

"I will give you double the money," said Solly.

"Not if you doubled it seven times. I am not interested in money."

Seeing there was nothing to be done, Solly went back to the Mayor and told him what had happened. The Mayor was soon bashing his head against the wall in desperation.

"Very well," he said at length; "here's another three hundred pounds. Go and try again; and if that's not enough promise him all the money I have. If you bring her back to me there will be a nice present for you."

Solly thought it over for a bit, and then he said:

"Very well, I will go; and if I don't manage to bring her back there will be no point in anybody else trying."

He took a spade, a pick, and a rubble-basket, and he went to the Devil's cavern. There he began picking and digging away near the mouth of the cave, and singing song after song.

The Devil down in Hell heard all this noise, and he came up to see what was happening. When he saw Solly he said:

"And now what?"

"I went to confession," said Solly.

"The more fool you, and no mistake! Didn't you have anything better to do?"

"That nettles you, doesn't it?" said Solly. "Well, scratch yourself – your nails are sharp enough."

"To confession! "cried the Devil. "You can put that in the pot and boil it."

"Where you won't boil anything for me is in Hell, if my confession is good. I know you well enough."

"Alright, let's leave it at that..."

"Well, who began it?" Solly replied. "Who sent you to ask me questions?"

"I heard picking and digging, and I thought I would see what was going on."

"The fact is," said Solly, "I have chosen to come here to carry out the penance that my father confessor imposed on me."

"What do you mean by *penance*?"

"I mean that I am doing it. Or do you think I'm one to put things off? The Doctrine says clearly enough that it must be carried out as promptly as possible."

"And what is this penance of yours?" the Devil asked.

"I am to put up some Stations of the Cross, and the first Station will be just here."

"What's that?" cried the Devil. "Are you going to plant a cross here?"

"I certainly am!" said Solly. "And it's going to be a good big one, to be seen from three miles away."

"Is there not somewhere else you could put it – not just here?"

"Here I have begun to dig, and here I am going to put the cross. You can kick as much as you like, but I tell you I have not dug this great hole just for fun."

"But, Solly, can't you see it's like cutting off my legs?" exclaimed the Devil.

"You can mend them," replied Solly.

"How can I come out if you put a cross here?"

"A good job if you never come out again. You can wait till we send for you."

When the Devil saw the game going so badly for him, he thought for a moment and then said:

"Very well; ask me for anything you want, and I will do it if I can – if only you won't put a cross here."

'What I want," Solly replied, "is the Mayor's wife."

"Is that all? Then wait a moment."

The Devil dived down into Hell; after a little he came back with the Mayoress and handed her over to Solly. Then Solly went off with her straight to the Mayor's house.

When the Mayor saw them coming he ran out to give them each a hug. He could not contain his happiness and joy; he threw his hat in the air and he jumped and danced with delight. He hardly knew what he was doing. Then he said to Solly:

"Look – the money that I gave you, the money that you took from me, the pair of oxen... it's all yours. I forgive you everything because you have earned it. You have made me see with my own eyes how wrong it is to give bad advice and to speak evil. I shall be more careful from now on."

Solly went home rich and as happy as could be. With his wife and children he lived in great peace and harmony for a good many years – until he died. And may we all meet him in Heaven.

Amen.

The Reaper and the Old Lady

THERE WAS ONCE a pious old lady who had a field of wheat ready for reaping. She hired a man to reap it for her; she gave him his dinner and reeds to tie the sheaves, and said:

"I don't know whether I shall be able to come to the field."

"Come if you can," he said, but without meaning it; he did not really want her to go at all. When the reaper reached the field the sun was well up, and he said: "It would almost be best for me to have breakfast now, and I can reap afterwards." He had his breakfast, and after that he lit his pipe; and then he felt amazingly sleepy. "It would almost be best for me to have a little nap, and I can reap afterwards." So he lay down, and he went to sleep and snored away.

About midday he woke up; he looked at the sun and sat up. "It would almost be best for me to have dinner now, and I can reap afterwards." He ate his dinner, and having a good bellyful was overcome with drowsiness. "It would almost be best for me to lie down for a bit, and I can reap afterwards." So he lay down again and slept and slept.

Half-way through the afternoon he woke up, lit his pipe, and puffed away, but he felt no urge to take up the sickle. He walked about a bit to stretch his legs, and behind a bush he found a great thing: a cluster of beetles the size of the crown of your hat, all doing what you may imagine.

What do you think the reaper did? He went and fetched his pitcher, and he put the whole cluster of beetles into it saying:

"I will tell the old lady it is a swarm of bees." Then he said: "It would almost be best for me to have a bite now, and I can reap afterwards." He had a bite, lit his pipe again, and sat there. The sun was setting, and the other reapers from round about had finished their work and were returning to the village tired out.

Our man said: "My goodness! I shall be left alone here and I shall be frightened. To hell with the old lady and her wheat; I am going, and that's the end of it."

He gathered up his things, took the pitcher, and set off for the village. He reached the old lady's house.

"Good evening," he said.

"It will be good with God's grace," she replied.

"Why did you not come to the field?" he said.

"I could not manage to. Did it go well?"

"Very well indeed! I have earned two days' wages."

"What do you mean?" she asked, surprised.

"What I say. I have earned a day's wage for the reaping, and besides I have found a swarm of bees."

"On my land?" she asked.

"Yes, certainly."

"Then the swarm is mine."

"Yours? Certainly not! I found it, and it's mine."

"But you were in my employ. Anyway, we must get this settled."

"Yes, let's get it settled. Let's go and see the Mayor."

"Alright we will go to the Mayor; but first I will pay you what you have earned." And the old lady paid the reaper his day's wage; then they went off together to see the Mayor.

They found him enjoying the cool of the evening with his shirt open. When he saw these two citizens approaching he guessed they had a problem; he looked as grave as the parish priest and said:

"What do you want?"

"I have found a swarm of bees," said the reaper, "and I think it should be mine, but this lady wants to have it."

"And what do you say?" the Mayor asked the old lady.

"What do you think? The swarm is mine; I had hired this man and he was working for me; he found the swarm on my land, and therefore the swarm is mine."

"I find the lady is in the right," the Mayor pronounced. "Give the swarm to her," he ordered the reaper.

"Well said!" exclaimed the old lady.

The reaper, pretending to be furiously angry, burst out: "May the bees turn into beetles!"

"Be quiet; don't be malicious," said the old lady.

"Quiet? I wish there were not an ear of wheat reaped on your land!" And the reaper went off quite happy with the day's wage in his pocket.

The old lady went off too, but when she got home she looked inside the pitcher, and of course what she saw was a swarm of beetles. She did not sleep all night with the shock, and the next day before dawn she went off to her piece of land, and... not an ear of wheat had been cut. She stood there frozen, thunderstruck, believing the swarm properly belonged to the reaper and that the Good Jesus had punished her.

But she soon learned that the reaper, instead of working, had been lying down all day. What do you think? The next year, and every year for the rest of her life, on the day her field was to be reaped she went to Mass very early and was at the field before the reaper himself. So nobody was ever able to deceive her again. There now!

If you own a piece of land, look to it.

Martin Heel

THERE WAS ONCE a cobbler who hated being hungry but shied away from work; he liked four feast-days in a row better than one working day. He was called Martin. One day he was cobbling outside, in the sun, and he noticed a bunch of flies settled on the end of a dried fig that he had thrown out.

He gave them a whack with his cobbler's last and saw he had killed four and knocked out eight.

"Look at that!" he said. "With one blow I have killed four and knocked out eight! I am not going to work any more; I will go and tell the King about this!"

He sold his lasts, his sole-leather, and the tools of his trade; he bought a new suit, and all dressed up he went off to the King's house.

He arrived there, presented himself, and said:

"My Lord King, here am I. And I have come to tell you that my name is Sir Martin Heeley, and with one *coup* I can kill *quatre* and knock out *huit*."

"Is that true?" said the King.

"It's more than true!" Heel replied.

"Then I need you!"

"I am at your command."

The next day the King summoned him, gave him breakfast, and said:

"There is a huge animal, as big as three oxen, which from time to time comes into the City, and I cannot tell you what havoc it wreaks. I don't know how many people it kills each year. All my forces have not been enough to rid us of it, and since I am King this distresses me. Now you who are so valiant are hereby charged to kill the monster; and it is understood that if by the evening you have not killed it, we will kill you. Take such troops as you need, and you may get going now."

I can tell you Heel found nothing to laugh about in this, but he did not dare to argue, for fear of the consequences.

After thinking it over he exclaimed:

"If I am to die the death I had better try my luck with the animal, and it will work out as God pleases."

He took forty soldiers and said:

"Forward, the company! Our job is where the animal lurks."

"Come on, then," said the soldiers, and they set off.

On the way the soldiers described to him the animal's powers: with every breath it would throw a man flat on his back; and when it had swallowed enough people it would take nine or ten skewered on a great twelve-foot horn that it had in the middle of its forehead, and would gobble them up when it was hungry again.

Heel did not know what was happening to him, such was the shock. When they had walked a good way they entered a very large pine wood, with a hill in the distance. The soldiers said:

"Sir Martin, do you see that hill?"

"Yes," he said.

"Well, the animal is there."

And suddenl, they heard the most deafening and terrifying roars.

"That's him! That's him!" the soldiers cried, and they turned tail and made off as fast as they could.

Sir Martin at first ran with them; then he stopped and said:

"Fool that I am! Where am I going? Back to the King's house to be killed there? I had better wait for the animal, and it will work out as God pleases."

The animal had smelled them; it was very hungry and it began to run towards Heel; it was coming straight at him with its mouth open a yard, and with every bound, if it struck a pine-tree, it laid it flat.

Sir Martin, when he saw the creature almost on him, tried to run away; but the more he ran the closer the monster came. In desperation he got behind the trunk of a pine-tree; the animal was going at such speed that it could not stop, and it struck the tree-trunk with its horn, which went in a foot deep and remained fixed.

Sir Martin brought out a knife and began stabbing away at the animal's chest and belly. He soon managed to kill it, and then he broke the horn with a stone.

The soldiers had come to a halt on a hillock, and they thought Sir Martin must by then have been eaten and half digested. But they suddenly heard shouts and cries; at first they did not know what it was, but after a while one of them said:

"Blow me down if that's not Sir Martin calling us!"

It was. He was running after them shouting like mad:

"Come and see! Come! I have killed it! Come and you will see."

"That cannot be," said the soldiers. "It's not possible, Sir Martin!"

They turned about and went back with him to where he had done the deed, and they found the animal with its horn broken, all over knife wounds, lying in a pool of blood.

"But, Sir Martin!" the soldiers exclaimed. "'How the devil did you manage to kill it?"

"I seized it by its horn and stabbed it with my knife," he said, while the soldiers exclaimed in amazement:

"But how the devil did you have so much courage and so much strength?"

"You don't know me!" he replied. "I am a man who with one *coup* can kill *quatre* and knock out *huit*."

They cut off the animal's head so that the King might see it. Sir Martin insisted on carrying it, and he held it by the remaining piece of horn.

When the King saw it his hair stood on end.

The news spread through the whole city; everybody was jumping for joy; they all wanted to see Sir Martin, and they carried him in triumph through the squares and streets, saying:

"But, Sir Martin, was it really you who killed the animal?"

"Well," he said, "it was not you, you feeble worms! You don't know me. I am a man who with one *coup* can kill *quatre* and knock out *huit!*"

The King loaded him with gold doubloons. The load was so heavy that he only just managed to reach home with it.

He began living like a lord and splashed his money about wherever he went.

"Doubloons," he would say to anybody who advised him not to spend so much, "were made round so they should roll." And he went on feasting and merrymaking.

A couple of years went by like this. If you will believe it, there appeared in the city where the King lived another great animal, even more ferocious than the first one, and with seven heads. Its lair was in a very deep ravine; when it was hungry it went where it saw it could get the most to eat, and it gobbled up all it could – men, women, children, animals – and left nothing alive. Against it neither weapons, nor troops, nor any human effort, could prevail. The whole city was in mourning.

The King in desperation issued an edict that whoever could kill this dragon should be married to his daughter.

But the dragon terrified everybody so much that nobody had the courage to go and fight it. There was nobody who could not live without the King's daughter.

Seeing nobody came forward, and the dragon was wreaking more havoc every day, the King exclaimed:

"There is nothing for it but to send for Sir Martin Heeley. He is valiant enough; he killed the other animal, so now he must kill this one."

No sooner said than done; the King sent a couple of his men to fetch Sir Martin.

"Set off at once," he said to them, "and don't come back without him."

The men went off, searching high and low for Sir Martin Heeley. In the end they found him.

"Sir Martin," they said, "the King requests you to come."

"What the devil does he want?" said Heel.

"Come with us, and you shall learn it from the King's own mouth."

He went along; the King was waiting for him eagerly, and said:

"If I don't tell you why I have sent for you, you will not know." And he told Heel about the dragon, about how many people it had killed, about how they had tried to do away with it, about the edict he had issued, and how nobody had come forward; and he ended by saying:

"I sent for you because you are so valiant; you killed the other animal, and now you must kill this one. If you kill it you can be married to my daughter; if you don't kill it, it will certainly kill you. So take as many soldiers as you need and get going at once."

When Heel heard these commands he was, as you may imagine, stunned. Then he started cursing and swearing:

"Would the King's men had never found the way when they came to fetch me. Would I had never found it when I came the last time. Who made me a killer of ferocious animals? What if I did kill the other one? How could I help killing it when it was caught with its horn fixed in the trunk of the pine-tree? And if it had not had the bad luck to be caught like that, what would it have done to poor me? And what will this dragon do? They say it has seven heads instead of one."

And he went on like this, and there was not a curse that he did not utter, until at length he exclaimed:

"But what is the use of talking? It is not words but deeds that will get me out of the mire. If you give a ball you must dance, and no argument. A bad road is best travelled over quickly, and what is an obligation has to be faced."

He took forty soldiers. "Come on, to the dragon!" he ordered, and the soldiers, with very bad grace, went with him.

When they were about a quarter of an hour's march from the ravine where the dragon dwelt, the soldiers said:

"Sir Martin, there is the ravine. Carry on walking and you cannot miss it. Let's see if you will be son-in-law to the King."

"Just a moment" said Heel. "You must come with me."

"Not likely!" they said. "We have done more than enough by showing you the ravine."

"To Hell with that! You will come with me."

While they were arguing like this they heard the most deafening and terrifying roars from the direction of the ravine.

"It's the dragon! The dragon!" cried the soldiers, and they turned tail and fled as fast as they could go.

Heel, without thinking what he was doing, fled too. Then he stopped and said:

"Fool that I am! What am I doing running away? If I escape from the frying pan I shall only fall into the fire. And I should deserve a worse fate. Moreover, *poltroons* have no *chansons* sung about them. Come on, face the dragon, and be it as God pleases."

He had hardly finished saying this when there came some ear-splitting roars, louder and more terrifying than before.

The dragon, from inside the ravine, had glimpsed him and was now bearing down on him like a cannon-ball. It was belching fire through its teeth and snorting enough to make your hair stand on end.

Heel turned and ran, and I can assure you that if he did not work his bunions any faster it was because he could do no more; and the dragon was gaining on him all the time.

At his last gasp he noticed a huge lime kiln, empty and open, and he began running round it, and round and round he went. The dragon was now and then almost within reach of Heel's clothes, and his buttocks, but it did not succeed in getting him, because he was doing his utmost.

Quite enraged and determined to cut him short and have done with him, the dragon gave a run and a jump straight across the kiln, but it could not reach the other side and it fell to the bottom.

Heel at once began to pelt it with stones, and more and more stones. The dragon was trying to climb out but the wall was so smooth that the creature could not get a foothold; and if it did find a bit of toe-hold it fell back again because Heel did not stop pelting it with stones. He hurled so many stones that he rendered the dragon senseless, and he smashed all its heads.

Then he ran off to see if he could catch up with the forty soldiers and give them the good news. He saw them running away and he began shouting at them like a madman.

The soldiers heard him, they stopped, and they waited for him, saying:

"He is the Devil, this Sir Martin! It's him coming now. He must have killed it! You will see."

When Sir Martin came up to them and told them, they could hardly believe it. To be quite sure they went to the lime kiln, and there they saw the dragon stretched out dead and smashed to bits.

They stood with their hair on end.

Heel was already beginning to be as boastful as ever, and he was careful not to say the dragon had fallen into the lime kiln by chance.

"But what the devil did you do?" asked the soldiers.

"What did I do? I just killed the beast."

"But how did you do it?"

"The dragon attacked me and so I began pelting it with stones, and I went on stoning it until it was dead."

"You are the very Devil!" the soldiers exclaimed in admiration.

"You don't know me," Heel said again. "I am a man who with one *coup* can kill *quatre* and knock out *huit!*"

They cut the seven heads off the dragon and strung them on a rope; Heel wanted to present himself before the King loaded with this string of heads; and he did so.

The King was amazed. They were all amazed. Soon the city was in a turmoil; everybody wanted to see Sir Martin,, and there was no mouth that was not shouting *Long live Sir Martin!* And they bore him in triumph through all the squares and streets.

"And was it you who killed the dragon?" they asked.

"Well, who would it be if not me?" he would reply. "You don't know me! Do you know what you are, all of you, no matter how much you brace yourselves up? A bunch of cowards, paper people, blind chickens! Do you know what you look like? Ants. If I put a hand on you, you would disappear. Haven't you looked at me? There is courage that never yields! With one *coup* I can kill *quatre* and knock out *huit!* And if you don't believe me let's have more animals with horns on their foreheads! Let's have more dragons with seven heads! You shall see that in the time it takes to say one Our Father they will all be dead!"

When people heard him talking so boastfully they had not the least doubt that he was as capable of doing it as of saying it, and they did not stop shouting *Long live Sir Martin!!! Viva!!!"*

Then the King said:

"A King's word cannot be gainsaid. You have killed the dragon: you shall be married to my daughter."

"Alright let's get on with it." said Heel.

They were married the next day; there was a great wedding feast and merrymaking galore, and everybody was talking about Sir Martin here, and Sir Martin there, and Sir Martin over there, and Sir Martin everywhere.

The King and his daughter were nobody beside him.

Sir Martin was such an eccentric man that he smoked a pipe, and to strike a light he used flint and tinder. He even smoked in bed; there was tinder everywhere and he dirtied the sheets, the pillowcases, and everything.

The King's daughter was greatly put out, but she could not say anything to him because he always came out with:

"What's this now? I am a man who with one *coup* can kill *quatre* and knock out *huit!*"

The King's daughter bore it for a couple of months, until she could stand it no longer; she told her father that nobody could live with Sir Martin.

"Very well," said the King after thinking about it for a while. "We will kill him. Tonight I will have four soldiers hidden under the bed, and when he is snoring they will come out and finish him off." The King gave these orders to four soldiers.

Sir Martin that day was walking about all puffed up like lights-and-onions, with plenty of wind to his trumpet. An old woman came up to him saying:

"Sir Martin, listen to me! Listen, Sir Martin!"

But Sir Martin did not even turn round.

After a while the old woman, who was following along behind him, called out again:

"Sir Martin, for God's sake listen to me! It's not for my good that I have come; it's for your good, Sir Martin."

"What's all this martining?" he said. "If I did not have to account to God, I would kick your guts out. Don't you know that I am a man who with one *coup* can kill *quatre* and knock out *huit!*"

The old woman said nothing but took another street and contrived to meet him.

"Sir Martin," she said, "I am here for your good. Don't be angry; listen to me, for God's sake! You will repent it if you don't listen. Look. I am warning you, Sir Martin."

"Let's see what this old devil wants!" he exclaimed, and he stopped to listen.

"Tonight they mean to kill you when you are asleep," she said. "I know it from the four soldiers who by the king's orders are to hide under your bed. As soon as they hear you snoring they are to chop your head off."

Sir Martin played it his own way, and instead of lying down he sat on the bed smoking and smoking away, pipeful after pipeful, and tinder and more tinder everywhere.

"Why not lie down now?" said his wife.

"Do you know, I don't at all feel like lying down."

"Well, try and feel like it – it's high time!"

"It is still early. And I am a man who with one *coup* can kill *quatre* and knock out *huit!*"

"We know that already," she replied rather crossly.

And there he was, sucking away at his pipe, scattering tinder everywhere, and grumbling the while.

"But don't you see you are preventing a person from going to sleep?" said the King's daughter.

"And my name is Sir Martin."

"Sir Martin? Sir Blockhead!"

"What's that? With one *coup* I can kill *quatre* and knock out *huit.* So watch out, everybody!"

And she could get no further with him. The more she tried the more obstreperous he became. After a couple of hours he said:

"There is somebody in here. I can hear breathing."

"You must be hearing yours and mine."

"I hear yours and mine and another's."

"We are alone here, you stupid!" she said. "You must be dreaming."

"I tell you there is somebody in here. Don't you hear breathing?"

Here one of the soldiers whispered to the others:

"Don't breathe so hard; he can hear us."

And they breathed as quietly as they could, so that he should not hear them at all.

Sir Martin again insisted there was breathing, and the King's daughter went on denying it. In the end he said:

"Light the lamp and we will look under the bed."

"I am not moving," she said.

"Then I will move," he replied. He stood up, lit the lamp, lifted the valance and found those four poor wretches, who were trembling like poplar leaves.

"Ten thousand thunderbolts!" he exclaimed. "And what are you doing under here, you miserable scum, you worse than scum? Didn't I say there was somebody in here?"

"Dear Sir Martin, mercy! Have mercy on us, dear Sir Martin!" said the soldiers, weeping like little children.

"No!" he said. "There is no mercy for you! You are as good as dead!"

"Dear Sir Martin," they cried, "we would never have done it if we had not been ordered to."

"Ah, no?" said Sir Martin. "Whoever does it shall pay for it! Even rats don't escape from me, and with one *coup* I can kill *quatre* and knock out *huit!*"

What with prayers and more prayers, and supplications and more supplications, for the love of God and for the love of his Mother, Heel allowed the four miserable men to go, and they went like ten thousand devils.

When the King had heard what had happened, he said to his daughter:

"My dear, this husband of yours is the Devil incarnate. He makes the sheets dirty with tinder? Patience! Nobody can say a word to him? Patience! He chooses to smoke the whole night through? Patience! For as he is we must suffer him."

The King's daughter did as her father said, and from then on she lived quite happily with Sir Martin, and when her father died the two of them reigned with peace and concord and joy among their subjects. And they are still living if they have not died.

Peter and his Cake

THERE WAS ONCE a man called Peter, who said to himself: "If I have a good harvest this year I will make myself a cake as big as a cartwheel."

He had a wonderful year, and he made his cake, just as big as he had said. When he was on the point of tucking into it, who should come by but the Good Jesus and Saint Peter, who in those days were walking about the world.

"The Lord be praised," they said in greeting.

"For ever," Peter replied. "If you would like to sit down, here are some chairs."

"What an enormous cake!" they said. "Will you eat it all?"

"Yes, and more if I had any more."

"Won't you give us a little?" asked the Good Jesus.

"No," said Peter, "because you pick and choose. Some people you let into Heaven and others you don't."

"But only the good may enter Heaven."

"I don't care about your arguments. I'm not going to give you any cake, so don't go on about it."

So the Good Jesus and Saint Peter went on their way. After a while the Devil came along.

"Is there enough for everybody?" he said, seeing Peter munching and munching away at his cake.

"There won't be any for you," Peter replied sharply.

"And why the devil not?" said the Devil.

"Because you pick and choose; some people you carry off to Hell, and others you don't."

"You fool! Don't you see it's my loss if I don't get them all? Do you suppose that to carry them off I have only to grab and dive down? Don't you know how my greatest adversary hinders me? To get anyone I have to persuade him to come, and to persuade him I have to use a thousand lies and tricks; I can get a soul only if I thoroughly deceive him, give him cat to eat instead of hare, make him see black for white, and make him believe the Mother of God was called Joanna. And when I have nearly broken my horns to catch him, and have done all I can, they still manage quite often to get him away from me."

"All that talk," said Peter, "is nothing but so much argument full of holes. Whatever you may say, you still pick and choose; and I'm not giving you any cake. So now you know."

The Devil had to shut his mouth; there was no danger that Peter's cake would give him a belly-ache.

After a while Death came by. She saw Peter digging into his cake – he had eaten more than half of it – and she said:

"Goodness, Peter! What a chunk of cake! What was it like before you dug into it?"

"Like a cartwheel."

"What an idea to make such a huge cake! Are you going to let me taste it?"

"Yes, you may have some; you don't pick and choose; you carry off everyone and you spare none. Here you are, my dear." And he gave her more than half of what was left. Death, famished as usual, swallowed it in a few mouthfuls.

"Look," she said as she was wiping her mouth. "I should like to repay your kindness. Whenever you see a sick man, look whether there is a fly buzzing by his head or by his feet. If it is by his head he will be well again within three days; if it is by his feet, within three days he will be dead."

When Peter heard this he exclaimed: "Blow me if I ever again touch a spade for the rest of my life!"

He sold his wheat harvest, he bought himself a doctor's gown, and he went off to the City. There he began walking up and down the streets as stiff as a rod and puffed up fit to burst.

People noticed him, of course, and they said:

"Look, a new doctor! A new doctor!"

"Where? Where?" cried those who had someone sick at home.

"Here I am," Peter would say. "What do you want?"

"Doctor, please, please come and look at our sick man and see if you can find a cure for him."

And Peter would go into the room and up to the bed, looking dead serious. He would speak to the patient, pretend to take his pulse, and say he wanted complete silence. The people there would stand with their mouths shut, hardly daring even to breathe. Peter, listening and looking carefully, would see whether there was a fly buzzing near the sick man. If it was by his feet Peter would say:

"There's nothing to be done; he will die within three days." But if the fly was by his head Peter would say: "It's nothing much. He will be right within three days." And he would pull out a scrap of paper and make a few scribbles on it with a piece of charcoal, saying to the people of the house:

"Here, take this to the chemist. He will make up some medicine for the patient to take."

"Doctor, does it matter if he sweats?"

"He can sweat till he has no sweat left; it does not matter at all."

"And may he eat a bit?"

"Yes, he may eat if he is hungry."

"May he eat anything he likes?"

"He may eat forked lightning and all, if he feels like it."

And without more ado Peter would leave the house; however hard they pressed money on him, he would take nothing.

"I will come back in three days' time," he would say. "If it does not work out as I say, we shall be quits; and if it does, you may give me what you like."

If the fly had buzzed by the sick man's feet, he was dead after three days; and when the new doctor turned up the people would always give him a little money – some more, some less – if they were not utterly mean. Now if the fly had buzzed by the patient's head he was fit and well after three days, and when the new doctor appeared they would all hug him so tight that he could hardly get free; and the more they could afford the more they gave him. If it was a fairly well-to-do family they would fill his pockets with money.

"There's one thing, doctor," they would say when things had quietened down.

"What's that?"

"The patient never took the medicine. There was not one chemist who could understand your prescription. We went to all of them."

How could they possibly have understood? Peter knew as much about writing as a donkey does about cooking.

"What's the matter with the chemists round here?" the rogue would say. "It seems I should turn chemist too."

When people saw that the new doctor knew what was wrong with every patient and never made a mistake, they were sure the trouble lay with the chemists, who did not know how to decipher such learned prescriptions.

"What a wonderful doctor!" everybody said. "He has only to see a sick man to cure him, if he can be cured. If only our chemists were not so stupid and could make out his prescriptions."

Soon none of the doctors in the City had any patients, only Peter. He never sat down all day, and he had to go to his inn to empty his pockets twice every morning and twice more in the afternoon, people gave him so much money.

After six months he found he had enough money to last him for the rest of his life, no matter how much he might spend. He took off his doctor's gown and went back to his village. He had to hire a cart to take the huge amount of money that he had made.

When he got home everybody made much of him and wanted to be his friend; he went about so puffed up and pleased with himself that he nearly burst, and he made himself respected no end. He bought a couple of farms and lived like a lord.

He had the prettiest and most delightful garden, where he always went to enjoy the cool of the evening. Years and years went by, and Peter had no worries; he filled himself up, he enjoyed every pleasure, and he left everything else to look after itself. One day he was sitting in the cool of his garden when Death appeared.

"Good evening," she said. "May I sit down?"

"Yes, do," said Peter. "Pull up a chair. You have not seen this garden of mine. Though I say it who shouldn't, it is a first-rate garden; there is nothing lacking."

"Yes, it is beautiful – but I have a better garden."

"Go on with you. Do you think you can match me? Take a good look at yourself. You're no more than a skeleton!"

"Never mind," said Death. "We can easily settle it; I will show you my garden."

"Good – let's go," said Peter, standing up.

"Don't be in such a hurry. This garden of mine is best seen at night."

"A fine sight that must be."

"You shall see for yourself."

And they chatted away until it was quite dark.

"Is it time to go yet?" Peter asked impatiently.

"Yes, we can go now," replied Death. "Come along."

They set off and she took him about an hour's walk away. They came to a walled enclosure with a small door in the wall; she opened it saying:

"Here we are. Come in."

"Is this all the garden you have?" said Peter like a fool.

"This is all," Death replied. "Come in quickly."

Peter went in through the door and looked all about, but he saw nothing except a light near the centre of the enclosure.

"But, my dear woman," he said, "where are the plants and the trees in this garden of yours?"

"There is only one tree," she replied, "but what a tree! You cannot ever have seen anything like it. Come with me, and you can look at it close-up."

They went towards the light, and it turned out to be a huge tree, with no leaves but lots of branches, and at the end of every branch there was a candle burning. Some of the candles were thin, some were middling, and some were good and fat; some were very long, as if they had just been lit, others were more than half gone, others were beginning to burn blue, and some were going out altogether, with nothing left but a bit of snuff.

That tree and all those candles gave Peter bad forebodings, and he was almost sorry he had come. To dispel the unease that was coming over him, he said to Death:

"What the devil are all these candles?"

"I will tell you," she replied. "They are the lives of people. The thin candles belong to people who will have short lives; the fat ones are those who will live long. The candles that are freshly lit belong to children just born, and those that are going out are people who are about to die."

Peter felt hot-and-cold all over. "Is my candle there?" he asked in anguish.

"Yes, of course," said Death. "Do you see that very short one there?" And she picked up a pebble and threw it at a candle that was burning its last.

"Do you see that one?" she said again.

"Yes..." said Peter.

"Well, that's your candle."

Peter felt his head spinning round and his legs turning to jelly. He had to sit down. He was as white as a sheet, his eyes were staring wide and his mouth was hanging open, but not a word came out. He was seized with trembling all over, his teeth began chattering, and he broke out into a sweat, and other things that you may imagine.

"Give me another candle, for God's sake," he managed to say at length, crying like a little child. "Change it for a longer one!"

"That cannot be done," said Death.

"Why can't you change it? Aren't we good friends?"

"Didn't you invite me to share your cake because I do not pick and choose? Come now, go home and pack your bag; and be quick about it because I shall be there before you know it."

Peter suddenly found himself alone in his garden. What had become of Death and the tree with all those candles, and the walled enclosure? He could not make it out, and he was so stupid that after he had thought about it for a bit he said:

"It must have been a dream. I can forget about it. How could my life be so short when I am as healthy as can be? She can't take me off without some good reason."

When he got to his house his supper was on the table, and to dispel all these gloomy thoughts he ate a tremendous bellyful.

"If we burst, here goes!" he said as he was stuffing himself. He went to bed as bloated as a pig that has got into a field of beans. He had hardly lain down when he heard a devil of a fly buzzing by his feet.

"Oh, horrors!" he exclaimed. He called his servant and said: "Go at once and fetch four men."

The servant went and brought them, and Peter said to them:

"Turn me round, head to feet." He thought he could deceive the fly. They turned him round but, as soon as he had his head where his feet had been, the fly was no longer there but buzzing away by his feet.

"Turn me round again," Peter said to the men. They turned him round, but they had hardly done it when that devil of a fly was buzzing away by his feet.

They went on trying and turning him round, but they could never make the fly buzz by his head; it would only do its buzzing by the idiot's hoofs. Believe it or not, Peter wasted all the time that was left to him in trying to deceive the fly; but it was he who was deceived. Almost before he knew it, Death was on him, and she mowed him down with her scythe. He did not even give a kick.

From Death's scythe he fell straight into the talons of the Devil, who was waiting there ready, and who said as he seized him:

"Now we shall see why you wouldn't give me any cake!"

The Devil pitched him headlong into the furnace of Hell, and when he had him there he poked and prodded him with firebrands, and he is still doing it if he has not stopped.

God preserve us all from such a fate, and may we all meet in Heaven.

Amen.

Feigning Dead to avoid paying Debts

THERE WAS ONCE a man who was in debt up to his neck; he owed so much money that he could not think properly, nor see what to do. He reached such straits that one day he took his wife aside and said to her:

"My dear, I cannot go on like this with so many debts weighing on my shoulders. I can see no way out but to feign death. I will pretend to die, and you will set up a great show of tears and distress, for all you are worth; you must go into the street and undo your hair in handfuls, as if you were pulling it out. And the more the neighbours tell you not to cry, the more you must weep and moan. First will come the neighbours to see what has happened, and they will be followed by the people whom we owe money to. When these come you must cling onto them, weeping in floods; you must show them the children, dressed in the poorest rags we have: and by pinching and slapping the children's bottoms or their necks and their cheeks, you will get them all crying, and the louder the better. The thing is to move our creditors to pity: perhaps, with me dead, they will see everything as lost and will forgive our debts, and we shall be able to make a big haul."

"That is a good idea," said his wife, "and for my part you can begin the farce when you like."

So what did he do? He lay down on his bed, well stretched out and stiff, and he looked just as if he were dead. Meanwhile his wife rounded up all their children – altogether quite a clutch of them because every year there was a new one. She never found it hard to remember how many years they had been married, because the children never let her lose count. Well, she dressed them all in the oldest and shabbiest clothes they had; rags of the most ragged.

When she had all the infantry dolled-up in this fashion, she set about distributing pinches and nips and good slaps on their bottoms, round their necks, and on their cheeks. I cannot tell you how those brats yelled and screamed and were all in floods of tears, while their mother cried even more than they did, and kept saying:

"Oh, dearest children, cry, cry, for your father is dead! See him stretched out on the bed! Oh, my precious man, beloved of my heart, dearest of my soul! How sad a death was yours! Suddenly cut down, and without Sacraments! Without the Sacraments you have had to go to the other world! Oh, my poor man! It is all up with me; I shall die of sorrow and they shall bury us together! Weep, my children, weep!"

And while she was reciting all this she kept on smacking them, pinching them, slapping them wherever she could, and she had the crowd of children all crying and howling and making a scandalous noise.

As you may suppose, the neighbours soon began to appear, asking: "What is all this? What is the matter? What has happened?"

"What indeed!" said the wife. "Go into the bedroom and you will see what has happened. My husband, I found him dead! See for yourselves, he is stretched out on the bed! Oh, my poor dear man! It is all up with me – they will bury me with you. The agony of it is killing me; it is killing me, I say, killing me... killing me!"

And she went out into the street crying like one in despair, undoing her hair and pulling at it as if she would have torn it out, and she kept on saying: "Oh, my neighbours all, men and women, have you ever seen a more unhappy woman? Suddenly a widow with this brood of little ones, all so young and so small, and with nothing to fill their stomachs! My poor man! What a sudden death! Who would have thought, an hour ago, that you were to die so soon! You were so healthy and strong! My poor dear man, my beloved companion! I shall never see you again! Oh, miserable me and my poor little ones! The agony of it is killing me, killing me; I say it will kill me here and now!"

By this time the whole street was in a turmoil; everybody came out on hearing that heart-rending lament, and they all went to the dead man's house. They piled into the bedroom as best they could, and there they saw the dead man on the bed, all stretched out and as stiff as a crowbar, and they said: "How sad! He is dead and gone. What a misfortune! And leaving so many debts and so many children! His poor wife, she has reason to weep and tear her hair out, and to do anything wild."

The women among the neighbours came and tried to console her, but she refused to be comforted, saying: "Don't tell me not to weep! I have too much cause to. Put yourselves in my shoes: a widow with all these little ones and not a crust of bread to give them, and loaded with debts. Let me cry – I have good reason to. You can see for yourselves how it is. Oh, miserable me, and my poor little ones! Oh, my poor dear man!"

And it was all tears and moaning and yelling from her and from the brood. The children hearing their mother wailing, and seeing the house and the street full of people, and their father stretched out on the bed and not moving, began to believe that he was really dead and gone, and then they were no longer crying from their mother's slaps and pinches, but because of all the turmoil and upheaval, like ten thousand devils, where nobody could be heard for the crying and weeping and the fearful noise.

Meanwhile news of the man's death had spread through the town, and naturally everybody was sorry for him, dying so suddenly like that and leaving so many children and so many debts.

"Poor kids! Poor wife!" everyone said.

Those who were most disturbed by the man's death were his creditors, to whom he owed so much. "You have seen the last of that money," each of them was saying to himself. "Yes, go now and demand payment; and unless you take payment in children... It was not such good business lending to this poor fellow. It would have been better if I had stayed in bed with a tertian fever on that day, instead of lending him money."

Even so, nearly all the creditors, out of compassion for the woman and the children, went one after the other to the house, to see how things were, and because of their dealings with the dead man. The choice thing was that, each time the woman saw one of the creditors approaching, she put on a great performance of howling louder and making her lament more heart-rending, so as to show how the pain of it all was killing her; and she really looked as if she were about to die and give up the ghost then and there. She would cling weeping to the creditor, showing him the children, all ragged as they were, and all wailing like bagpipes.

"Look at us," she would say. "Have you ever seen such an unhappy woman and such unfortunate children? How can we possibly pay our debt to you when we have nothing to eat? How am I to feed all these mouths? My dear husband would have paid you in time, good man that he was, but, unhappy me and my poor little ones, all unhappy too, how can we ever manage to repay you?"

And the creditor, faced with this picture of misery and misfortune, would feel his heart touched and would say: "We will say no more about the debt, neighbour. The Good Jesus will pay me; he has a good money-bag."

"And is it really true you forgive us the debt?" she would say. And the creditor would reply: "I would not tell a lie at a time like this." Then the woman, to make him say it clearly so that everybody should hear, would ask him again if it was true he forgave the debt, and the creditor would repeat that it was so.

Then another creditor would appear, and another, and another, and for each of them this cunning woman would put on the same performance: great distress, showing him the children, a heart-rending lament, and cries and moans and floods of tears, and lots of noise. And the creditors all fell into the carefully laid trap; they all said there should be no more talk about the debt; they could see very well that she could never manage to repay it, and she would have enough to do to find food for herself and her brood of children; and this clever actress, as cool as you please, made them all repeat before the people present that it was true they forgave the debt. The creditors, to appear generous and noble, all agreed; they saw that in any case they would never be paid, because where there is nothing the creditors – even the King – will lose out.

When the woman saw how all the creditors had appeared and all of them had said, and repeated before the people present, that they forgave the debts out of compassion and pity for this terrible death, she threw herself on the ground as if she were in a dead faint. They quickly applied brandy to her temples, and they fanned her, to bring her round; but she did not stir nor utter a sound. Four men picked her up and took her into the house, and laid her on the chest with a rug and a pillow beneath her; they kept on dabbing her temples with brandy, and two women fanned her.

At length she opened her eyes, looked around her, and again burst into floods of tears, but without throwing herself about or tearing out her hair. While she was carrying on her lament the neighbours set about wrapping the dead man in a shroud, and they sent word to the sacristan to bring a coffin for him to be buried in; and everybody present made the sign of the Holy Cross and said a Rosary over him.

Then the sacristan arrived with the coffin; he put it on a table, took the lid off, and with two other men arranged the dead man in it, and closed it. Then, as darkness was beginning to fall, they took the coffin – with all the crowd following – to the church, where they set it on a table with four candles alight and the lid taken off, as was the custom, with the idea of burying it the next day, twenty-four hours after the man's death. So they left the dead man alone in the church.

Well, believe it or not, one of the creditors who had sold the man some beans, and had never been paid for them, had seen how the dead man was to be left alone on a table in the middle of the church, and he said to himself: "Am I such a fool as to let everything go? I will take his shroud, and I shall at least have something, so the loss of the beans will not seem so bad." Saying this he went off to the church. He went in and saw nobody but the dead man stretched out in his open coffin on the table with the four candles burning. "If I go now and take his shroud," he said, "I run the risk of somebody coming in to say a few prayers and catching me red-handed doing it. It will be better if I hide behind one of the altars; then after midnight I can come out and take the shroud off that rascal stretched out in his coffin, and then run home as fast as I can." He did as he thought; he hid behind an altar, and he waited and waited for midnight, to steal the shroud off the rascal in the coffin.

The rascal in the coffin was beginning to be tired of the farce that he and his wife had set up to avoid paying his debts, and he was thinking: "How are we going to come out of this comedy? Must I wait till they throw me into the grave? The joke of shamming dead would no longer be a joke, and I should be well and truly dead. There is no way out; if I let them throw me into the grave it will be the end of me; what will become of my body? I shall rot away without remission. Do I fancy such a deal? Definitely not! Anyway, between now and dawn I have time to think out what to do. When all is said and done, I think the best thing will be, come midnight, to take to my heels and scurry off to where nobody knows me."

While the dead man was making his plan, stretched out in his coffin, on top of the table in the middle of the church, with the four candles burning – and spluttering all the time because they were made of the poorest wax, provided by the sacristan who foresaw that he would never be paid unless it were in children, which he had no need of, being himself already too well favoured; and he had enough to do filling their bellies, which were pretty capacious and always ready to be stoked up, with the particularity that the better the food the more they went at it, and would not stop until they had finished it or it was taken away...

Well, while the dead man was making his plan, on the stroke of midnight a gang of robbers came into the church after making a big haul at a property where the farmer handled his money by the shovelful; they had cleared him out and left him high and dry. It was said he was a miser and so avaricious that nearly all his money was ill-gotten. The robbers, after stealing this huge amount of loot, believed they had done a good deed, as it is said that to rob a thief earns you a hundred days' pardon.

Anyway, these rascals came into the church to share out the stolen money by the light of the sanctuary lamp; but they saw the dead man stretched out in his coffin on the table with the four candles alight, in the middle of the church, and one of the robbers had an idea.

"Listen," he said, "Do you know what? We should take this dead man off the table; then we can put the money on it and by the light of the candles we can sort it out and divide it up like good brothers."

"Good idea! Good idea!" they all said.

So four of them took up the coffin with the dead man in it and put it on the floor a little way off. Then they emptied onto the table the sacks of money they had stolen, and they began sorting it out, making piles of florins, crowns, guineas, doubloons, and so on. When the piles were made then came the business of sharing them out; each of the robbers demanded preference because he claimed that he alone had done more than all the others together. And there they were squabbling like cats and dogs.

One of them, the smallest and feeblest of the gang, was shouting loudest for the biggest share, while the others thought he had more than enough with the smallest. He was a small man, and of him more than of any of the others you could have said *Short man, long tongue.* He had enough tongue for sixteen, but deeds very few.

Well, believe it or not, he got so angry that he brought out a weapon, an eight-inch knife, and threatened them with it. The others, who knew him well and were quite familiar with what he was capable of, all began to laugh, saying:

"Come on! Put away that knife of yours. What do you think you are doing with it open, brandishing it like that when you are not even capable of sticking it into the dead man lying in the coffin!"

"It's a bet you will not thrust it into the dead man!"

"Into the dead man and into all of you!" said the long-tongued fellow. "Right now you shall see!" And he went over towards the dead man, who had heard all these exchanges and had his eyes wide open to watch the movements of anybody who should come near, and was ready to do his best to keep out of trouble.

He saw the loud-voiced man coming at him, knife in hand and on the point of plunging it into him; so he let out a yell, as loud as he could:

"Help, all the dead!!!"

"Here we are, all ready!!!" shouted the creditor – he of the beans – from behind the altar where he was hiding. His idea was to help the dead man frighten off the robbers.

And were they frightened! Imagine! They believed that all the dead were coming out of the graves, tombs, and sepulchres.

"Fly for your life!" they cried and fled double-quick, like hares. They abandoned all the money on the table rather than end their days in the clutches of the hordes of dead that they imagined were advancing on them. And away they went as fast as they could, some to the east, some to the west, with their heels kicking their buttocks.

The dead man saw the robbers had all fled, and there was no sound of them, so he sat up, somehow managed to undo the shroud, and jumped out of the coffin. The creditor behind the altar, who was peeping out and watching everything, saw the dead man getting out of his coffin, and he said.. "Hey! What is going on? Are you dead or aren't you?"

"Hey to you! Let's not talk about being dead. I have had enough of it! And you over there, are you the one who responded when I cried out, when that robber was going to plunge his knife into me?"

"Yes, I am," said the man from behind the altar. And with that he came out from his hiding place; they came closer together and of course they recognized each other.

"Alright," said the altar man, "but were you dead and have come back to life, or were you only shamming dead?"

"Not that dead!" he replied. "I had no way out, I was so deep in debt. By pretending to be dead I hoped my creditors would take pity on my wife and children and would forgive my debts."

"That was a good idea you had, considering," said the creditor.

"Very well," said the debtor, "what we have to do now is to share out this pile of money the robbers have left on the table – half each."

"A good idea," said the other, "but look: those beans that you owe me for; you must pay up."

"Of course I will pay you, to the last penny."

And so they divided up all those piles of florins, crowns, guineas, and doubloons, like good brothers; and then the creditor said. "Now pay me for the beans."

"Alright, and what is the price I am to pay?"

"As we agreed."

"Wasn't it at fifteen pence a bushel that I bought them?"

"Fifteen and a half," said the creditor.

"Not likely!" said the debtor. "Only fifteen. Remember, you have always been a bit weak in the memory."

"Weak indeed? I see you are trying to do me out of my half-penny."

"Let the halfpenny go, man. Don't bother about little details. Don't you know that who goes in for mean dealings will be caught by mean dealings."

"What you are doing," said the creditor, "is trying to cheat me out of my halfpenny a bushel; and you are not going to get away with it. I want my halfpenny, in the teeth of the Devil and all."

Meanwhile the robbers, running as hard as they could, were finally quite out of breath and had to throw themselves on the ground; and they all lay stretched out here and there, panting furiously. When they had recovered a little one of them said: "Are we going to be such fools that we consent to losing all the money we left on the table in the church?"

"You are right," said the others.

They talked about it for a while and then decided to return as stealthily as they could; and one of them was to go close to the church to see if it were possible to go inside again and save the huge fortune they had lost through their fear of the dead.

So they did that. They set off towards the church. Before they reached the town they sent one of the gang ahead to see how it was at the church; he got there just when the debtor and the creditor were arguing over the halfpenny on the beans.

The robber listened outside for a while, but then he was seized with fear again, and he took to his heels and fled. He went back to his companions and said:

"Fellows, don't dream any more about the money. The whole church is full of the dead, who have shared it all out; the shares must have been so small that they are arguing about a halfpenny. You should have heard them, mates! There was one who never stopped saying 'I want my halfpenny, the halfpenny that is mine by right! And he shouted loud enough, but he did not get it."

When the robbers heard all this, they took to their heels again without any more argument; they feared that people might see them and that the Arm of the Law might come down on them.

By then the man who feigned dead to avoid paying his debts had paid for the beans at fifteen pence and a farthing, as he and the creditor agreed to split the halfpenny. And he went home with the money that he had got from the robbers. Then he called all his creditors and he repaid his debts to the last penny.

He had enough money left to live well and honestly, with his wife and children, for many many years. And – What do you think? – they lived until they died.

And if you don't believe it, go and find out for yourself.

Who will make the Bread?

THERE WAS A MAN who had a most obstinate wife; and he was not easy to persuade, either. One day when there was hardly any bread for their dinner he said: "Wife, will you make bread tomorrow?"

"You can make bread if you feel like it," she said.

"No. You will do it."

"I will not, however pig-headed you are about it."

Knowing how talkative women are, he thought he would catch her out, and he said: "Alright; the first of us to speak shall make the bread." And she nodded her head in agreement.

You should have seen them, both with their mouths shut the whole blessed afternoon and all the evening; they went to bed, and they went to sleep without having said another word.

They woke up in the morning, but neither of them moved from the bed or attempted to get up, so as not to meet anybody and be tempted into talking. Eight o'clock came, nine o'clock came, midday came, and there they were, the two of them, stretched out in the bed, back to back, their mouths shut, just as if they were dead.

The neighbours, seeing the house all closed up, began to feel uneasy and asked each other if anybody had seen them open the house or go away. Nobody had seen a sign of them; nobody had heard or seen them open the house.

"Do you think something might have happened to them?" the neighbours began to ask each other. So they went up to the door and – *knock-knock!* No answer. They knocked again, louder, but still got no response.

They went and reported the matter to the Mayor. Then the Mayor came along with the locksmith. He knocked, and knocked again; but the two idiots in bed refused to move or to answer, so as not to have to make the bread.

Then the locksmith, on the Mayor's orders, fitted a tool into the lock and opened the door. They went in, but did not see or hear anybody. Then they went into the bedroom and found these two stretched out in the bed with their eyes closed, hardly breathing, acting dead.

The neighbours called them and shook them in vain; they could not get a word out of them nor make them open their eyes.

"That's enough!" said the Mayor. "It means they are dead. So wrap them up in shrouds straight away and take them to the cemetery to be buried; and that will be the end of the matter."

Would you believe it? These two, rather than utter a word, let themselves be wrapped in shrouds and put in coffins, and they even allowed themselves to be taken to the cemetery. On the way there each of them was thinking: "We shall see who makes the bread."

When they got to the cemetery it chanced that the grave-digger had a grave already dug for anybody who happened to come along; so he said to the bearers:

"Shall we bury them together?"

"Good idea; together in life, together in death."

"Alright, bring them here," said the grave-digger.

The bearers brought the coffins up to the grave-side, and one of them said:

"Who shall we put in first?"

"The man; he is the heavier," said the grave-digger.

Here he, seeing that it was all happening in earnest, could not go on any longer, and he cried out:

"Just a moment! I don't want to go underneath!"

"Then you will make the bread!" said his wife at once, sitting up in her coffin.

The grave-digger and the bearers fled in terror, and the quarrelsome couple went home.

And he had to make the bread.

The Man who made a Gift of his Estate

A CERTAIN WIDOWER had three daughters, all getting on in years; and the three of them were always asking him to make over his estate to them. They kept on at him so much that at length they persuaded him, and he made a gift to them of everything he owned, which was not much but was something.

When the gift was duly recorded by the notary, things changed entirely in that family: the three daughters took no further notice of their father. This upset him very much; so he went to see a friend, and told him about it. Then this friend handed him a bag of gold coins.

"Take this bag of money," he said, "which I lend to you for a week. This is what you must do: shut yourself in your room; then spread the coins all over the lid of your wooden chest, and begin counting them, making plenty of noise. Your daughters will hear you and will come and spy on you through the key-hole; they will see the gold and will naturally suppose it is yours. Then you will see how they will be nice to you, to get what they can out of you. To each of them, without the others knowing, you must say: 'If you are good to me you will have nothing to complain of'."

The widower very much liked his friend's scheme. He took the bag of money, went home, shut himself in his room, and locked the door. Then he spread out the money on the chest and began counting all those gold coins, bouncing them on the wooden lid.

The daughters soon heard the sound coming from their father's room, so they went up to the door and looked through the key-hole; and they saw all those gold coins on the chest, where their father was counting them and bouncing them to see if they were genuine.

The three women were staggered at the sight of all that money, even just seeing it through the key-hole.

"Well, what a thing!" they said. "Who would have thought father had all that gold! And we believed we had squeezed everything out of him when we made him give us his estate."

So those three greedy women set themselves thinking how and by what means they could manage to get hold of all the money. Each of them decided to be kind to her father, in the hope – one way or another – of getting her hands on that gold. After some time their father came out of his room, locked the door with the key , and put the key in his pocket; and from then on he did not allow anybody except himself into the room.

This gave the three schemers even more to think about, and they paid great attention to their father, to ensure that those gold coins did not go off in another direction.

"Father dear," said one of the three, "would you like a fried red mullet for your supper, after the soup?"

"I certainly would," he said.

She went and bought a mullet and in the evening she fried it and gave it to him for supper, after the soup. Their father tucked in and soon finished it, leaving only four bones.

The next day another of the daughters said:

"Father dear, wouldn't you like a stuffed pigeon?"

"I should indeed," he replied.

"Very well, I will stuff one today for you to have in the evening." So she stuffed and cooked a pigeon and brought it to him after their soup. He went at it with gusto and ate it all; he left nothing but the bare bones.

The next day the other daughter said to him:

"Father dear, would you be cross if you had a roast hen for dinner?"

"Cross, did you say? I should be very pleased indeed."

So she roasted a hen for him and brought it in after the stew; he tucked in and went at it until there was no hen left on the table. Meanwhile he would say to each of his daughters, without the others knowing:

"If you are good to me you will have nothing to complain of."

What do you think? From then on those three odious women made great efforts to treat their father kindly. They hardly let him put his feet to the ground.

At the end of the week the widower took the bag of money back to his friend, with countless thanks for the advice that he had given and for the week's loan of the bag of gold. As a result, he said, his daughters were as kind and attentive as if he had been the Pope.

The old man ate so well with the good fare that his daughters gave him that he got fatter and fatter. Then, when it was least expected, he had an attack of apoplexy, and four days later he died and went to see Saint Peter.

And what did his daughters do? They took him to be buried and they actually said a half-hearted Office for him. They did not trust each other, and they waited until they had said the Office before opening the chest where they believed their father kept his money. They opened it all three together.

Inside the chest they found nothing but a huge hammer. They lifted it out to see what was underneath it, and there they saw a paper with writing on it that said:

Who should sign away his estate
Use this hammer to smash his pate

The three schemers were stunned, speechless; they looked at each other and they thought it was best to say nothing about the trick their father had played on them. They took the blow in silence. That was the best thing they could do.

Old Miss Wind and Old Miss Block

THERE WERE TWO AGED SPINSTERS called Old Miss Wind and Old Miss Block. They had always been for sale in marriage, but what they had never had was a man who was willing to put his neck under the yoke of holy matrimony with either of them. They were so ugly that no man had ever had enough courage.

Old Miss Wind ruled over Old Miss Block, who was so stupid that she spent her time sucking two of her fingers; she had made them quite fine and white.

Well, believe it or not, the King got tired of being single, and he issued an edict stating that he had decided to marry, and therefore all pretty girls between the ages of thirteen and twenty-one should present themselves, and he would choose the prettiest of them all.

A good many girls came, but he was so choosy and critical that he found them all common. Of the many girls who came, not one really pleased him. At length Old Miss Wind went to see the King.

"My Lord King' she said, "I have a girl, the finest and most beautiful creature you ever saw."

"Very good," said the King. "Could we not see her?"

"The truth is, my Lord King, she never goes out of the house, not for anything in the world."

"To come here, would she not leave the house?"

"Oh no, sir," said Old Miss Wind. "You have no idea how sensitive and shy she is."

"Alright then, we will come to your house," the King replied; and he thought: "She must be marvellous if her people are so careful of her. What will she be like?"

Later the King arrived at the house, and Old Miss Wind said: "Your Royal Majesty must have come to see our girl."

"How ever did you guess?" the King replied. "Where is she?"

"In her room, my Lord King."

"Then let her come out."

"She does not like to come out. You don't know how shy she is; and she is so sensitive that the slightest little thing is enough to upset her."

"But how am I to know if she is as fine as you say she is?" the King demanded, beginning to be rather annoyed.

"Do you know what we can do?" said Old Miss Wind. "She will put out two fingers through a crack in the door, and Your Royal Majesty can see them; then if you do not marry her it can never be said she has been seen by anybody."

The King agreed to this. They went to the door of the bedroom and Old Miss Block put out through a crack the two fingers she was always sucking – the only part of her that was fine and white.

The King looked closely at these two fingers and exclaimed: "Oh, how white they are, and how fine!"

"If only you could see the rest of her!" said Old Miss Wind. "I can assure you these two fingers are the darkest and roughest part of her body."

The King swallowed it all. "She is to be the lucky one," he said. "We will be married in a week's time."

Everything was made ready for the marriage ceremony and for a proper wedding feast. When the day of the celebrations came, Old Miss Wind turned up at the King's house leading Old Miss Block covered with a thick veil reaching down to her feet.

The word had spread about that the bride was the most delicate creature, and everybody came to the wedding to see the cat let out of the bag.

"Oh, she must be so sensitive!" they said when they saw her all heavily veiled. When the marriage ceremony was about to begin everybody was saying: "Is she not going to take the veil off now?"

The King thought the same, but Old Miss Wind said: "For Heaven's sake, don't speak of it! Can't you see she is much too shy before all these people. She has never shown her face – never! She would refuse to be married sooner than take off her veil."

When people saw she was not going to show her face they believed all the more that she must be very delicate, and they wanted all the more to see her. The one who most of all wanted to see her was the King.

When the marriage ceremony was over, the festivities began; and Old Miss Block still carefully kept her veil on. Bedtime came, and when the King found himself alone with her he said very firmly:

"Come on, off with that veil!"

"I will take it off tomorrow," she replied.

"Tomorrow?" said the King. "Tonight! Tonight!"

"Tomorrow," she repeated in pathetic tones.

"No! It is going to be now, this minute!" he said, furiously angry. And he had hardly said it when he gave a tug to the veil; it came away in his hands, all torn, and there appeared before his eyes... Old Miss Block.

When the King saw the horror, the dark face, all wrinkles, with no teeth and no hair, he stood frozen. Then he became so angry that he beat her and threw her out of the window – and down she went.

The window gave onto the garden, and Old Miss Block fell into a lemon tree. She was riddled with thorns; her body was running blood from head to foot; and there she was caught, uttering the most piteous groans and sobs.

In the morning three fairies came by; they saw her in that plight and asked her what she was doing there. She told them and they exclaimed: "We could make this poor woman happy. Come on!"

So the first fairy said: "By weird and weird and by my mother's powers, let what I say come true: this old woman shall become nineteen years old." And Old Miss Block became nineteen years old.

And then the second fairy said: “By weird and weird and by my mother’s powers, let what I say come true: she shall become the most lovely and beautiful girl ever seen.” And at once Miss Block became the most lovely and beautiful girl you ever saw.

And the third fairy said: “By weird and weird and by my mother’s powers, let what I say come true: whenever this girl speaks there shall be music of the sweetest. And it was so; Miss Block, bursting with joy, said to the fairies: “May God repay your kindness, my dears.” And as soon as she opened her mouth the music played, and you could have heard sounds of the most, most, most...

At sunrise the King jumped out of bed and said: "Let us see what happened to yesterday's nightmare – that horror of last night." He opened the window and looked out into the garden; there he saw, caught in the lemon tree, a girl as resplendent as the sun; you could not look at her without being enchanted.

It was Miss Block. The King looked at her thoroughly, all over, and the more he looked the less he could make out what had happened.

He said to himself: "Is this the one I threw out of the window last night? Either I was drunk or it is not her." And then he called to her: "Listen, pretty one; are you the woman I threw out of this window last night?"

"Yes, I am," she replied, and the music played with the sweetest and purest sounds.

The King was then even more astonished, and he went on: "And was it to you that I was married yesterday?"

"To me, yes, to me," she said, and the music played and played. And every time she spoke the music played away for all it was worth, making the most enchanting sounds.

"Men and maids!" cried the King. "Go at once and bring up here the light of my life!"

They went and they brought her up; but they had to put her to bed because the early morning dew had caught her; she was shivering with cold and was desperately sleepy.

Miss Block was then the Queen. She had a crowd of ladies-in-waiting and chamber-maids who did not let her put a foot to the ground.

Old Miss Wind came to hear of this, and she went straight off to the King's house to see for herself. She said she was the Queen's sister, but nobody believed her; still she swore and swore she was, and made a shocking row about it. She went on so much that, to get rid of the annoyance, they let her in.

She went into the bed-chamber and up to the bed, and she put her face close to her sister's till she touched her with her nose, which was not small. When she saw her sister looking so young and beautiful she exclaimed: "Either my eyes deceive me or you are not my sister."

"Your eyes do not deceive you," said the Queen, "and I am your sister."

"But you were even older and uglier than I am, and now you look about twenty years old and stunningly beautiful!"

"I became like this."

"And how did you do it?"

"I had myself planed."

"Who planed you?"

"A carpenter over the road."

"I should like to go there!" exclaimed Old Miss Wind.

"A very good idea!" said the Queen. "He will take off the wrinkled crust, as he did for me, and the skin will be left smooth, firm, and pink and white."

"Good. I will go straight away!"

"Yes, do," said the Queen, "and you can tell him I sent you."

Old Miss Wind, leaving her sister in bed without another word, ran off as if her shoes were on fire, straight to the carpenter's shop.

"Good morning to you," she said breathlessly. "Don't you know why I have come?"

"Not if you don't explain, madam," said the carpenter.

"Well, I have come with instructions from the Queen that you should plane me."

"Plane *you*?"

"Yes, me, me. Don't pretend you don't know what I mean."

"Madam," said the carpenter, "I don't understand you."

"Don't you? And I speak quite clearly, thank goodness."

The carpenter found her so determined, and again and again saying the Queen had sent her, that at length he said:

"Very well; so you want me to plane you?"

"That is why I have come!" said Old Miss Wind.

"Then lie down on this bench."

And she lay down on it. The carpenter took the largest plane he had and began running it over her, and on he went. Here he took off a piece of cheek, and there an ear, now he laid bare some ribs, and then took a slice of calf off her leg. And Old Miss Wind, between sobs and groans, kept saying:

"Suffer to be beautiful! Bear it to become young."

She so badly wanted to become young that she suffered till she could bear no more. She had had a mirror brought, and she looked at herself from time to time, to see if the wrinkles were going away and if any trace of beauty was beginning to appear; but the more it went on the worse she looked. There came a point where she no longer looked like a human being; she was a terrible sight.

At length she told the carpenter not to plane any more; and she turned up her toes and died.

God will have forgiven her.

Amen.

Dogs and Hares

THERE WAS A TIME when dogs and hares were the best and closest of friends; they were never apart, they were always seen together, and there were never any differences between them.

One summer's day they went out to stretch their legs and to look for some fun; they happened to come on a large cistern, which was nearly full of the clearest of water and invited a swim.

Moreover, there was a very hot sun that was burning the hares' backsides and making the dogs pant furiously with a hand's breadth of tongue hanging out. In those days dogs were just as hot-blooded as they are now, and just as fond of diving into water and getting wet. So it was that as soon as they saw the water in the cistern they said:

"Shall we have a dip?"

"You jump in," said the hares. "We would rather watch you from the side."

"Will you wait for us a while?"

"Of course we will. Have a nice swim."

"Alright," said the dogs, "we will have a dip; but we must take off our shoes, because if we get them wet they will not last any time at all."

They took off their shoes and left them near-by, and then – *Splash!* – they all jumped into the cistern, and there they were jumping and plunging about and pushing each other in all directions. They were enjoying it wonderfully and were taking no account of the time.

What do you think the hares did when they saw the dogs so taken up with their swimming? They put on the dogs' shoes and ran off as fast as they could.

When the dogs were tired of playing frogs they came out of the cistern, and they found no shoes and no hares.

"Those rascals have made off with our shoes!" they said, cursing.

"They will pay dearly for this!" Furiously angry, they went off looking for the hares, determined to finish them off wherever they should find them.

From then and for ever after, dogs have been unable to abide hares; they will search for them ceaselessly, and if they find one they will chase it and will not be satisfied until they have caught it. When dogs see hares with such good shoes*, stolen from them, while they have to go barefoot, the Devil fills them with anger, and they will never forgive the hares the trick they played at the cistern.

After all, it was a bit too much.

* Hares' feet are covered in fur; hence the saying that they wear shoes.

The Vixen and the Hedgehog

IN THOSE FAR-OFF DAYS when animals talked – as stones do today – a Vixen and a Hedgehog together contracted to do a job of cutting thistles. They agreed on a payment of fifteen pounds with no extras but a jar of honey, to be given to them straight away.

It was given to them, and the Hedgehog said:

"Do you know what I think? We should put it aside for finishing day."

"No, you are wrong," the Vixen said. "Let's have it now while it is fresh, it might go rancid later."

"How could it go rancid if our job is for only four days?" said the Hedgehog. "Besides; if we eat it now what shall we have for finishing day?"

"Alright," said the Vixen after a moment's thought. "You want us to put it aside? We will put it aside, and no more argument."

They hid it away in the stump of a wild olive tree; and the next day at the crack of dawn they went to the thistles and began working.

The Hedgehog went at it with a will, but the vixen hung back all she could. When the sun was two hours up she was overcome with the most terrible lethargy. Then she moved away a little and began to cry out:

"What's that? What do you want? What's the matter? What is happening?"

"What's all this?" the Hedgehog asked.

"Would you believe it?" said the Vixen. "A neighbour of a sister of mine is calling me. I will just go and see what she wants."

The Vixen went off a couple of hundred yards, and came back.

"My dear fellow," she said to the Hedgehog, my sister has had a baby and has sent for me to be Godmother. I told the neighbour I could not go because of my obligation under our contract, and that I did not have the face to leave you. But she said: 'Watch your step! Don't do such a thing to your sister; she does not deserve it, and let me tell you she would take it very much to heart'."

"Never mind," said the Hedgehog. "You go, and don't worry. I am not that much bothered. Anyway, I might find myself in the same position, and I think you would not mind at all if I were to leave."

"But of course I would not!" the Vixen exclaimed. "I should be glad for you to go. So, very well, I will go."

Where the slyboots went was straight to the jar of honey. She held it to her lips and she sucked and sucked, and she took a good pull at it.

Then she saw a shady spot that she liked; she lay down in it and stayed there until the sun was setting. Then she got up, stretched a few times, and went off to find the Hedgehog.

She found him, giving no rest to his jaws, cutting and cutting thistles; he had cleared a huge area.

"All this time?" said the Hedgehog to the Vixen when he saw her.

"My dear fellow!" she said. "Don't speak of it! I am quite done in! I feel I might be seriously ill through being so angry! Oh, what tiresome people! In vain I told them I was in a hurry, that I was needed, that I could not stay. But they kept on saying: 'Come on! Don't be so impatient on the one day in the year that you come!' And there was I fuming away. At length I said: 'To hell with you all!' and I came away. As I am a vixen, they will never again drag me into being a godmother."

"And what name did they give the baby?" the Hedgehog asked.

"Commencella," said the Vixen. "It's a girl."

"What an awkward sort of name," the Hedgehog said.

"It is a name that suits her very well," the Vixen replied.

"Commencella," the Hedgehog was muttering to himself. "I cannot see the sense in it."

What a commotion he would have made if he had known that what had Commenced to disappear was the honey in the jar.

The next day they went again to the job and they set to work; but if the Vixen was not feeling like work on the first day, she was feeling even less like it on the second day.

The Hedgehog nearly burst working and never complained; but the vixen was really afraid of those thistles and it grieved her soul to do them any harm. When the sun was two hours up lethargy overcame her completely, and she whispered, very softly so the Hedgehog should not hear:

"Fools can get on with the work; I am not doing any more." Then she began crying out: "What's that? What is it? What is all this shouting? I heard you!"

"What now?" asked the Hedgehog.

"The neighbour of a cousin of mine is calling me. I will just go and find out what she wants." And the Vixen went off a couple of hundred yards and then came back.

"What is it?" said the Hedgehog.

"Would you believe it? Another complication: a cousin of mine has just got married and is inviting me to the wedding feast. I said to the neighbour 'Tell her I am grateful for the thought; but she must not take it ill if I don't go. I cannot conceivably go. I have a contracted job that I cannot leave; I have already abused my partner's kindness, and I am the last person to leave somebody else doing the donkey-work, or to eat the juicy tops and refuse the dry stalks.' But, my dear fellow, the neighbour went on and said: 'Look, you should not insult your cousin like this; she does not deserve it. And what a one she is! It is enough that she said: 'She must come! If she does not come, let her never look me in the face again! Tell her that'."

"There's nothing for it; you will have to go," said the Hedgehog.

"But it is not right," the Vixen went on "that you should have to toil away here with the thistles while I am away on family affairs."

"But it is your cousin, and one must respect one's relatives," said the Hedgehog. "Anyway, you will make it up another day."

"Very well then; if you really don't mind, I will go."

"You go and don't worry!"

Where the cheat went was to the jar of honey. She put it to her lips and sucked and sucked away until the jar was half empty. She wiped her mouth, she lay down in the shade, and went on lying there with no desire to get up. Towards evening she said:

"Heavens! The sun is down among the trees and the Hedgehog will eat me alive!"

She got up, stretched a bit, and went off to find the Hedgehog. She found him sweating away cutting thistles, dead tired.

"All this time?" He said when he saw her.

"Oh, my dear fellow! Don't speak of it! I have never been so angry! I am sure to get the colic! The little that I ate was bound to be like lead inside me. I shall never again go to a wedding feast. What a way to die! There was dish after dish, each better than the last; and they made a fuss if you did not try them all: 'Taste this, take some of that, just a mouthful to see how good it is! Come on! Don't be shy! Don't you like it?' And there was I saying: 'Will this never end? Do they think my stomach is a bottomless pit?' And then there were nuts, and toasted almonds, and dried fruits, and doughnuts with honey. And then came the ball. 'Won't you dance?' And the ball was in full swing while I was fuming away. And I had to do all sorts of tricks to extricate myself."

"And what is the name of this tiresome cousin of yours?" said the Hedgehog.

"Midella."

"What a funny name" said the Hedgehog to himself.

What a commotion he would have made if he had known it was the honey in the jar that was mid-way down.

The next day they went again to the thistle-cutting and got down to the job.

The one who really got down to it was the Hedgehog; the Vixen went at it much more calmly. She needed half an hour for each thistle, and every few moments she had to get rid of the prickles.

The sun was hardly two hours up when she said to herself:

"I cannot go on like this. May I turn into a thistle myself if I ever contract another job of thistle-cutting! Let the Hedgehog cut them down! Or the Devil himself if he wants to!"

Then she began shouting loudly: "What is it? What is it? What do you want? I heard you; I am not deaf."

"Now what?" said the Hedgehog.

"Somebody is calling me; I think it is a neighbour of a daughter of a first cousin of mine."

"I can tell you one thing," the Hedgehog said; "these neighbours and cousins of yours are making things pretty difficult for us."

"Don't speak of it! It sets my teeth on edge. Anyway, I will go and see what she wants."

She went off a couple of hundred yards and then came back.

"What an affair!" she cried. "It's as if there were a conspiracy."

"And, what is it about this time?" the Hedgehog asked.

"Would you believe it? An aunt of a first cousin of mine has died, and a neighbour has come to tell me, and to say they are expecting me to be there for the burial."

"That is really too much!" said the Hedgehog. "And do you have to go?"

"What do you think?" the Vixen went on. "The first thing they will say is that I have behaved badly; and the neighbour made it quite clear: 'Come on, we must go! They are all waiting for you, and they will not take her away or bury her if you are not there.' 'But I have contracted a job of thistle-cutting, and for three days I have not done a stroke of work because of commitments that have arisen.' 'But you cannot rebuff her by not coming,' the neighbour said. 'You cannot do that to her. You don't want people to speak ill of you'."

"There is nothing for it," said the Hedgehog. "You have to go."

"I hate to go, and I hate not to go," said the deceiver.

"Never mind; go and don't worry. You will make it up another time. Come back as soon as you can."

"Never fear about that!" said the Vixen.

And off she went straight to the jar of honey. She had barely reached the spot when she put it to her lips, and she sucked away until there was no honey left. There were only the dregs, a little sediment.

She saw a nice shady place, stretched her bones out flat, and lay there until the sun was well down among the trees. Then she got up and went to find the Hedgehog. She found he had not eased off from the morning until then, and all the thistles were cut down.

"All this time?" he said, more than half angry.

"Yes, all this time," she replied. "Hang me if I ever go again to a funeral! I thought it was never going to end. If they had not been so keen to sing – which I was not – we should have been done quickly. But they went at it hard, as if they could not stop, and they walked to and fro; and sometimes they stood, sometimes they sat, and sometimes they squatted. I don't know how many times I wanted to get hold of the dead aunt and throw her into the grave; then we could have been finished with it at once. How sorry I am I did not do it."

"Don't say that!" said the Hedgehog. "That is not the sort of thing to do."

"And is it a good thing to finish off a person's patience?" the Vixen retorted with flashing eyes.

"My dear," the Hedgehog went on "in a case like that you just have to put up with it and keep your mouth shut."

"But it is very hard on a person with a tender conscience" she exclaimed. "I am a hard worker, and it is not in my nature to be idle, nor to see others so. God alone knows how I have suffered and how angry I have been! Moreover I am quite sure the annoyances I have had these past three days will come out and make me ill."

"And what was the name of this aunt of your cousin's whom you have buried?" the Hedgehog asked.

"It was Finishella," the Vixen replied.

The poor Hedgehog saw no sense in such an outlandish name.

"Finishella." he muttered, "what strange names! I never heard anything like them."

The next day the Hedgehog had to go alone to the thistles. The Vixen had had a very bad night; she had only been able to sleep from when she went to bed an hour after sunset until dawn the following day. There was no part of her body that was not ill; she had a fever too. It was because of the three annoyances she had suffered through having had to be godmother to Commencella, having to go to Midella's wedding and to the funeral of Finishella, and having hardly been able to cut any thistles at all.

The Hedgehog swallowed it all and said:

"Don't move, my dear. Perhaps you will sweat it out and it will go. Forget about those three annoyances, and don't worry; I can finish off the thistles on my own. The important thing is that you should be well for finishing day."

And he went off to the thistles. There was half an hour to go before sunset when he had them all with their stalks in the air. He went back, very pleased, to tell the Vixen. She was so glad, and the news gave her so much pleasure, and restored her so well, that she was just like a lamp that is going out altogether for lack of oil and is suddenly filled up again.

"My dear darling Hedgehog!" she said. "My beloved sweet friend, I think tomorrow we could celebrate finishing day. If you will believe it, I have sweated plenty. I am a new vixen. I don't know why, my dear – this morning so prostrate and this evening feeling so lively."

"Tomorrow then," said the Hedgehog, "we will go early to the farmer and get the work accepted."

The next day they both went; the farmer accepted the job and gave them the fifteen pounds. Then, as cheerful as an Easter morning, they went to celebrate the finishing with that jar of honey.

The Vixen felt its weight and said:

"It does not weigh as much as sawdust! What can have happened to this honey?"

The Hedgehog looked inside, and he turned pale.

"This is awful" he said. "It's empty!"

"Empty?" said the Vixen. "Did you only say you wanted to keep it for finishing day, without meaning it?"

"I said it and I meant it" the Hedgehog protested.

"I see," said the Vixen. "If I were you I would keep quiet about it. Is that a trick to play – to guzzle all the honey?"

"I will be hanged if it was I who ate it! It must have been you."

"You will be sending me back to bed if you go on like that," said the Vixen grimacing.

After much arguing the Vixen said:

"Look, it is easy to find out who has eaten the honey."

"How?"

"We lie down on our backs with our bellies in the sun. The one whose belly shows shiny will be the one who ate the honey!"

"Yes, I like the idea," said the Hedgehog. "Let's do it."

They lay down on their backs with their bellies in the sun. The poor Hedgehog, exhausted by the past three days' hard work, at once fell asleep like a log. The Vixen was not so sleepy; when she saw he was sound asleep she got up and. fetched the honey jar; she turned it upside-down over the Hedgehog's belly, and a trickle of dregs came out. With her paw she spread it about, and of course the Hedgehog's belly was shining like anything.

She put the honey jar back in the same place and then began to shake the Hedgehog.

"Come on, you rascal! Look at this belly of yours! Open your eyes and take a good look at it, and you will see whether it shines or not."

The Hedgehog woke up and looked at his belly. When he saw it so shiny he was quite taken aback.

"It is true my belly is shiny," he said, "but it is even more true that I never touched the honey."

"You will deny there is God!" retorted the Vixen, and for good measure she heaped insults on him.

The Hedgehog was as furiously angry as Nero, and then he thought up a good ruse.

"Look," he said to the Vixen, "I am not satisfied with this test we have tried. You say it was I who ate the honey; I say it was you. God in Heaven knows who it was, so let's not argue any more. We will run a race, and the winner shall take the fifteen pounds from the thistle contract."

"You a runner?" exclaimed the Vixen. "You may be, but you don't look as if you were."

"Do you know what that is? The excuse of a bad payer, fear of losing."

"You are the liar!" she retorted. "We can run the race when you like."

"Tomorrow morning, then" he replied.

Near-by there was a good straight wall separating two arable fields, and it must have been half a mile long.

"The course shall be this wall," said the Hedgehog. "We shall start at this end, one on each side; when we reach the other end we turn round and come back; the first to arrive back here will have won the race."

"Alright, alright!" said the Vixen, quite sure of winning.

She could not understand why the Hedgehog wanted to challenge her at running. Her confidence was her undoing.

The Hedgehog that night went in search of some of his relatives, and he stationed one of them every so many yards all along the wall, hidden in the rosemary plants and bushes there. At sunrise the Hedgehog was at the end of the wall where they had to start. The Vixen turned up and said:

"Come on! What has to be done let's do it and get it over quickly."

"Come on then!" replied the Hedgehog.

The Hedgehog placed himself on the side of the wall where he had all his relatives hidden, and the Vixen took the other side. Then. *Ready , Steady , GO!* and off they went.

The Vixen went at good speed, and from time to time she called out:

"Hedgehog, where are you?"

"I am here," called back the hedgehog-relative hidden a little farther ahead.

"The devil you are!" said the Vixen, hearing him ahead of her. And she pressed on, calling out again:

"Hedgehog, where are you?"

"I am here," called back another hedgehog farther ahead.

"The devil you are!" cried the Vixen, trying to run even faster.

She nearly burst with running, and whenever she called out "Hedgehog, where are you?" she was answered by the hedgehog hidden ahead of the spot where she was. Every time she heard that the reply came from farther ahead, but she never noticed they were different voices.

In the end, when she was a hundred yards from where they had started, the Hedgehog – who had not moved from there – looked round the end of the wall saying:

"Come on, lazy-arse! As if you were going to your death! By the time you move one foot the other has taken root! The fifteen pounds are mine!"

The Vixen did not finish the course. She turned tail and ran off cursing and swearing and letting out a string of oaths enough to set the whole place on fire.

The Hedgehog gave a shilling to each of his relatives who had helped him, and with the rest of the money he lived rich and contented until he died.

I came along today
With a little bit of cheese,
But the cats along the way
Attacked me if you please,
Miau! And took it all away.

Why it is that when Bees Sting they Die

WHEN THE GOOD JESUS had created bees, they found that the honey they made was very good, and they saw how from their combs wax candles were made and used in church; then they became full of vainglory, and they were so presumptuous that they dared to confront the Good Jesus with this:

"Seeing we make such precious and exquisite things, we need to guard them from people who would take them from us; so we ask you to grant us the grace that when we sting we may kill."

"Oh, really?" said the Good Jesus. "You mean you want to kill people? Don't you know I cannot in any way suffer those who are vengeful? Alright, I am telling you now that in future when you sting, far from killing others, you shall yourselves die. So be careful."

Ever since then, when bees jab their stings into you their guts run out and they die. It is not good to be so spiteful.

The Dog, the Cat, the Ram, and the Cock

ONE DAY TOWARDS EVENING Bill's Dog went for a stroll. He passed near Peter's farmyard where he saw the Cat and said:

"Come on, let's go and stretch our legs a bit."

"Good idea," said the Cat; "let's go." And off they went.

"Do you think we shall catch anything?" said the Cat.

"I have no idea," the Dog replied.

And he had hardly said it when – *Whoosh!* – he raised a rabbit: he dashed after it – *yip! yap! yip! yap!* The rabbit saw a tree trunk looking like a burrow, and dived into it in a flash. The Dog was checked; but the Cat went in after the rabbit and, as you may guess, caught it and pulled it out.

"Now I have my supper," said the Cat.

"Just a moment, my friend!" said the Dog. "I am the one who has supper here. The rabbit is mine."

"Yours? When it was I who caught it? Not likely!"

"Do you know what you have? Too much lip!" said the Dog. "Do you think you are a hunter? You know nothing about hunting. Don't you know that a rabbit belongs to the one who raises it and a hare to the one who catches it?"

"What I do know," the Cat replied, "is that if I had not pulled it out the rabbit would still be in that burrow."

At this the Dog, beginning to get angry, said: "You don't want to give way; neither do I. We must settle it in court. Let's go to town."

"Let's go straight away then," said the Cat; and off they went towards the town. On the way they came on a Ram. "O Ram," said the Cat, "will you come with us? We are going to court with this rabbit, and you could be my advocate."

"Seeing it is you, I will come," the Ram replied, and on they went, all three. Farther along the road they came on a Cock. "O Cock," said the Dog, "will you come with us? We are going to court with this rabbit, and you could be my advocate."

"Seeing it is you, I will come," the Cock replied, and on they went, all four, and on and on.

By the time they had reached Vincent's farm it was beginning to get dark. "Gentlemen," said the Cock, "I cannot see any longer, and I will go no farther." The others begged him to go on, but they could not move him. At length they said:

"Alright, let's stay the night at this farm, and we will move on again early tomorrow morning."

When they came up to the farmhouse they heard voices inside:

"I have nine."

"I have ten."

"I have ten."

"I have nine."

The Dog said: "These must be robbers sharing out money that they have stolen. Let's see if we can give them a fright!" Then he went up to the door, knocked loudly and shouted:

"Open, in the King's name!"

When the robbers heard this they jumped up and, leaving all the money and everything, fled like ten thousand streaks of lightning, and never looked back. And they ran until they were completely out of breath. Meanwhile the Dog, the Cat, the Cock, and the Ram were bursting their sides with laughter.

Then they went into the house; they found a table with a pile of gold and silver coins on it, and in the kitchen a pot of meat and rice boiling away on the stove.

"What the devil!" said the Cat. "The Dog claims the rabbit is his, and I claim it is mine. If we go to court it will not be mine or his, but will end up with those pen-pushing animals that live there. Don't you think it would be better if we put it in the pot – then we can all have a share of it."

"A good idea! Good idea!" they all cried. And what they did was to take the meat and rice out of the pot, because it was done, and

then they put the rabbit in the pot with the broth, and put it back on the fire. It was soon cooked; they mixed rice and meat with rabbit, and they tucked in; they were soon as fat as pigeons.

Then they shared out the money, and they went to bed. The Cat curled up in the hearth, the Cock perched on a shelf in the kitchen, the Dog lay down behind the door, and the Ram slept in the cool of the yard outside.

When the robbers were tired out and nearly dead with running, they stopped; and when they had rested a bit one of them said: "Are we such cowards that we are not going to see if we can recover what we have lost?"

"You are right!" the others exclaimed, and they started back. When they were near the farmhouse they all stopped; fear gripped them again and they did not dare go any farther.

At length one of them summoned up his courage and said: "Alright. You wait for me and I will go and spy things out." Making as little noise as possible, he went up to the house; he reached it without noticing the Ram; he tried the door and found it was not locked; he opened it very slowly and went in. There was not even a fly to be heard, and it was all in darkness; he could see nothing at all. Feeling his way, he went into the kitchen and put his hand up to the shelf to get a lucifer match. He had hardly done so when the Cock, perched on the shelf, pecked out one of his eyes. So as not to make a noise, he suffered without uttering a sound, determined to go on. When he had got his match he went towards the hearth to light it; he saw two things glowing and, thinking they were embers, he thrust his match at them. But they were the eyes of the Cat, who with a fierce hiss dug all the claws of both fore-paws and hind-paws into the man's face. He could bear no more and took to his heels. Then the Dog attacked him and tore off one of his buttocks; and in the yard, as he went, the Ram gave him such a ramming that it split his rectum.

The luckless man, as you may suppose, fell to the ground more dead than alive, with the most piteous groans and sobs. As best he could he got up again and, at times on his hands and knees and at times limping along, he came near his companions, who heard his moans and groans and went to help him.

"Oh! Oh!" he cried. "Oh! I am dead I can do no more!"

"But what happened?" they asked. "Tell us what happened."

"Oh! Oh! I am dead, I tell you."

"Not likely! You are caterwauling too hard to be dead. Tell us what happened."

"Well, I went in; the house was all dark. I went to the shelf to find a match, and I found one; but there was a shoemaker there who took my eye out with his awl. I tried to light the match at a couple of embers that I saw in the hearth, but there was a wool-carder there who left my face a wreck. I fled for my life, but behind the door there was a blacksmith who attacked me violently with his pincers and took off one of by buttocks; and to finish me off, out in the yard, up came a barber, syringe in hand, and he gave me such a syringing that he has split my rectum. Oh! Oh! Oh! I tell you I am dead!"

The others picked him up and carried him to a cave in the mountain near there.

Early in the morning the Cock woke up; he called the Cat and the Dog and the Ram, and, feeling well in the stomach and even better in the pocket, they returned each to his home.

And I came along with a morsel of cheese, but on the way the cats – *miaow! miaow!* – got at it and left me not a bite.

The Charcoal-Burner's Daughter

ONCE THERE WAS a Charcoal-Burner who had one son, one married daughter, and two unmarried girls. The King was out hunting one day and he passed by the Charcoal-Burner's cottage; there he saw the youngest daughter, a girl of sixteen, as pretty as can be, whose name was Cathy.

"The Lord be praised," he said in greeting.

"For ever, my Lord King," the girl replied.

"What are you doing?" the King asked.

"I am cooking up-and-downers," she said.

"Up-and-downers?" exclaimed the King, quite perplexed. Then he noticed a large basket full of something. "What is in that basket?" he asked.

"Whispering," said Cathy.

"Whispering?" the King repeated, without any idea of what that might mean. And then he said:

"Where is your father?"

"Pulling people out of their homes."

"And your mother?"

"She is weeping for last year's pleasure."

"And your brother?"

"He is out hunting. He will leave what he catches and will bring back what he could not catch."

The King was quite mystified by all the things that this cheeky girl came out with.

"Tell your father to come and see me this evening," he said to her; and he went on his way.

In the evening the Charcoal-Burner appeared at the King's house and said: "Good evening, my Lord King. Are you well? What can I do for you?"

I am well, thank God." said the King. "I passed by your cottage today and met your daughter; she is a very bright spark. I asked her a few questions and she gave me answers that have left me mystified. She said she was cooking up-and-downers."

"She was right," said the Charcoal-Burner. "They were chick-peas; when the pot boils they come up and go down; one moment they are up, and then they are down."

"She is the very devil, that girl!" said the King. "She also said that inside a large basket there was whispering."

"It is true," said the Charcoal-Burner. "Our other daughter was there with no clothes on. The two girls have only one dress between them; they wear it for a day each, and the girl who is not wearing it hides in the basket if anybody comes, and she whispers so that nobody shall know she is there."

"She is the very devil, that girl!" said the King. "And she told me you were pulling people out of their homes."

"That was true," replied the Charcoal-Burner. "I was pulling up vine-stocks."

"She was quite right, then. And she said her mother was weeping for last year's pleasure."

"Indeed she was. Last year one of our daughters was married, and the day before yesterday she died – may she be in Heaven with all the departed – with my wife there, you see, to lend a hand. And she and all of us were weeping, and weep now, for the pleasure we had last year at the wedding."

And the Charcoal-Burner burst into tears.

"Don't cry," said the King. "God willed it; he knows what he is doing and never errs. Another thing that your clever girl said to me has mystified me more than anything. She said her brother had gone hunting and that he would leave what he caught and bring back what he could not catch. Who could understand that?"

"I will tell you," the Charcoal-Burner replied. "He went to delouse himself; he killed and left the lice he caught and brought back on his body those he had not been able to catch."

"She is the very devil, that girl!" said the King, full of admiration. "Look, if I cannot outwit her I will marry her."

And what do you think he did? He took three eggs and broke them into a bowl ; he beat them for a good while and then said to the Charcoal-Burner:

"There. Take these eggs to your daughter; tell her to put them to hatch, so we may have some poultry when we are married."

"My poor child! How will she manage this one?" the Charcoal-Burner was saying as he returned to his cottage. When he got home he gave his daughter the message.

"Are you worried by that?" she said. "Wait a moment and you shall see." She took several handfuls of oats, ground them thoroughly and said to her father:

"You see this flour? Take it to the King and tell him to sow it, so we may have some oats to give to the poultry when we are married."

The Charcoal-Burner went and did as Cathy had told him; the King was left speechless. After thinking about it for a long time he took a piece of cloth and cut it into very small pieces, no bigger than your finger-nail.

"Here," he said to the Charcoal-Burner. "Take these to your daughter and tell her to make swaddling clothes for when we are married and may have a child."

"My poor girl! How will she manage this one?" the Charcoal-Burner kept saying as he returned, all upset, to his cottage. When he got home he gave Cathy the King's orders, and she exclaimed:

"Is that all?" She took a couple of handfuls of twigs, broke them up as much as she was able, and gave them to her father.

"Take these to the King," she said, "and tell him to make a cradle, just in case."

He went off to the King's house and repeated Cathy's order. How could the King have known what to reply? He thought and he thought how he was going to outwit her; at length he took a basket and said to the Charcoal-Burner:

"Here, take this to your daughter and tell her to fill it with laughter."

"My poor child! You will never get out of it this time!" the Charcoal-Burner kept saying on his way back to his cottage. And with his head in the basket he went Ha! Ha! Ha! with the most forced laughter. And could he fill the basket? Not likely!

When he was home and Cathy had heard the King's command she said to him:

"Are you worried by that? Go and catch three dozen small birds; put them in this basket and cover them with a cloth. Then go to the King's house and wait until he is at table; give him the basket, as from me, and tell him to take the cover off."

The Charcoal-Burner did as she said. It happened that the King had a large party of guests. He took the cover off the basket and out came that crowd of birds; some of them flew at the jugs of water and the carafes of wine; others upset plates and bowls as they flew about; others went for the heads and the shoulders of the guests; others brushed the diners with their wings on the forehead or the cheeks or the ears; and there were some well-favoured noses that got quite a few pecks. Things were upset, wine was spilled, stains appeared everywhere, and there were shouts and turmoil; everybody had to burst out laughing, and they nearly died laughing so much.

The King, quite worried that he was still coming off second best, thought about it very hard and then came up with an idea that he was sure would defeat the Charcoal-Burner's daughter.

"Alright," he said to her father, "tell her to come here neither dressed nor undressed, neither on the road nor off the road, neither riding nor on foot."

"My poor girl! This time you will not be able to do it!" he kept saying, all upset, as he returned to his cottage. When he got home and Cathy had heard the message she said:

"Are you worried by that? Go to Ses Planes and bring me back a mountain billy-goat – a good wild one."

Her father went, bought the goat, and brought it home.

Cathy undressed and wrapped herself in a net; then she mounted the goat and set off for the King's house. The goat, as you can imagine, was jumping and leaping about, bucking and

kicking. At one moment it was keeping to the road, and at another it was off the road; it would throw Cathy and she would mount it again; it would throw her again and she would remount.

So she was neither dressed nor undressed, neither on the road nor off it, neither riding nor on foot.

When the King saw her he said: "A King's word cannot be gainsaid. I have not been able to outwit you, so let's be married."

"The sooner the better," she said.

"It will be soon enough, please God," said the King, "but it is subject to an agreement."

"What is this agreement?" she asked.

"That you may not give advice to anybody. If you do, you will have to go back to your father's cottage."

"And shall I not be allowed to take anything away with me?"

"Well, so you shall have nothing to complain of, you may take one jewel," said the King.

"Only one? Large or small?"

"It does not matter; any jewel you like."

She thought about it for a little while, and then she said:

"Alright. I agree."

They were married. The King celebrated it lavishly; there was a great banquet and festivities beyond all describing.

After about a month a man from Mahon, with a mare, came and stayed the night at the King's house.

"Where shall I put my animal?" he asked.

"In the stable," the servants told him.

He looked into the stable and he saw a horse there.

"Shall I put her next to the horse?"

"Yes, put her in there," they said.

The next morning the mare had a foal.

The King claimed the foal as his because, he said, it had been born in the stable where there was no animal of his other than the horse; therefore the horse must have produced the foal.

"But there was the mare belonging to the Mahon man," they said.

"Don't argue with me," he retorted. "I don't need you to tell me what day of the week it is. I had no other animal in the stable but the horse; if a foal is born it must have been by the horse."

When his men found him so obstinate they gave up. The man from Mahon too was careful not to cross the King.

The Queen heard about it, and she showed the Mahonian a dry pond that there was near-by.

"Go there with a fishing-rod and line," she said, "and act as if you were fishing. When the King goes hunting he will pass that way and will say to you: 'What are you doing?' You must say 'I am fishing.' 'What are you fishing for?' he will say. 'Sardines,' you must reply. 'How is it possible,' he will say, 'with no water in the pond, to fish for sardines?' Then you must say 'It is as possible to catch sardines without any water in the pond as it is for a horse to bear a foal.'"

The Mahonian followed the Queen's advice and did as she had said.

The King passed near the dry pond and saw the man with his rod and line like an angler expecting a big catch, and said to him:

"What are you doing?"

"I am fishing," said the Mahonian.

"What are you fishing for?" the King asked.

"Sardines."

"Idiot!" said the King. "There is not a drop of water in the pond and you are hoping to catch sardines! How could you possibly catch any?"

"It is just as possible to catch sardines without there being any water," said the man, "as it is for a horse to bear a foal."

The King was taken aback by this rejoinder, and to get out of the awkward spot he said:

"Alright; go back to the house, take your mare and the foal, and get going from here as quickly as possible."

The Mahonian did as the King told him. Meanwhile the King was thinking: "It must be the Queen who advised him to do that." And he turned about and went back home.

"It was you," he said to the Queen. "It could not have been anybody else."

"What's this now?" the Queen said.

"Yes, just now! You gave advice to the man from Mahon; you cannot deny it!"

"I gave him advice so that you should not do him the injustice of taking the foal from him."

"Don't argue with me!" the King replied. "You gave advice when you should not have done. Do you remember the agreement we made when we were married?"

"Yes," said the Queen.

"Very well, you can go when you like."

"Could we not have dinner first?" she said.

"Alright," said the King. "We will have dinner and then you can go."

They had dinner, and the artful girl gave him a sleeping potion.

When she saw he was sound asleep she had the coach harnessed; she put him inside it, and then gave orders to drive to her father's cottage.

They were soon there, and she had the King laid on the pile of charcoal dust in the shed, where the cobwebs in the roofing hung down on his face.

When the King woke up and found himself in that hole he thought he must still be dreaming.

"Where am I?" he said. "Am I dreaming or am I awake?"

"You are not dreaming," said Cathy. "You are at my father's. The agreement was that if I had to leave I could bring away any jewel I liked. I looked everywhere in your house but I saw no jewel like you; I did not see any that I liked so much. Therefore I have brought you."

When the King heard this he said:

"Let us forget about it. Let's go back home, and you may give as much advice as you like, so long as it is good."

So they went back to the King's house and lived in peace and concord for years and years; and they are still alive if they are not dead.

Cap-Doffing Friends and True Friends

THERE WAS ONCE A MAN who was so well-off that he could count his money by the shovelful. He had only one son, called Andrew. This lad never had empty pockets, so you can imagine how many other young fellows wanted to be friends with him. His father was always saying: "Be careful, Andrew, of cap-doffing friends, of those who are more interested in your pocket than in any real friendship with you."

"You should not suppose, father," Andrew replied, "that all those who make much of me are not sincere friends. You sometimes think too ill of people."

"Andrew, I have seen too much to trust people easily. When you reach my age you will see things as I do."

"No, father, don't think that! The many friends that I have cannot all be false; I take them for true friends."

"Very well," said Andrew's father one day, "let's put your friends to the test, just to please me, and to show you the truth."

"Alright," said Andrew, "we'll do it, to show you the truth."

"Look then," said his father, "this is how we will test them. We will kill a lamb and put it in a sack; in the evening, after dark, you sling the sack over your shoulder and go to the houses of your friends, one after the other. You knock on the door; someone will open it, so you ask for your friend, and then you say to him very secretly: 'Look, old chap, I have in this sack a dead body, which I had the misfortune to kill; let me bury it in your yard, so it may never be known that I am the culprit.' Then we shall see which of them will let you bury the body in his yard."

Andrew found his father's idea very strange, and he said:

"What ideas you have, father! Isn't it asking a lot?"

"It's finding out whether they are false or true friends."

Then his father took a good fat lamb, the biggest in the flock, and they killed it. In the evening, after dark, Andrew put the sack over his shoulder and went off to do the round of his friends' houses.

He came to the first house and *Knock-knock!*

"Who's there?" called someone inside.

"A friend of yours."

The door was opened by the father of Andrew's friend.

"Is your son at home?" Andrew asked.

"Yes, he is."

"Could you ask him to come to the door? I need to speak to him."

"Yes, of course," said the man. He went in, and after a moment the friend came out. Andrew said to him:

"Can anyone overhear us?"

"No," said the friend. "Is there something wrong?"

"Indeed there is... I take you to be a good friend..."

"You may he sure I am. But what's the matter?"

"Look, my father and I have a dead body on our hands – we had the misfortune to kill ..."

"*What are you saying?*" cried the friend in horror.

"Just what you heard," Andrew replied. "and I have the body in this sack."

"But what is all this to me?" cried the other, aghast. He hardly knew which way to turn.

"The point is," said Andrew, "that I trust you to help me to avoid being found with this body."

"Me?" the friend said. "Not likely! What could I do?"

"What you can do is to let me bury the body in your yard; and if you don't tell anybody it will never be found out who did the killing."

"But suppose someone happened to see us doing it and reported us to the police, and they were to come and dig up the body. They would be sure to think me or my father guilty. What's more, Andrew, I could not do such a thing without my father's permission; and do you suppose he would agree to such a thing? I have not the courage even to ask him."

"So," said Andrew, "you will not give me any help?"

"I cannot give you help of this kind. It's asking too much. I hope you won't be offended, Andrew."

"Never mind," Andrew replied. "forget that I ever said anything about it. Good night to you."

"Good night," said the friend.

Andrew stepped back and the friend slammed the door in his face. Then he made for another friend's house, but he was already beginning to have doubts about the loyalty of his circle of friends.

"If this fellow," he thought, "whom I regarded as my best friend, can behave like that, what will the others do? What if my father is right? And the thing is that it didn't occur to this fellow to ask me whether the body was an animal or a person. when he heard there was a dead body he took it for granted it was a person. Well, well ..."

With that he reached the house of another friend whom he wanted to try, and *Knock – knock!*

"Who's there?" called someone inside.

"A friend of yours," Andrew replied.

The door was opened by the mother of his friend.

"Is your son in?" he asked.

"Yes, he is," she replied.

"Could you ask him to come to the door? I should like to have a word with him."

"I'll tell him," she said, and went back, into the house; after a moment the friend came.

"Oh, it's you, Andrew," he said when he saw him.

"Yes, it's me, old chap."

"Is there anything wrong?"

"Indeed there is," Andrew replied, lowering his voice. "Can anyone overhear us'?"

"I don't think so, but to be on the safe side let's speak softly."

"I'm in pretty serious trouble," said Andrew.

"Well, get to the point," said the friend. "Out with it!"

"My father and I have a dead body on our hands – we had the misfortune to kill ..."

"*What are you saying?*" cried the friend in horror.

"Just what you heard; and I've got the body in this sack. I thought, to make sure the police never discover that it was we who killed him, the best thing would be to bury the body in the yard of another house; so I thought of you, hoping you would let me bury it in your yard."

When the friend heard all this he found it very unpleasant. In short, he said *No*, and again *No*, and would Andrew be kind enough to go away as quickly as he could; he had no right to compromise his friends in this way.

Andrew picked up the sack again, and – *Good night! Good night!* – went off towards the house of another friend; but he was turning it over in his mind and saying to himself:

"Well, well! My father must be right! I wonder whether any of my friends will help. At least they might ask me what kind of a dead body it is. But not they! As soon as they hear the tale they lose their wits and don't know what happened; all they want is for me to get out and be as far away as the Man in the Moon."

With that he reached the house of a third friend, and *Knock-knock!* Here it was the friend himself who opened the door. Andrew told him the story, as he had done to the other two, and all he got was a flea in his ear – I mean, when this third friend heard how Andrew and his father wanted him to let them bury a dead body in his yard, he sent Andrew packing, saying such things were not to be asked of any friend and telling him to go away at once.

Andrew, as you may well imagine, went off thoroughly downcast, rebuffed, disappointed and disillusioned about his friends. He did not go to see any more of them because he said to himself:

"If these three, my closest friends whom I most trusted, turn out like this, what would the others do? They would kick me out pretty quick; they might, even go and inform the police that I and my father had committed murder."

Andrew returned home; when his father saw him so crestfallen and saddened, and still carrying the sack, he said:

"So you have had to bring back the dead body."

"I'm afraid I have," Andrew replied.

"Do you mean not one of them would let you bury the body in his yard?"

"Not one," said Andrew. "They said it was compromising them, and was not a thing to ask of any friend."

"There you are," said his father. "You see how all these are only cap-doffing friends? Never mind; now we have tested them we will try out a semi-friend of mine, who lives in so-and-so street at such-and-such a house. Go there with the sack, knock on the door, ask for him, and tell him as secretly as possible, as from me, what you told those friends of yours. Let's see what he says."

Andrew did as his father said. He took up the sack once more and was off to the house of his father's semi-friend. He got there and *Knock-knock!*

"Who's there?" called someone inside.

"A friend of yours," Andrew replied.

The door opened, and it was the man himself.

"Good evening," said Andrew.

"Good evening to you. Is there anything wrong, that you come at this hour?" the man said, seeing Andrew with the sack over his shoulder.

"There certainly is," Andrew replied. "I'll tell you in a few words. My father and I have a dead body on our hands – we had the misfortune to kill – and my father has sent me, with the body in this sack, to ask if you would let me bury it in your yard, so that we may not be found with it."

"Friends, Andrew, are for when they are needed. If your father sends you to ask me for help, that is enough and I will give it. And it will be best to get it done at once. Wait while I bar the door so that nobody can come in and surprise us in the act."

The man shut and barred the door, and then started off for the yard with a spade, to dig the grave for the body.

When Andrew saw this he was utterly amazed at the fine friendship of this man towards his father and himself, and he exclaimed:

"Sir, you can put down the spade. Thank God, my father and I did not kill a person, but only one of our lambs. The point of it is that I thought I had a lot of friends, but my father kept saying they were only cap-doffing friends; and today he said: 'Let's kill a lamb and put it in a sack; then in the evening you can go to these friends of yours and tell them you have the misfortune of having a dead body on your hands; you ask each of them to let you bury the body in his yard. Then we shall see if there is one among them who says *Yes*. So we did that, and there was not one of my friends who would help me. Then my father sent me to you, to see if you would do it. Now I have seen for myself that mine are cap-doffing friends – friends in name only – but you are a friend indeed, and true to my father and me."

"If I had not done what I did," said the man, "your father could have spat in my face. Friends must be loyal; nothing less will do."

"You are right," Andrew replied. "And that's how the world ought to be, but it isn't."

Andrew took his leave of the man and returned home; he told it all to his father, who said:

"You see, Andrew? This semi-friend of mine is worth more than all the friends you thought you had."

"It's true, father," said Andrew. "You are quite right." But he still could not understand why his father had said *semi-friend* of the man who had been willing to bury the dead body in his yard. He said he found the man had acted not as a semi-friend but as a good full-friend. His father then replied:

"To convince you still more of the truth of what I say, I will tell you about my father – may he rest in peace – and a friend of his in the City. You will see that what happened between them showed an even greater friendship than was shown by the man who was willing to bury the body in his yard."

"Do you mean," asked Andrew, "it is something that actually happened to my grandfather, your father?"

"Indeed it is," his father replied. "It was like this."

❖ ❖ ❖

My father had a friend in the City, who one day sent for him to come. My father went, and he found his friend was about to be married and wanted him to be at the wedding. My father was then still a bachelor. The first thing his friend did was to take him to meet his girl; and if you will imagine and believe it, my father liked that girl so very very much that he was quite smitten and fell deeply in love with her.

His heart was so gravely wounded that the wound had perforce to show. I mean it soon became clear there was something wrong with the poor man, try as he would to hide it. He became sadder and sadder; he would not eat or drink; he even had to go to bed. They called the doctor; the doctor felt his pulse, examined him very thoroughly, and then said: "As for any injury or any sort of fever, I can find nothing. What I do find is a very severe ailing of the heart; if it does not pass off soon he is finished, because the heart has little resistance."

When the doctor had gone the friend shut himself in the bedroom alone with my father and said:

"Now, what is wrong? Out with it! You heard what the doctor said."

"Wrong with me?" said my father. "Well, nothing really."

"No," said his friend. "There is something wrong. You came here from Manacor fit and well; now suddenly you have fallen ill, and the doctor says it is an ailing of the heart. What is this ailing of the heart?"

My father did not want to say, but his friend pressed him so hard that at last he came out with it.

"I had sworn to myself never to tell you, but you are so determined to make me speak that I shall have to say it. The fact is I liked your girl so very very much, from the moment you took me to meet her, that I fell in love with her. But she is going to be your wife, and therefore can never, never, be mine; this is weighing on my heart and breaking it. I think in a few days I shall give up the ghost. Now you know, dear friend, what is wrong with me. Don't tell anybody, and let me die as God wills."

When the City friend heard this he went and shut himself in his own room; he stayed there for twenty-four hours without sleeping or eating. At the end of this time he came out and went back to my father, and he said:

"Dear friend, I want to save your life."

"How can you?" said my father.

"How can I? Like this. Here and now I give you my girl, if she is willing, for you to marry her. I will find another girl. If you are going to die of a broken heart without her, I cannot as your true friend allow that to happen. I will find another girl whom I can like as well as this one."

When my father heard this he thought at first that his friend was joking, and he did not take him seriously. But in the end he understood that his friend was in earnest.

Well, believe it or not, they both went to the girl's house, and the City friend took her aside and explained the whole thing to her. She looked my father up and down and found nothing bad about him, but rather that he was nice and attractive. Her parents heard where he came from, how he was one of the best farmers in Manacor, and was very well-off. So in the end they said to her:

"If you like him, dear, take him."

So the girl said *Yes* to my father, and they were married. That girl was my mother – may she rest in peace with all the departed.

"So you see, Andrew, how my father and that City fellow were true friends. You see how that man gave my father proof of a friendship that was even greater than the friendship of the man who would have let you bury the dead body in his yard. Imagine what it means for a man who is about to marry a girl to give her up to marry another man, just to make him happy."

"There's no doubt about it," said Andrew. "You are quite right:

what the City friend did for my grandfather was even more than what that friend of yours would have done for you."

"But wait, Andrew," his father went on; "I have not finished. I will tell you of another proof of true friendship between that City man and your grandfather."

"What was that?" Andrew asked.

"It was like this," his father said.

As you may imagine, after my father was married to the City girl they came to Manacor, and they lived in peace and harmony like Joseph and Mary, with all the bounty there has always been in this house, by the grace of God.

It did not go so well for the friend in the City, because – do you know what happened? – he thought he would find plenty of marriageable girls whom he would have liked, but he was quite mistaken. He searched high and low but he did not find one who really pleased him; there were many who at first sight were attractive, because they were well-shaped and pretty, but on closer acquaintance they proved stupid or suffered from one defect or another, and so were no good.

This began to prey on him a great deal; he did not want to say anything about it for fear that his people might blame him for having given to my father the girl whom he had first chosen and had so much wanted to marry. This began to gnaw at his heart like a worm, gnawing and gnawing away, and this hidden distress made him very ill, so that he nearly died. He managed. to recover a little, but everything began to go wrong for him, until he almost gave up only half-way through his life. Then he said to himself:

"I will go and see my friend in Manacor; perhaps he will be able to help me a bit. I am sure whatever he can do he will do."

He set off for Manacor; just as he was getting there, and was almost at his friend's house, he came on two men in the middle of the road who were quarrelling so violently that they brought out their knives. Then one of them plunged his weapon into the other's chest; he dropped dead, and the one who had done it dived like lightning into a house, sped through the stable yard, which faced out of town, and ran off as if he had a hundred thousand devils after him.

The man from the City saw all this and stood there horror-struck, not knowing what to do. Then people began to appear, and more and more of them; they were all saying: "Who killed this man? Who could it be? Who couldn't it be?" Then they saw the stranger there – the poor fellow from the City – and one of them said:

"It must have been this man here!"

"No doubt of it at all." said another.

"It couldn't have been anyone else!" said a third.

"You may be sure it's he who did it!" said a fourth.

"Then this is the man!" everybody shouted.

Then the police arrived. They arrested the City man, they locked him up and they charged him. In all truth he denied having killed the man, saying it was another man, whom he did not know and who had run away. The Judge did not want to listen to arguments, and he said:

"There are no two ways: anyone who kills must die. It is quite clear this man did the murder; therefore he must be hanged."

The poor fellow from the City was put in the condemned cell, and you can imagine how he must have felt. My father was not in Manacor just at this time, but he came back on the day that his City friend was due to be hanged. My father, not knowing it was his great friend, went to see what was happening. When they brought the condemned man out to the gallows, my father looked at him and saw it was his friend from the City. He thrust his way through the crowd until, he was close up to him, and said in dismay:

"My dear friend, what is this? How can you have killed a man? You cannot possibly have done it!"

"I assure you I did not do it. I will swear to that by the Cross of Christ!" said the poor fellow weeping.

And what do you think my father did? He went to the Judge, who was there in person, and said:

"Mister Judge, this man is innocent. This man had nothing to do with the murder. I will answer for him."

"Oh, you answer for him?" said the Judge.

"Yes, I say I answer for him."

"And will you put yourself in his place?" asked the Judge.

"Yes, now – at once," my father replied.

"Look here," said the Judge, "I am not to be trifled with."

"Nor am I," my father retorted.

"Well," the Judge went on, "if you put yourself in this man's place, we will hang you instead of him."

"That's alright," said my father. "Just as I am sure this man had nothing to do with the murder and is entirely innocent, so I am sure Your Honour will not be capable of hanging me."

"Did you say 'not capable'?" exclaimed the Judge, getting angry.

"Yes, I did say it, and I will say it again!" replied my father, by then even more angry than the Judge.

"Hey, you!" cried the Judge to the bailiff and the other officers there. "Arrest this man and take him to the gallows to be hanged!"

They took my father to the gallows. As the hangman was putting the rope round his neck, there was suddenly a great shout from a man in the crowd who cried out:

"Mister Judge! It was not either of these men who did the murder. It was I who did it!"

This man was telling the truth; it was he who had killed the other fellow. He had run off, and nobody had seen him with the weapon in his hand, except for the poor man from the City who did not know him; so nobody had suspected him.

He was not at all a bad man, but the other had done him a really dirty turn; he had been blinded by anger and had stabbed the other in a fit of violence. In his right mind he would never, never, have done it.

Well, this man was there, and he had heard and seen the discussion between my father and the Judge, and he had seen the poor City fellow – who had had nothing to do with it – being taken to the gallows; and he had seen my father, equally innocent, with the hangman putting the rope round his neck. And all this because of the obstinacy of the Judge, who was too proud to be 'trifled with'. When the man saw it all he was overcome with such remorse that he said to himself:

"This must not happen! I could not go on living. What would become of me before the Tribunal of God if I were the cause of these two innocent men going to their death? It is I who should be hanged."

Thus it was this man cried out, and went up to the Judge and told him quite clearly that it was he, and nobody else, who had killed the other man.

The Judge was all confused by these goings-on. When he had done cudgelling his brains he gaoled the City man and my father, and the man who had confessed to the murder. Then he went off to the City to tell the King about this remarkable case.

When the King had heard the story and saw what a tangle it had become, he issued the following verdict:

"Release all three of them: the City man and the man who answers for him, because it is clear they are innocent and because of the fine friendship they have shown, and the man who committed the murder because of his goodness in not allowing two innocent men to be hanged; but tell him to be careful never again to put a foot wrong, for that would cost him his life."

They did as the King said. They released all three men. My father brought his City friend to this house and said: "This is your home. Eat and drink your fill and don't worry. So long as I have a piece of bread in the house, half of it will be yours."

His friend was no longer so keen to be married, and he lived here with my father and mother, just like a brother, until he died. I remember him as a little old man who always treated me kindly and used to take me for walks.

"That's what I call friends," said Andrew's father at the end of this story. "My father and the City man were what you may call true friends."

"You are quite right," Andrew replied. "I see it is not easy to find a friend in deed, rather than a friend only in word. From now on I will not trust those who merely say they are friends, but rather those who by their actions show that they are friends at heart."

And I say the same to you who hear this tale. Your relatives you must take as they come; but for your friends choose good ones. Beware of cap-doffing friends; don't trust them – any more than you would trust a house that is falling down.

Donkey's Eggs

A MAN FROM Sa Pobla was once on his way to the City with a donkey. In the panniers the donkey was carrying two enormous pumpkins; just with them alone it was bearing a really good load.

The man met a charcoal-burner coming down from the mountains of Lluch with a donkey and a load of charcoal. This fellow noticed the great pumpkins and was quite dumbfounded; he had never seen any of such a huge size, not by a long way, and he did not know what they were. Moreover he was a simpleton.

Of course, he could not refrain from asking the man from Sa Pobla:

"What are those huge things in your panniers?"

"Have you no eyes?" the other replied. "What do you think they are? Donkey's eggs of course."

"And do donkeys lay eggs?" the charcoal-burner asked, with his eyes wide open like saucers.

"Of course they lay eggs, man!"

"And do they hatch out, these eggs, if they are set?"

"Of course they hatch out if they are sound, and quite quickly."

"And do they hatch out donkey foals?"

"Would they hatch out locusts, stupid?"

"You are not joking?"

"Why should I be joking now?" said the man from Sa Pobla, who was an inveterate joker and as wily as a weasel.

"Anyway," said the charcoal-burner, "I must do this myself, whatever it may cost. Look, would you be willing to exchange loads, one for the other?"

"It's a deal. What a good idea!" exclaimed the man from Sa Pobla. And he at once unloaded the pumpkins, arranged the two baskets of charcoal on his donkey, and went straight back to Sa Pobla as cheerful as a pair of castanets.

The charcoal-burner managed to load the pumpkins onto his donkey, and he set off for home very pleased with the deal.

The man from Sa Pobla had said: "Look: if you want these eggs to hatch out you must keep them warm in your bed for a week. Put them there, a little apart from each other; then lie down between them, stretched out. And take care not to move for the whole week and not to utter a single word. If you move or speak they will not hatch." The charcoal-burner had all this firmly fixed in his mind.

He reached home. His wife was out fetching water; so what do you think he did?

He unloaded the pumpkins and led the donkey into the stable, where he gave it some feed. Then without more delay he put the two great pumpkins on the bed, a little apart from each other; then he lay down between them, well stretched out and with as much bed-covering as he could find. He was resolved and determined to do everything to make those eggs hatch out.

Then his wife came back; she found the house open and she saw the donkey in the stable.

"I wonder where the rascal has gone," she said. "He is back early today. He must have been able to sell his load on the way. He has probably gone to the tavern to have a drop. He will come back when he wants to."

After a while she went into the bedroom and saw all that bulk on the bed.

"Now, what is all this?" she exclaimed, slightly alarmed. She went up to the head of the bed, and there she saw him with only his face showing, looking as solemn as a potato.

"But what is all this?" she said again "Are you not well? You might at least have said something."

"Ssh! Ssh! Ssh!" he went, with a finger on his lips.

"Alright!" she said, beginning to be angry. "But what is the matter with you, in bed at this time of day and all covered up? And what is this making these lumps? Have you got a swelling on your stomach, or on your back? Or have you got somebody under there in bed with you...?"

But he kept on going "Ssh! Ssh! Ssh!" with his finger on his lips.

She could not resist having a look to see what the lumps were, and she lifted the bed-cover at one side; but he, as quick as a flash, brought his arms out and pressed them with all his strength over the cover on each side of the pumpkins, so that she should not uncover them.

His wife kept on scolding:

"You pig-headed rascal! I want to know what this is. I will see what you have put in my bed! If you think you are going to get away with something you are very wrong. Come on, now. No more nonsense. Let's see what you have here."

Meanwhile he kept on, with his finger on his lips, going "Ssh! Ssh! Ssh!"

His wife was in a fury; a thousand of the maddest ideas came to her mind.

"What can it be?" she was saying to herself. "A sensible man like him behaving in this way? His mind must be upset. He has never done such a thing as this. It must mean that his brain has suffered."

Then she went and told her neighbours about it.

They all came into the bedroom, and of course they found him hatching his eggs, lying in bed covered up to his nose, with his eyes darting about and watching them closely.

"But what is this, good man?" they said, coming close. "What has happened? What is the idea of going to bed at this time of day? What do you mean by not replying to your wife? Just like a man!"

In vain they questioned him and re-questioned him; in vain they shook him and prodded him; they got nothing out of him but "Ssh!" and more "Ssh!" with his finger on his lips when his arms were not holding down the bed-cover defending those famous pumpkins from all the women who were dying to know what the lumps were.

After a little while one of the neighbours said:

"My dear girls, I would not go on like this. I would send for the doctor; I don't like the look of this man."

"You are right," said another. "There is something wrong with him. He has never before been like this; he was the most sensible man in the village. There is nothing for it but to fetch the doctor."

The wife agreed, and one of the neighbours was very quickly at the doctor's house. The doctor soon turned up, panting from the run they had made him do.

"Now, what is this?" he said, coming into the room and going up to the bed.

The wife took up the tale and told Sir Doctor everything in detail, without omitting a jot, and begging him for the love of God and Holy Mary to cure her poor husband.

The doctor spoke to him, but he did not utter a word. He watched the doctor closely and did not take his eyes off him, for fear that he might damage the eggs.

The doctor got tired of asking questions and getting no answers so he tried taking the man's pulse.

"Well, he has no fever," said the doctor in surprise, "but there is something about his eyes that is not normal."

"And what has he got?" they all asked.

"It could be quite serious, or it could be nothing much," replied the doctor, not knowing what to say.

"Could it be an attack in his brain?" one of them asked.

"It could be," said the doctor.

"And could he suddenly become unconscious?"

"He would be exposed to that danger," the doctor replied.

"What I would do," said another neighbour, "is tell the Vicar and get him to give Extreme Unction, just in case later on he might not be in time."

"That can never be wrong," the doctor said.

The neighbour dashed off, as if her shoes were on fire, to find the Vicar. The Vicar soon appeared with the Extreme Unction, and while the wife was pulling her hair about, in floods of tears, he and the acolyte began saying prayers and more prayers. The Vicar was about to anoint the eyes of the dying man, and he told them to uncover his feet.

At this point the charcoal-burner saw he was lost and in danger of being taken off and buried alive.

So this should not happen he gave a jerk and sat up straight in the bed, still without the heart to abandon those two eggs that he had taken such care of. Then he let fly, shouting with all his might:

"Damnation! Now they will not hatch out!"

And he jumped out of bed in one bound and ran off hitting himself on the head and cursing and swearing without pause.

The bed-cover fell off, and there were the two pumpkins for all to see.

When people heard the charcoal-burner was hatching the pumpkins, hoping to get two donkey foals, or two fillies, or a filly and a foal, I cannot tell you what a commotion they made about it.

And they are still at it if they have not stopped.

A Soldier after Ten Years

ONCE THERE WAS a Soldier who served for ten years and was then sent home with nothing but a standard loaf of barracks bread. He found this hard to bear and as he walked – *tramp-tramp* – towards home he kept saying:

"Well, look at that! After ten years serving the King and without wasting a penny, all I get is a loaf of barracks bread. Is this how the King rewards those who serve him? Blow me down if that makes him a king or even a gentleman."

The thing was on his mind so much that at length he stopped in his tracks and exclaimed: "Now if somebody does something to me I always make him pay for it. The King has done this to me? Then he will have to pay for it. I will go straight away and throw this barracks loaf at his head; and if he does not like it he can do something about it."

He turned about and made for the King's house. On the way there, he passed through an enormous wood, where it so happened the King was hunting; and he was not wearing anything to show who he was. If you will believe it, the Soldier met him in the wood, but did not know who he was, never having seen him; he mistook the King for his regiment's cook, who was called Bruno. So of course the Soldier greeted him:

"Well, blow me down Bruno! What the devil are you doing here? And how is the regiment managing without its cook?"

The King was taken aback by this greeting, but he saw that the Soldier had mistaken him for the regiment's cook, so he said to himself: "Alright, we will play the cook for a bit and see what comes of it". And he said to the Soldier: "Well, old chap, I came to stretch my legs a bit. And where are you making for?"

"I?" said the Soldier. "I am going to throw this loaf of barracks bread at the King's head."

"Oh, really?"

"Yes, mate. I have served the King as well as I could for ten years, and now they have sent me home with nothing but this loaf; and so as to be able to say I owe the King nothing I am going to throw it at his head."

"Well, what an idea!"

"I am like that. If somebody does something to me, he has to pay for it."

The King was so struck by this, and found it so amusing, that he forgot about hunting and went on chatting with the Soldier. They walked and walked a long way, without looking where they were going, till nightfall overtook them in the heart of the wood, with no road or path out of it.

Suddenly they found themselves at the mouth of a big cave, which was very dark and went a long way back. "What is this?" said the Soldier, and he went in. Looking around he saw hanging on the walls were pistols, shot-guns, muskets, blunderbusses, swords, daggers... "This can only be a robbers' cave," he said; "and luckily they are not here, or are sleeping."

"Let's get away!" said the King, "Without more talk."

"Get away, did you say?" the Soldier replied. "Not on your life, Bruno, by order! Try and run away and I will pepper you with one of these blunderbusses!"

"But, old chap, what can we do against this band of robbers? We should be wiped out!"

"It remains to be seen whether we should be wiped out or should be able to wipe them out." And the Soldier went on: "What's more, we are here now and here we have to defend ourselves. Either we make an end of them or they of us. So no more argument, and let's see to our defences at once."

The Soldier saw an axe in the cave; he cut down two pine-trees which he fixed at the mouth of the cave. He and the King found gunpowder, bullets, and shot, and they loaded shot-guns, muskets, blunderbusses, and pistols; they fixed these weapons to the pine trunks, all aimed outwards, with a string attached to each trigger, so that with one pull one man could discharge them all.

When they had everything ready and just so, the Soldier said:

"Now one of us must watch and the other can sleep for a while."

"I will watch," said the King.

"Alright; you watch and I will rest my bones for a bit."

The Soldier lay down in a corner, and there was the King watching and watching. A couple of hours before dawn he began to hear footsteps and a murmur of people approaching; so he called the Soldier and alerted him.

The Soldier jumped up and said: "For sure, it's them. Come on, then; we will give them the works, as planned."

He looked at the shot-guns, muskets, blunderbusses, and pistols, to see that they had not moved at all. The footsteps and voices of the robbers came nearer and nearer, and it was plain they were returning relaxed and unsuspecting.

When they were about thirty paces off, and the Soldier judged they were within range, he pulled the strings on all the triggers, and – *bang!* – gave them a fusillade in their faces that inflicted severe losses on them. Six or seven of the robbers fell dead, and as many were badly injured; the rest took to their heels as fast as they could. I can assure you none of them looked back to see what had struck them; they made off as quickly as they were able. Now and then one of them would fall, wounded, with no strength left.

The King thought, since they had come through the adventure with success, that the best thing was to get away, in case the robbers came back in greater strength.

"What's this, Bruno?" said the Soldier. "Unless the Devil himself carries you off, you are not moving from here. We have not yet finished trimming this gang of robbers; so let's load our battery again, and pretty quickly!"

The King could do nothing but bow his head and submit. So there they were loading and loading away shot-guns, pistols, muskets, and blunderbusses, and fixing them again on the two pine-trunks, in case the robbers should return to the attack.

"You will see," said the King. "They will make mincemeat of us."

"Oh? Mincemeat? They will not mince anybody who is not minceable."

What do you think? They had their battery all reloaded when they heard footsteps again. It was the same robbers who had worked up their courage and were coming back to get into the cave or die in the attempt; all their wealth was inside it.

The Soldier, watching and watching intently, with the trigger strings in his hands, saw the robbers creeping up silently, like cats. When he thought he had them within range, he pulled the strings and – *bang!* – the shot-guns, muskets, pistols and blunderbusses all went off; and if the robbers suffered losses from the first fusillade, they suffered worse losses with the second. A good many fell dead; others were badly wounded and died soon after. Only two or three survived, and that was thanks to having good hoofs and knowing the paths in the wood, because the Soldier and the King went after them with swords; and if they caught one they skewered him, to teach him to be more careful next time.

Meanwhile day broke; the Soldier and the King went back to the cave and searched about; in a recess they found a tub full of gold coins. "Very good! Let's take half each," said the Soldier.

"No; all for you," the King replied.

"Certainly not, Bruno. I cannot take your share; I would sooner leave it here."

"Alright, then; we will leave it here."

"But Bruno, you must be mad!"

And, believe it or not, they were both so obstinate that Bruno would not take his share and the Soldier agreed to leave it there rather than take more than his own share.

"Well now," said the King, still acting Bruno, "I must go back to the barracks. God be with you."

"God keep you," replied the Soldier. "I shall go along to the King's house and throw this barracks loaf at his head, and then I shall make for home double-quick."

They parted company and each went his way.

The King knew his way about better, and he was soon out of the wood. When he reached the city he gave orders to all the sentries and officers that if a soldier of such and such an appearance should arrive, they were to give him the honours of General of Land and Sea Forces, because this was what he was, even though he might not appear to be.

After a good deal of walking the Soldier reached the city; the first sentry that he came to cried:

"The General of Land and Sea!" And everybody saluted him as the King had ordered. He asked his way to the King's house from an important-looking senior officer, who thought it right to accompany him there. And whenever they passed a sentry outside a barracks the place rang with the cry: "The General of Land and Sea!" And everybody saluted him as the King had ordered.

The Soldier could not understand all this and was saying to himself: "If this is a joke they are playing on me, it's a bit too much. And if it is serious, it's much too much. Never mind; press on and we shall see what comes of it." And on they went towards the King's house. At length they arrived, and the sentries nearly burst crying out: "The General of Land and Sea!"

All the doors opened and the Soldier resolutely went in, passing through hall after hall, until he found himself in the largest of them, where there was a group of generals and other important people, with the King among them. But the Soldier did not realize he was the King and knew him only as Bruno, the man he had spent the night with killing those robbers.

"Well, blow me down, Bruno!" he exclaimed cheerfully. "Fancy finding you here! Strange how we keep on meeting! And what are you doing with all these important people?" As he was saying this, and noticing the faces the senior officers were making and the respect they were showing to Bruno, he realized it was not the regiment's cook but the King, and he saw what a great fool he had made of himself. He was speechless, utterly ashamed, and he went all sorts of colours.

Then the King came over to him, friendly and laughing, and embraced him, saying: "I am not Bruno; I am the King. And so that you shall not throw the barracks loaf at my head – though I admit I deserve it – and because of your great action last night in killing off that gang of robbers, which nobody has ever been capable of doing, you are appointed General of the Forces of Land and Sea, for life."

You can imagine how the Soldier was astonished and bewildered. Then he was quite overcome; he burst into tears and fell on his knees before the King, begging his forgiveness for having treated him with so little respect.

"All is forgiven," said His Royal Majesty. "Don't give it another thought."

Then the Soldier made his way home; he found his father and mother alive, he married the girl he had been courting before he did his military service, and he took them all to live with the King, who welcomed them with open arms.

And they all lived and enjoyed a good many years, until they died and were buried. And may we meet them all in Heaven.

Amen.

Peter and the Good Cloth

A CERTAIN FATHER AND MOTHER had but one son, who was called Peter. They were poor and thin, and you may be sure there was never enough bread to go stale in that household.

Their only wealth was three lengths of very good cloth; they did not know where this cloth had come from, but they were so fond of it that they would have starved sooner than part with it. But, if you will believe it, they suffered so much from the feeling of rats in the belly and were so tormented by hunger that eventually the wife, half fainting, said to her husband:

"We can't go on like this. We must sell those pieces of cloth, and never mind the consequences."

The husband took them up as best he could and, staggering with weakness, went from street to street crying out:

"Come, ladies, some good cloth! Who will buy? Come on, ladies, while there is a chance!"

He went through street after street and made himself hoarse with shouting, but all in vain. Dead tired, he went home.

"Let's see if I have more luck than you did," said Peter. He took one of the lengths of cloth and went into the streets shouting out:

"Come on, ladies, some good cloth! Come quick if you want to buy it! Wake up, ladies!" He went all round the town, and at the bridge he came on a gang of boys who were carrying a cat and shouting like lunatics.

"Where are you taking that cat?" Peter asked them.

"We are going to throw him in the river," they replied.

"Will you swap him for this length of cloth?"

The boys did not care for cloth, but it happened that two of the mothers of those lads were passing by at that moment, and when they heard about a length of cloth they were interested and made a deal. Peter handed over the cloth, they gave him the cat, and he went home with it.

You can imagine what his father and mother said when they saw him with that piece of luggage, and particularly when they heard of the deal that he had made. Luckily for him they were rather sluggish people, and being so starved they could not raise their voices much. So it all passed off with nothing more than scolding and sour faces.

The next day Peter took another length of cloth and went along the streets as before, shouting out like mad:

"Come, ladies, some good cloth! Who will buy? Come on, ladies, hurry! Wake up!"

Nobody took any notice of him. In Moon Street he came on a gang of boys dragging along a dog and making a great deal of noise.

"Hey!" cried Peter. "Where are you taking that dog?"

"We are going to throw him in the sea."

"Will you swap him for this piece of cloth?"

"Who wants a piece of cloth?" said the boys with crude jokes. Just at that moment two of the mothers of those lads happened along; of course they heard what Peter said and they took him up on it. They took the length of cloth, and Peter got the dog. He was delighted.

He went home with it; when his father and mother heard what had happened they would have made mincemeat of him if they had not been so weak with hunger.

"What's the use?" they said. "If we haven't got enough to fill our own three bellies, how can we fill two more?"

"You are wrong," said Peter. "The more we are the better we shall manage, believe me." And they could not budge him from this idea.

What do you think happened? The next day, without his parents' knowing it, he took the last of the lengths of cloth and went off through the streets shouting out like mad: "Come, ladies, good cloth! Come quick, ladies, if you want to buy! Wake up, ladies – some good cloth!"

Half-way along Hand Street he met a very well-dressed lady who said to him:

"What is it you are selling?"

"Some good cloth," Peter replied.

"I will buy it from you."

"I will sell it to you."

"Come in, then." The lady's house was right there. Her husband was a ship's captain who had just returned home. He had brought her many things – in particular a gold ring with diamonds, which was a wonder to see, and which she was already wearing. Her husband had gone to bed – he was tired out and sleepy from his long voyage – and he had said to her:

"Will you make me some shirts, please? They must be of good cloth or I shall not want them."

That was why the lady was so quick to accost Peter and take him into her house; as soon as she saw the cloth she said: "What do you want for it?"

Peter at that moment noticed the ring that the Captain had brought her, and he said:

"What do I want...? The ring that you are wearing."

"No," she said. "I will not sell or part with this ring. My husband brought it specially for me."

"Then you can't have the good cloth!" Peter replied.

She thought about it for a bit and said to herself: "He has brought me so many things; I could part with this ring to get the good cloth that he wants."

Eventually they made a deal. She kept the cloth and Peter went home with the ring.

This time his father and mother did not grumble so much when he got home; they understood the ring could mean money.

There was trouble at the Captain's house. When he woke up and his wife showed him the good cloth that she had got for his shirts, he asked:

"What did you have to pay for it?"

"Guess!"

"Don't expect me to cudgel my brains. Tell me."

"Well... the ring."

The gold ring with diamonds?" he exclaimed in dismay.

"Yes, dear," she said, "To get you some good cloth I parted with the ring."

The Captain stood as if frozen, speechless.

"But what is there about the ring?" she asked, afraid that she had done something very wrong.

"What indeed!" he exclaimed. "Its special quality is that it will provide whatever you ask of it."

"What's that you say?"

"Just what you heard. But the thing is: do you know the fellow who sold you the cloth?"

"Of course I know him, and quite well."

"Then let's go at once and find him."

They went and found him, but Peter was not to be budged.

"Come on!" said the Captain. "Let's call off the deal."

"Oh no," Peter replied.

"Will you take a handful of gold coins?"

"Not even four handfuls."

"Ask whatever you want."

"No, I say."

Finally the Captain saw there was nothing to be done, and he would just have to say *good-bye* to the ring. He went off crestfallen, leaving Peter looking at the ring with the cat on his lap caressing him and the dog at his feet wagging its tail and making up to him.

Then the cat opened its mouth and said:

"You did well, Peter, to refuse to call off the deal."

"Do you mean," asked the dog, "that the Captain knew what he was doing when he tried to call it off?"

"All too well he knew!" replied the cat. "The ring, you know, has the special quality that it will provide whatever you ask of it."

"Is that so?" replied the dog.

"Good heavens!" Peter exclaimed when he heard what they were saying.

"Try it, and you will see," said the cat. "But watch out! Don't let anybody take it from you. If you should lose it, or if it were taken from you, it would go straight back to its rightful owner, Queen Pomeretta."

"Queen Pomeretta?" said Peter. "And where does she reign?"

"You don't need to know," said the cat. "Never mind about that. Try the ring and. see what happens."

"And what shall we ask it to provide?" said Peter.

"A well-set table, of course, so that we may all satisfy our hunger," the cat said.

Peter was delighted with this idea, and he said:

"O Ring, let us have before us a well-set table with more on it than we can finish, no matter how much we eat."

And at once there appeared a table with big dishes piled with saffron rice, stuffed capons, roast sucking-pig, grilled sausages, and black puddings.

I don't need to tell you how Peter and his father and mother tucked into all that and made short work of it. The cat and the dog went at the sausages and puddings until they were stuffed.

Nobody at Peter's house was ever hungry again. Every day, at breakfast-time, lunch-time, and supper-time, they sat down at the table; and the cat and the dog took care not to be far away. Peter would bring out his ring and say:

"O Ring, let us have such and such things before us."

And at once the things would appear; and you may be sure they never had beans, nor barley bread, nor mouldy dry figs, nor worm-eaten olives, because Peter took care not to ask for such things. They had, rather, fried eggs, omelettes with bacon and red sausage, rice with game or chicken, lamb or beef casseroles, stuffed capons, roast sucking-pig, red sausage with honey, grilled fillet of pork, and black puddings.

Whatever appeared on the table was soon finished by the five hungry mouths in the house; and it was hard to say which of them had the strongest teeth or the most bomb-proof stomach. Soon they were all so fat that they hardly fitted into their skins.

Naturally, people noticed and, because they did not know how to explain the change, they began to suspect something and to suppose that Peter and his parents had done a robbery somewhere or had made a pact with the Devil.

Just at this time there was a big robbery at a house in the town. The police searched high and low but could find no trace of the thieves.

"It must be the people at Peter's," said a malicious gossip. And then everybody repeated: "It's sure to be them."

The police wasted no time. They went to Peter's and said to his father and mother:

"Come on, now, don't deny it! It was you who did the robbery! How can you be so well fed if you didn't do it?"

"Gentlemen," said Peter's father and mother, "that has nothing to do with it: we cross our hearts. The fact is our son brought us a ring, and this ring gives us whatever we ask of it. That is the whole truth."

The police did not believe it; so to convince them Peter brought out his ring and said:

"O Ring, let us have a first-rate meal for the police." And at once there was a table lacking nothing in good food. The police tucked in with a will; then they began to have an idea, and they said among themselves:

"Why should this silly oaf have this ring and be able to fill his belly so easily? It's not right. The best thing for us to do is to take possession of the ring then lock him up, and then hang him; and then he won't bother us any more."

No sooner said than done. They tied Peter up, they took the ring from him, and they locked him up in the prison.

But – would you believe it? – the ring disappeared and they never saw it again. It went tlirough their hands straight back to Queen Pomeretta, who had had no joy since it had been taken from her by trickery. To make sure nobody should take the ring from her again, she put it in her mouth and kept it there all the time. "It will be the devil of a job for anyone to steal it again," she said.

Meanwhile the police were furious that the ring had disappeared, and they searched for it like mad – but how should they ever find it!

Peter, locked up in the prison, was very wretched; they gave him nothing but bread and water, and he was lucky if they remembered to do even that.

The busy ones were the cat and the dog, who had been under the table when the police were planning to take the ring from Peter and hang him. They had not missed a single word.

When they saw Peter being tied up they set off straight for the Port. On the way they found a pumpkin; they split it open, they hollowed it out, and they made a boat of it, they made a rudder with a piece of prickly pear. Then they launched it into the sea and got into it. The dog paddled like mad with his forelegs while the cat handled the rudder, and they set off for the kingdom of Queen Pomeretta.

Would you believe it? They soon sighted land, and in no time at all they were at the shore. They happened to come on a cat and a dog squabbling over a little rabbit that they had caught.

"Brother cat," said the cat, and "Brother dog," said the dog, "would you please tell us what land this is."

The other two stopped their squabbling for a moment and said: "This is the kingdom of Queen Pomeretta."

The cat and the dog in the boat were amazed and could hardly believe their good luck.

"And what are you seeking here?"asked the squabblers.

"We want Queen Pomeretta's ring," said the two in the boat.

"Then you may as well go back where you came from. She is so careful of it and guards it so closely that she keeps it in her mouth, so nobody shall steal it again."

"Was it stolen from her before?"

"Yes, and it's not long since she got it back."

"Are you sure of all this?" asked the two in the boat.

"We should be," the others replied. "We are from the Queen's house."

"Where shall we find her just now?"

"In the garden, beneath a huge orange tree that stands in the middle, where she goes to enjoy the shade. But look out – she has devilish ways with her."

The cat and the dog, jumped ashore, they put their boat in a safe place, and off they went to the Queen's garden as fast as they could, and they did not stop till they were there. They saw the Queen under the orange tree enjoying the shade.

"Brother dog," said the cat, "this is where we must do our very utmost. You must do the acting; go close to the Queen and make as if to do your business, and I will do the rest."

The dog did that, and there he was, straining away.

When the Queen saw this she was furious; she was a fiery character and, forgetting about the ring, she shouted with all her might:

"Get out, you dirty beast! Get out of here!"

She yelled it with all her force, and she spewed out the ring quite a good distance. The cat was watching for it as if it had been a mouse; he caught it in the air before it touched the ground, and then darted off like lightning, making, for the boat, with the dog following full tilt.

They got to their boat, they jumped in, and the dog paddled away like mad, with the cat at the tiller keeping the boat dead on course. Away they went into the open sea, heading for their home port.

"I can't go on!" said the dog after some time.

"You must go on," replied the cat. "Perhaps Peter is already at the gallows; we should deserve to die if we were not in time to save him, remembering how he saved us."

And the little dog went on to do even more than his utmost.

What do you think? Almost before they knew it they were in the Port. They jumped ashore and. dashed up to the town as fast as they could go. When they reached the market square Peter was already up on the gallows, with the rope round his neck. The cat shot like an arrow between people's legs, climbed up the gallows and up Peter's legs, and gave him the ring.

When Peter felt the ring in his hand he nearly burst with joy – and so I should think! At once he said:

"O Ring, may the rope that is round my neck leave me and go round the necks of the judge, the police, and the hangman, until I say *stop*."

He had hardly finished saying it when the rope left his neck and was round the necks of all those who represented Justice, including the hangman; and there they were with a hand's breadth of tongue hanging out. Strangled, because Peter never said *stop* – but went off leaping and jumping for joy, and hugging the cat and the dog and embracing and kissing them. And his father and mother did the same, weeping for joy like little children when they saw him safe and sound.

Nobody bothered them again, and they lived together for many years; and they must still be alive if they are not dead. And may we all meet together in Heaven.

Amen.

The Miller's Daughter and Stepdaughter

ONCE UPON A TIME THERE WAS A MILLER in a country town who had a daughter called Kathy; she was pretty, attractive, and very bright.

The Miller's wife died, and he got married again to a widow who had a daughter called Kate. This girl was loud-mouthed, good-for-nothing, and disagreeable.

One day the Miller said to Kathy: "Kathy, will you take the flour to the Giants in the cave at Marlpit Farm?"

There is a cave in the Marlpit property, which in those days was inhabited by a group of Giants who lived on the game that they caught. They were very good folk who never said a word to anybody so long as nobody tried to cross them. The people of all that neighbourbood knew this, so nobody crossed them; people gave them a wide berth and let them be.

These Giants used to bring wheat to the Miller, who milled it and returned the flour to them, after taking his normal due, of course. The Miller employed a man who usually took the flour to Marlpit Cave, but it happened the man was off sick that day, so the Miller decided to send Kathy.

He loaded the sack of flour onto the mule, sat the lass on top, handed her the halter, and said *Gee-up*. The mule then set off for Marlpit Cave. When they reached the cave the mule stopped; Kathy dismounted and went into the cave calling out:

"Is there anyone at home in the house? Is there anybody here? Please come! I have brought your flour."

She went on calling out, but nobody answered. So what do you think she did? She somehow managed to unload the sack and to take it into the cave. She saw it was all rather dirty and untidy inside; so she swept and cleaned and dusted, and she soon had it all neat and orderly.

Then suddenly the Giants arrived back; they saw what Kathy had done inside the cave, and they were very pleased and grateful. Then they put their heads together, and the Chief Giant said:

"This lass deserves a gift from us; she has truly earned one."

"A good idea! Good idea!" they all cried. "And the Chief shall say what the gift is to be."

"Very well," said the Chief. "I will say what it shall be. The gift is to be: that whenever Kathy opens her mouth to speak, a silver coin shall come out with every word she utters."

"Agreed! Agreed!" said all the Giants.

"Very many thanks." said Kathy then, and at once three silver coins came out of her mouth for the three words she had said. She picked up the coins and pocketed them; then she mounted the mule and set off for the Mill.

When her father and stepmother and stepsister saw how whenever Kathy uttered a word a silver coin fell from her mouth, you can imagine how they goggled. Her father was delighted; but her stepmother and stepsister could not bear it. They were filled with envy and anger.

Kathy, being the good girl she was, gave her father all the coins that fell from her mouth when she spoke, and her father was overjoyed; but her stepmother and stepsister were grinding their teeth with rage, and the Devil was making them green with envy.

One day the stepmother said to the Miller:

"Have we not had any more grain to mill for the Giants of Marlpit Cave?"

"Yes, we have," the Miller replied.

"Well, mill it; and my Kate can take the flour to them."

"Is it your idea," he said, "that she should come back from the cave, as my Kathy did, with a silver coin falling from her mouth for every word she speaks?"

"You've guessed it!" she said. "And wouldn't you like that?"

"Yes, of course. Come on then, let's mill the grain for the Giants of Marlpit Cave."

They put the grain in and it was soon milled; the Miller took his due, filled the sack, put it on the mule, and called his step-daughter:

"When you like, you can take the flour to the Giants."

His wife heard and said: "Come on, Kate, get moving; and see if you can come back as Kathy did."

"I will do what I can," said the wench.

She mounted the mule and set off for Marlpit Cave. She was soon there; she dismounted and went into the cave calling out: "Hey, you people in here! Come out quick! I have brought your flour. Come on, you great lazybones, get moving! Do you expect me to carry the sack in? If you don't come quick I'll dump it on the ground and go."

At this point the Giants returned from their hunting, and she – being all worked-up as she was – began scolding them without consideration or respect.

The Giants unloaded the sack and took it in to their kneading trough. They left Kate outside because she was so loud-mouthed and disagreeable; and – would you believe it? – when she saw the Giants disappearing without saying anything about a gift such as they had given Kathy, she shouted out:

"Hey. you great louts! Are you sending me off like this? Am I to go back just as I came?"

When the Giants heard that they got together and said:

"What a rude, disagreeable, stuck-up girl! She is expecting us to give her the same gift as we gave Kathy; but good things are for those who earn them; Kathy deserved her gift, while this girl has earned nothing. But, so that she shall not go home just as she came, let us plant a trumpet in her backside, which shall sound off *Tarrarah! Tarrarah!* whenever she speaks."

"Very well," said the Chief. "Let the trumpet be so planted, and whenever she speaks let it sound off *Tarrarah! Tarrarah!*"

When Kate found that the Giants did not come back out of the cave, she jumped on the mule and set off for the Mill, disappointed, angry and hurt. The joke was when she got home; at the first word she spoke the trumpet in her backside went off *Tarrarah! Tarrarah!* And whenever she said anything it went on sounding off *Tarrarah!*

You can imagine the rage that she and her mother got into, and how the others laughed when they heard the music of the trumpet in her backside. The Miller could not help laughing aloud, and Kathy had to shut herself in her room; she could not stop laughing at such a funny thing, but she did not want her stepmother to catch her with the laughter on her lips.

The Miller's wife was furious at having her daughter in this plight. What worried her most was that, as Kate was courting, her young man would come and hear the *Tarrarah!* that never failed to sound off whenever the girl spoke. Kate's mother was afraid he might take it amiss and never come to the house again. So what do you think she did? She went to see him and announced:

"Look, my Kate has been to confession, and the father confessor has imposed on her the penance that she shall not speak a word until she is married."

The young man was a bit stupid; he had not found any other girl who would have him, and he hoped Kate would inherit something, because the people at the Mill were well-off. So he resigned himself to marrying the dreadful girl.

The wedding was arranged, and a week later they were married, without Kate having opened her mouth to say a word. The joke was when they came out of the church, with everybody congratulating them; there she was with her mouth shut, not speaking a word for fear of the consequences.

Her husband began to be annoyed and said:

"Well, woman, you can speak now. Christ spoke even when he was on the Cross. Your confessor gave you the penance of not speaking till you were married; now you are married, so speak!"

She was so hard pressed that she had no choice but to open her mouth to thank people for their congratulations. It was no good! The trumpet that the Giants of Marlpit Cave had planted in her backside sounded off *Tarrarah!* for every word the poor girl said.

It was a riot! Everybody burst out laughing, and they all laughed and laughed; the bridegroom and his people were more upset than I can say; the Miller's wife was furious; the Miller too was embarrassed, but also greatly in fear of bursting out laughing as well.

It all ended badly. The bride fainted and had to be taken home on a ladder and put to bed; the bridegroom said he had been deceived and therefore regarded the wedding as not having taken place. He sent back all Kate's trousseau and other things, and would have nothing more to do with her.

She was never able to get rid of the trumpet planted in her backside by the Giants of Marlpit Cave; it went on sounding off *Tarrarah!* every time the wretched girl uttered a word.

Well then, she should not have been so ill-tempered, so rude, and so disagreeable. She thoroughly deserved it.

Be warned, you girls who hear this tale; if you want to keep out of trouble mark the lesson of Kathy and Kate.

John the Charcoal-Burner

THERE WAS ONCE A BACHELOR FELLOW named John who worked as a charcoal-burner. His mother was alive and he lived with her; the house was in the village, but he spent his time at his kiln and came home only once a fortnight. He never washed, and as for his clothes you could not tell whether they were cloth or charcoal, they were so dirty and ragged.

Eventually his mother died. May she rest in peace and her soul be saved, as all the faithful departed. Amen.

Then the neighbours began to say to him:

"John, you should get married."

"Is getting married the only thing to do?" he would say.

"The point is you should have a woman at home to look after your house and wash your clothes and mend them, to see you don't go about in rags. Then people cannot say when they see you: 'If you are worth anything, look at yourself'."

They went on singing this refrain until at last he said:

"I don't know any woman who would suit me, and I've no time to look for one. You find me one."

They searched around and at length they found a girl who was nothing much but seemed quite good enough for John. They told him about her, and he went to see her.

"It's not that I am very keen to be married," he said to her; "it's the neighbours who keep pushing me. So, to keep them quiet, and if you are willing, say the word and we can be married when you like."

She said *Yes*, and they were married.

The next day he went off to his kiln, and he did not come home until a fortnight later.

And what do you think? That idle girl had not put any water in the pitcher for him to wash, had no clean clothes for him, and had not prepared any supper.

John did not say a word, and the next day he went back to his kiln. After a fortnight he appeared at home once more, and again he found no water in the pitcher, no clean clothes, and no supper ready.

He kept his mouth shut, and the next day he went off to his kiln as quickly as he could. Another fortnight went by; he came home and found the same welcome – the pitcher empty, his clothes unwashed, and no supper made.

John never said a word to the silly woman, but he went to the neighbours who had found her for him, and said:

"I think I made a bad buy with this girl. Three times now I have come back from the kiln, after a fortnight, and found no water in the pitcher, no clean clothes, and no supper made. Would you tell her, please."

The neighbours went and told her, but she answered them back with:

"I have hired an ass, and he must keep me and support me in sickness and in health."

"Pig-headed are you? Is that a thing to say?"

"Then don't stick your noses in where you're not wanted."

The neighbours told John of this. Then he went off to his kiln and was away for three weeks; when he came home he found no water in the pitcher, no clean clothes, and no supper.

Then he grasped his buttocks in both hands and pushed himself to see the Vicar who had married them, to tell him what was happening and to ask him to give the girl a bit of a sermon.

The Vicar later sent for her and said:

"My dear, what is this I hear about you and your husband? He says when he comes home from his kiln every fortnight he finds no water in the pitcher, no clean clothes, and no supper ready. Don't you see, my dear, this won't do. You must look after him and care for him; he is your husband."

The woman was silent for a bit, and then she came out with:

"I bought an ass, and he must keep me and clothe me and support me, in sickness and in health."

"Oh, really?" said the Vicar. "Then look out this ass doesn't break his chain and kick you where it hurts."

The Vicar told John of the stupid girl's reply; then John went off to his kiln and was away for four weeks without coming home. And what do you think? When he did come home he found not a drop of water in the pitcher, no clean clothes, and no supper ready. He was incensed, and without saying a word he went off that same evening back to his kiln. A fortnight went by, and another fortnight; six months went by, and still John did not show up, neither in the village nor at home.

About this time the midwife began calling at John's house – not for him of course but for his wife, who in time gave birth to a strong healthy boy.

The neighbours sent a message to John, who turned up to take the baby to be baptized; but once this was done he went back to

his kiln as quickly as he could.

His wife then began to think. John did not come home and did not send her any money, so that with the expense of having the baby and supporting him she came to the end of her money. She got thin, and then she had no milk, and soon she and the child began to suffer real hunger.

At length she said: "There's nothing for it; I must go and find John and see if he has any human blood in his veins and will take pity on this little angel, and on me who have to suckle him."

She summoned up her courage, and early one morning she took the baby in her arms and set off for the kiln. She was thinking and thinking how to approach John when God gave her light, and at once she saw how to do it.

She got to the kiln about nine o'clock; she found John sorting out charcoal, and she greeted him humbly, saying:

"Praised be the Lord."

"May he be praised for ever," John replied, looking at her rather closely, and even more closely at the baby.

"Is this the child?" he asked.

"Yes," she replied. "Isn't he a little angel?"

John noticed how thin they were, child and mother, and that struck him to the heart; but he said nothing.

The woman laid the baby down on the ground and set to sorting out the charcoal alongside John. Neither of them said a word, but both had pounding hearts going *thump-thump.*

About eleven o'clock she said:

"Shall I light a fire and cook some dinner?"

"Yes, do," he said. And he went and showed her the things for making a fire and cooking. He left her to it and went back to his charcoal. He found the baby asleep there and could not refrain from picking him up; he kissed him again and again, and he shed many tears. He held the baby in his arms for a good while, until she came to tell him their dinner was ready. When she saw him holding the child her heart swelled up and she burst into tears. John almost did so too, but he restrained himself and said:

"Alright, let's have dinner."

They went and had it, and I can assure you she ate a very good meal. When they had finished she washed up, and then she tidied the hut where John slept – where there was plenty of room for her and the child too.

From that day on she was diligent in all the housework, and when that was done she helped John at the kiln, and with the other jobs that had to be done. She was able to eat enough, and so her milk came back and the baby could have all he wanted.

John began to play with him and hold him in his arms, and the little angel soon got to know him; when John was holding him he was always good.

So peace and happiness came to that marriage, thanks to the child. John became another man, and his wife another woman. And they lived like Joseph and Mary for years and years, and by now they are old, if they are not dead.

May we all meet them in Heaven.

Amen.

A Farmer's Wife who Outwitted the Devil

THERE WAS ONCE a tenant Farmer whose rented farm was put up for sale leasehold; he bought a large part of it without having the money to pay for it; and he did not even have enough to make improvements that would have earned money to pay what he owed.

In desperation he one day promised his soul to the Devil if he could have enough money to finish paying for the land and to make the improvements that were needed.

What do you think? The Devil appeared with a bag of money enough to complete payment for the land, and he said to the Farmer: "As to the improvements, I will send some people along to do the work. All you have to do is to be on the land at midnight exactly; then you whistle and we shall appear."

"At midnight?" said the Farmer. "Do you work in the dark?"

"Indeed we do," the Devil replied. "We don't care for bright light and it is in the dark that we do best. We shall begin work at midnight and we shall be busy until daybreak."

"So you do your work when there is nobody about?"

"You have got it! Alright; when you need us, remember, you go to the land where the improvements are to be made, you whistle on the stroke of midnight, and we shall not keep you waiting at all."

When he had said this the Devil disappeared into thin air. The Farmer went and paid for the land, and that same evening at midnight exactly he was there. He whistled and – *whoosh!* – there appeared a huge crowd of devils all shouting:

"Work, Master, work! We want work."

The Farmer was taken aback by this flock of lucifers; but when he realized that they were not coming at him and showed no evil intentions, he plucked up courage and said:

"You want work? Alright, you shall not be short of it. This land, as you can see, needs to be cleared of stones and weeds. I want to sow crops and to plant almond trees, fig trees, vines, apricots, apples, pears, carobs and olives. For this we must prepare the land; we must bring manure and spread it, we must plough it, and we must dig pits to plant the almond trees, the fig trees, the apples, the pears, the apricots, the carobs and the olives; and we must make trenches for the vines. You can see there is work for some time."

"Then what is our task now?" said the devils.

"The best thing will be for you all to clear the land of stones. Make piles of the stones and then dig pits and throw the stones in; cover the pits with earth and level it all off, and then it will be right for weeding."

The devils were so many and so active – and they all went at it with a will – that they soon had the land cleared of stones; they dug pits here and there, threw the stones in, covered over the pits with earth, and left it all level and as smooth as the palm of your hand. Then dawn broke, and the Farmer said:

"That's enough for today, boys; see you again at twelve o'clock tonight. Go your way now, and *au revoir!*" He did not say *God be with you*, as he thought that was hardly suitable.

He went and lay on his bed to get a little sleep. Later in the day he got up, had breakfast, and set himself to thinking what task he should give the devils, to make the best use of the time and advance the work.

In the evening he had a good supper, lit his pipe, and went off to his land, where he waited and waited. At twelve o'clock he whistled and – *whoosh!* – the huge crowd of devils appeared again, all shouting like mad:

"Work, Master, work! We want work!"

"Just a moment," he said. "I will give you a job right enough, and we shall see if it keeps you busy!"

He showed them where he wanted to sow beans, where he wanted the vineyard, where the almond trees should be planted, where the fig trees, where the olives, where the apricots, where the apples, where the pears, and where the carob trees.

"There!" he said to them. "You can divide up the work among yourselves, like good brothers, and you can set about the job now. The land that is to be the bean-field you must weed; you must bring manure and spread it, and then plough the land with the right furrows; when it is ready I will bring the seed and we can sow it. Where the vineyard is to be, make the necessary trenches; and where we are going to plant almond trees, fig trees, olives, apricots, carobs, apples, and pears, dig pits of the right size and depth. Meanwhile I will get the saplings that we are going to put in, and I will go about my business. At daybreak you may stop work until midnight tomorrow, when you will be back on the job. *Au revoir*, then!"

The Farmer went on his way and the devils gave him a big *Farewell!* and then went on with their work, each in his particular job, until daybreak, when they all stopped working and disappeared into thin air.

Well, what do you think? The next day, on the stroke of midnight, the team of devils on the job of the bean-field soon had it well weeded; then they ran all over the neighbouring fields where herds of oxen, pigs, sheep, and goats were grazing, and gathered up all the droppings, which they brought onto the Farmer's land and spread over the part to be sown with beans, with the result that there was a complete covering of manure all over the field; then with their finger-nails and toe-nails, and their horns, they dug over all that land better than if it had been ploughed six or seven times, and the field was ready for the seed. The Farmer brought several sacks of beans, and in one night the devils had sown them all, well spaced out, and covered with plenty of soil. The Farmer was there, and the head Devil too, who asked him:

"Do you accept as properly done the job of sowing the bean-field?"

"I certainly do," said the Farmer.

"Well, this fulfills one part of my promise to help you with the improvements. We shall not be long finishing the other jobs and then we will submit them for your approval."

Some days later the Farmer went at midnight and found teams of devils working away furiously with their finger-nails and toe-nails, and their horns, digging trenches in the part that was to be the vineyard, and pits where the almond trees were to be, and where the fig trees, apricots, carobs, olives, apples, and pears were to be planted; and that same night all the pits were ready. Then the head Devil said to the Farmer:

"When you like you can bring the saplings for us to plant in these pits, and the stakes and supports we must put with these young trees."

"Very good," said the Farmer. "In a week it will all be here." And within a week the Farmer had bought the vine cuttings to plant in the trenches, and the saplings of almonds, figs, apricots, carobs, olives, apples and pears. In one night the devils planted all those vine cuttings and all those young almond trees, fig trees, apricots, carobs, olives, apples, and pears; and they put in the stakes and supports needed, and they left it all as neat as could be.

Then the head Devil said to the Farmer:

"Do you accept the task as properly completed by the work of these my minions?"

"I certainly do," said the Farmer.

"Well then," the head Devil went on, "now you can prepare yourself to fulfill your part of the pact that we made."

"And when is this to be?" the Farmer asked, rather upset by the warning.

"When?" said the Devil. "When you have harvested your beans and the first fruits of your almond trees, fig trees, apricots, carobs, olives, apples, and pears. I think I have not spoken wrongly, nor said anything unreasonable."

"No, you have not," replied the Farmer, more than a little put out. Then the head Devil and the troops of little devils all vanished into thin air.

The case of the Farmer's land – where in silence and all unnoticed, there had been so many improvements in so short a time, without anybody being able to find out who had come and done the work – caused a lot of surprise and everybody was amazed; some people were very worried by it.

The Farmer was hard put to it, and he had to employ men to look after all those sowings and plantings, and to do all the jobs that had to be done.

In the bean-field there grew up a huge harvest such as has seldom been known. All the vines rooted and after two or three years began to bear fruit; the almond trees, the apricots, the apples, the pears, the figs, the carobs, and the olives, all took root and grew very quickly, and in due course began to bear fruit.

The Farmer, on the face of it, should have been bursting with joy and satisfaction; but as it was he was hardly ever seen to laugh, and he went about looking worried, down-hearted, and depressed; worse than if he had sold something on tick.

This was because, when the carob trees and the olives began to bear fruit – and they are the slowest to do so – the Devil appeared and said:

"Look; you know what our pact is: there is fruit on all the trees that we helped you to plant in the land you bought with the money I gave you. Agreements are agreements: you must deliver your soul to me. It is mine because you promised it to me, and what is promised must be fulfilled. On such and such a day I shall come to take it away."

You can imagine what a bitter draught this must have been.

The Farmer's Wife saw there was something wrong, and she asked him over and over again what the matter was; but he kept his mouth firmly shut. But at length he had to tell her, weeping like a little child.

"All this fuss just for that?" she said.

"Don't you think it is enough?"

"Goodness, no, man; it is hardly enough to begin with. Look, I will settle this business. When the Devil comes to demand your soul you must tell him you have made over the land to me, with all the improvements, and he must deal with me – and, as everybody knows, 'who has the land has the upper hand'."

The Farmer heaved a sigh of relief, and at length said to his Wife:

"Do you mean it? Have you the courage to put yourself in my place and tackle this horrible business?"

"Of course I have," his Wife replied. "Don't worry about it any more. When Old Nick turns up, just send him along to me, and you will see how I get rid of him."

What do you think? On the day that the Devil had told the Farmer he would come to carry away his soul, he duly appeared, ready for action; but the Farmer said:

"Look; I have made over the land and all the improvements to my Wife, who says she stands in my stead; therefore you must arrange matters with her."

So the Devil went along to the Wife and demanded her soul.

"Oh, you want my soul, do you?" she said. "You are not asking for much, are you?"

"Agreements are agreements," said the Devil. "Your husband promised me his soul if I would give him money to pay for the land; I brought him money and he was able to pay. We helped him with the improvements and all the trees are bearing fruit. I have fulfilled my part; now you must fulfill yours."

"I don't have any agreement with you. I have never promised you anything."

"But your husband promised me, and you are standing in his stead."

"I tell you," said the Wife, "I have never promised you anything, least of all my soul, which belongs to the Good Jesus, who bought it with his holy blood."

"Don't mention that name; he is my worst enemy."

"Well, you have made a bad bargain with me, because whatever happens I am his, and that's that."

When the Devil heard this he was nonplussed and did not know which way to turn; because it was true the Wife had not promised him anything and he had no claim on her.

When she saw that the Devil was losing his arrogance and was wavering, she took courage and tried a joke on him.

"Look," she said; "did you not say you wanted my soul?"

"I certainly do want it! It is mine by rights because you are standing in place of your husband, who promised it."

"His he promised, not mine!" she said. "But never mind that; you say you want mine?"

"I want what is mine."

"Well then, first of all I want you to straighten this tuft of hairs that I have between my jaw and my left ear, below my cheek; they all curl like corkscrews." And she showed him the tuft of hairs which she kept covered with her scarf; she never cut these hairs with scissors nor shaved them, so that they should not become coarse and end up like bristles.

The Devil so much wanted to carry off the Wife's soul and throw it into a furnace in Hell that he at once attacked the tuft, and there he was pulling away at those hairs with his nails. And he pulled and pulled, but when he let go they were as curled and twisted as ever. When Old Nick was tired of making so much effort with no result, he whistled and there appeared a team of devils eager for work.

"Now then, my minions," he said, "let's see if you can straighten out this tuft of hairs that the Farmer's Wife has between her jaw and her left ear, just below her cheek. When you have straightened them we can take her off to Hell."

And all those devils worked away at the tuft, and there they were pulling and pulling away at those obstinate hairs. But what a hope! Those wicked hairs, though they were pulled hard enough to break, as soon as they were let go remained as twisted and corkscrewed as ever. What do you think? Those devils nearly burst with pulling, until at length they said:

"Enough! Let Pilate straighten them out – or whoever likes to try."

And they all took to their heels, leaving no trace.

The Farmer's Wife, very resolutely, went to find her husband.

"There!" she said. "I have got rid of the Devil. And don't you be so feeble as ever again to promise anything to that Old Nick."

"I promise to be more careful," said the Farmer. "On my word."

She was the very Devil, the Wife! Anyhow, don't argue with women if you don't want to come off second-best.

And this Wife and her Farmer, and the Farmer and his Wife lived for years and years, and they must still be alive if they have not died.

And may we all meet in Heaven.

Amen.

The Rivals

THERE WAS a married couple on a farm who had one daughter, named Mary. Her father and mother died – may God keep them in his Glory – and Mary went to live with her godfather.

She grew up; she was by no means ugly, and the chief ploughman, Tony by name, fell in love with her. She liked him too, but because he was so poor they kept it secret.

At the same time another young fellow from the town, called James cast an eye on Mary and asked if he might court her. She let him come to the house, but she liked Tony better.

About this time two friars came through the place, begging as usual for money to rescue captives from the Moors. They called at James's house and his father promised them a hundred pounds, saying: "Tomorrow my son James will take the money to you in the City." The friars called the same day at the farmhouse where Mary lived with her godfather, who was the farmer. He too promised the friars a hundred pounds for their mission and said that the following day his chief ploughman, Tony, would take the money to them in the City.

The next day James set off from the town on horseback, and Tony from the farm on a mule, each with a hundred pounds in his pocket, making for the City. They met on the road, they joined up, and in the course of conversation found they were both bound on the same errand.

James's horse began to behave badly; James lashed it again and again, and the more he did so the more the horse got out of hand. In the end it refused entirely and there was no way of making it move a step. Seeing this Tony said:

"James, I think I should push on. If you like to give me your hundred pounds I will take the money to the friars along with the hundred from our boss, and then you will not have to go any farther."

"That's a good idea!" said James. And he brought out his hundred pounds and gave the money to Tony, who trotted on towards the City. He found the friary, handed over the two hundred pounds, and then he turned about and set off for home.

When he reached the place where he had left James with the boggling horse, he found the horse tied to a bush, but no sign of James. He called out, in case James was somewhere near, but there was no answer. So what did Tony do? He went into the town, to James's house, where he told them about the horse, and about James himself. They were greatly surprised by this, and they at once took steps to find out where James was.

They found the horse alright, tied to the bush, but of James they could not find any trace.

They went and reported it to the police, and the police searched and searched. The police knew Tony and James were rivals, both courting the same girl, and at length they suspected it must be a question of jealousy; that one of the rivals, finding they were alone, had taken the opportunity to get rid of the other.

So they arrested Tony and put him in prison, and the case began to look very bad for him; not that there was any formal evidence against him – only unfounded suspicions.

Would you believe it, in court the case went so badly wrong that they passed sentence on Tony – and not just any old sentence but a sentence of death. And Tony was put in the condemned cell for three days.

On the morning when he was to be executed there arrived at the City a ship-load of rescued captives. Usually, whenever such a boat-load arrived at the port, crowds of people would go to the quay to see who the returned captives were; but on that day hardly anybody appeared. The sailors found this very surprising and they asked what the reason could be.

"It is because," people said, "today they are going to execute a certain Tony, who is said to have killed a certain James, of the same town, because they were rivals."

One of the rescued captives heard this and cried out:

"Wait a bit! It is not true! I am that James. When Tony left me with my boggling horse half-way to the City, I was attacked by a gang of Moors from a ship that had made a landing near there; they kidnapped me and took me to Algiers, where I have been until now."

Everybody was amazed. They all went with James to the place where Tony was to be executed; he was already beside the gallows and on the point of being hanged. James repeated before the Justices what he had said to the sailors, and Tony was ordered to be released. They released him, and the poor fellow went off, as you can imagine, in a sorry state. James accompanied him to the farm, and he had to go to bed because of the shock. But instead of recovering he got worse and worse, and finally he died.

He made a will wishing Mary to marry James; but when Mary heard he had died she said:

"Tony is dead? Then for me all men are dead."

And do you know what she did? She shut herself up in a convent and became a nun. And when James knew of this he followed her example and went off to become a hermit.

And Mary in her convent and James in his hermitage lived for years and years, and they are still alive if they are not dead.

And may we all meet in Heaven.

Amen.

A Lazy Bride

THERE WAS ONCE A LAZY GIRL who would gladly have seen all kinds of work done away with. She was not unattractive in face and figure, and she owned several parcels of land in good order, so there soon appeared a wide-awake fellow wanting to marry her.

He went straight to the point, and she – can't you imagine! – resigned herself to the idea. The neighbours warned this fellow over and over again about the girl's laziness; but he carried on as if he had not heard, and kept to his purpose.

They were duly married, and they had a wedding feast according to their means. The man had wanted everything to be just right in their bedroom, so that his bride should find nothing to complain of. Even so, there was one thing that at once caught her attention: there were twelve well-polished sticks arranged here and there about the walls of the room.

"I say!" she said, "What are these twelve sticks doing in our bedroom?"

"They are the twelve Apostles," he replied.

"But what's the idea of having so many sticks in the room?"

"That's a little hard to explain just now," he said. "I will tell you in time, and I am sure that with your keen intelligence you will understand at once."

She did not bother to go on about it, and said nothing.

When the wedding festivities were over the bride and groom were left alone; neither of them was hungry for supper, so they went to bed – this being the best thing to do. The next morning he woke up at dawn; he jumped out of bed and got dressed. He saw she was still asleep, and he left her in peace.

She did not get up until late in the morning. He said nothing to her that day, though he did not see her at all busy doing any housework.

The following morning he woke up at dawn and got out of bed; he saw she was sound asleep, and still he said nothing. She got up late and idled away the whole blessed day.

A couple of days went by like this; he was always diligent in his work, while she was lazy over everything and never got busy; she left the household chores undone as if it were not her job to do them.

One evening she said to him:

"Look, the bread left over from the wedding is coming to an end; some more will have to be baked."

"Is that so?" he said. "You mean the bread from the wedding is finished, and tomorrow we must bake some more."

They went to bed. The next morning at dawn he woke and got up; seeing that she went on sleeping, he called her and said:

"Listen, dear! We have to bake bread today."

"Yes," she replied, sleepily rubbing her eyes.

"Well then," he said, "the point is that you should get up at once and make a start on mixing the dough."

He went on getting dressed and then left the bedroom saying: "Don't be long. It's time we were at work."

He went and lit the fire, heated the water for mixing the dough, and made all the usual preparations.

Time went by, but for all he went on calling her she did not appear out of the bedroom. Eventually he went in and found her stretched out under the bedclothes as if she did not intend to get up until much later.

The fellow lost his patience; he seized the first of the sticks on the wall, went up to the bed and pulled off the bedclothes. She saw there was trouble and turned her back on him. Then he gave her three of the best – *thwack! thwack! thwack* across her back; and he meant to hurt.

She did not wait for him to hit again; she jumped out of bed as quick as she could, got dressed in a trice, and went out of the room and straight to the kneading trough. She worked beside her husband and did not stop until they had mixed and kneaded the dough, made the loaves, and baked them. And then she went on to do the other work in the house until the evening, when they went to bed.

The next morning – would you believe it? – as soon as he kicked off the bedclothes, she did the same; she got dressed quickly and went about the work in the house like a proper woman.

From that day on he never had to call her in the morning, and never had to say anything to her about the housework and all the jobs that had to be done. She was quite changed; she became another woman. Instead of being lazy, she was diligent and orderly, and she became a wonderful wife to the man.

One day her mother said to him:

"How is it my daughter has changed so much? How has she become so hard-working?"

"It was Saint Peter who did the miracle," he replied.

His mother-in-law did not understand and did not care to ask for an explanation. Saint Peter was the stick he used that morning to beat his wife. Those twelve sticks, if you remember, he called the twelve Apostles, and the first of them was of course, Saint Peter.

Apostles of that kind can certainly perform miracles if there is a hand that knows how to wield them properly.

And if you don't believe it, try it out yourself when you have a chance.

The Soldier and the Bag

THERE WAS ONCE a lad, a poor widow's son, who decided to enlist as a soldier. His mother was in tears about it, but he would not be moved, and off he went to serve the King.

At the end of his service they sent him home with a loaf of bread and three guineas for travelling costs; and with this capital he set off for home.

In those days the Good Jesus and the Apostles were walking about the world. They were sitting in a pine-wood resting when the Soldier passed by without noticing them. When he was six or seven hundred yards down the road, the Good Jesus said to the Apostle Saint John: "John, go and ask that soldier for alms."

Saint John went off after the Soldier, crying out as loud as he could: "Some little thing, good soldier, for the love of God! For the love of God, something, please!"

"What is that?" said the Soldier when he heard this.

"A little charity for God's love."

"I have only a loaf of bread and three guineas, and I have not eaten anything today," the Soldier replied; "but that's no matter. Come here and we will divide it like good brothers." And he broke the loaf in two and gave one half to Saint John. "Take this guinea," he said, giving him one. "You should have half a guinea more, but as we cannot divide it we will toss for it. Say: heads or tails?"

"Never mind that," said Saint John. "What you have given me is enough; in God's name be it, and God be with you."

"Amen! Just what we need," said the Soldier, and he went on his way while Saint John went back.

"How was it?" the Good Jesus asked. "You see what a good heart that soldier has. Look, James; you go now and ask him for some little thing for the love of God."

Saint James went off. As the Soldier was going at a good pace, the Apostle had to move fast to catch up with him. From some way off Saint James began to cry out: "Some little thing, good soldier, for the love of God! For God's sake, something, please!"

"What? Another one?" said the Soldier. "They seem to be pretty thick about here. And a lot of largesse I can give! Never mind, I will walk faster and perhaps he will not catch up with me."

The Soldier lengthened his stride. Saint James noticed this, so he began to run, shouting away: "Some little thing, please, for the love of God!"

"I heard you all too well," said the Soldier to himself. "I have given half of what I had to another man; I have a long way to go, and I have not eaten anything yet."

As the other did not stop crying out and was now quite near, the Soldier began to be angry, and he broke off a shoot from a wild olive tree that there was near the road, and brandishing this stick he said: "Come on, and see if I don't give you some little thing with this!"

Saint James did not stop until he was right up to the Soldier; and – would you believe it? – the Soldier felt such compassion for him that the stick fell from his hand. Then he broke the half-loaf into two pieces and gave one to Saint James; and he gave him one of the guineas, saying: "Take this; we shall have one each."

"May God repay your kindness!" said Saint James, and he went running back to tell the tale.

"How was it?" said the Good Jesus. "You see what a good heart that soldier has. Anyway, Bartholomew, you go now and ask him for some little thing."

Saint Bartholomew went off and ran and ran. He saw the Soldier in the distance and began to cry out as loud as he could: "Good soldier! Oh, good soldier! Some little thing for the love of God! For God's love, something, please!"

"Another boil has broken out!" said the Soldier when he heard; and he saw that the other was coming at a great pace. "They must be in league. What can I give? And nothing has yet gone down my gullet today. Oh well, I will try running, and perhaps he will not catch me up."

And away he went running as fast as he could. But if the Soldier ran fast, Saint Bartholomew ran faster, and there they were both running for all they were worth; and the more they ran the louder and clearer was the voice of Saint Bartholomew crying out: "Some little thing for the love of God! For God's love, something, please."

The Soldier, seeing himself defeated, seized another wild olive shoot that he saw by the roadside, and he stopped to pull off the twigs. Breathing heavily he muttered between his teeth: "I am ready for you here, you villain. You shall see whether I give you some little thing more than you bargained for. You rogues, all! A mouthful of bread is all I have left, and would you cheat me of that? You are the very devil – so many of you, and so good at begging. Have I to support you all when I need someone to support me?"

But what do you think? When the Soldier saw Saint Bartholomew close to him, and could have touched him with his hand, he again felt in his heart such deep compassion that the stick fell from his grasp, and he said: "There! Here is all I have! Let's have done with it, once and for all. God will provide." And he gave him the piece of bread and the guinea that he had left.

"May God repay your kindness," said Saint Bartholomew, and he ran back to the Good Jesus to tell him the tale.

"How was it?" asked the Good Jesus. "You see what a good heart that soldier has. He really has won a prize, and we will give him one. Philip, you take this bag and give it to the soldier; explain to him that he has only to say, to anything, *Into the bag* and it will go in."

Saint Philip took the bag and went off with it. By dint of running hard he at last descried the Soldier and began to cry out loudly: "Good soldier! Oh, good soldier! Listen a moment! Stop a minute! Wait for me! Stop!"

"What? Yet again?" said the Soldier when he heard this. "It will be hard for me to give anything this time." Saint Philip never stopped shouting out like mad: "Hey! Stop! Stop, for the love of God!"

"'What the devil do you want with all this shouting?" the Soldier said at length. "I have given everything I had; I have nothing left."

"Stop, I say, for your own good," cried Saint Philip.

"What's that?" the Soldier asked testily, and he stopped.

"It is this. Take this bag."

"Empty?"

"Yes."

"That's a fine present! What am I supposed to do with it?"

"Look, whenever you say to anything *Into the bag!* that thing will just have to go in."

"Thank you, then, and for the love of God be it."

"Let all be for the love of God," said Saint Philip. And each of them went his way.

The Soldier walked and walked and at length came to a city. I cannot tell you how hungry he was; his belly was empty and wrinkled. He passed by a bakery where there was a table full of bread just out of the oven, most appetizing.

"One of those loaves into the bag!" He said promptly. And one of those loaves went straight into the bag.

"This is going well," he said; and he saw farther along the street a pork-butcher's shop full of red sausages, black sausages, bacon, and hams. Naturally he said: "A string of red sausages and a string of black sausages into the bag!" And a string of red sausages and a string of black sausages went straight into the bag.

"That's good," he said, "now we have something for dinner and for supper. He sat down in a square near a fountain, broke the bread and a red sausage and a black sausage, and went at them, taking a bite of each; and he took good large mouthfuls with the keenest appetite you ever saw. He ate until his belly was like a bagpipe, and then he went walking about the city.

Going along one street after another, he came on a group of people. He went near and saw they were surrounding a lady who was clearly upset and distressed.

"Is there something wrong?" he asked bluntly.

"There is too much wrong," said the lady. "Are you a stranger here?"

"Yes, madam, at your service."

"Well, this is what is wrong: I am the owner of this great house that you see here, and for several weeks I have not been able to live in it, because it is haunted. The bravest, most courageous men do not like to sleep here, still less to stay here."

"Don't want to sleep here? They must be easily put off."

"How about you? Would you sleep here?" the lady asked.

"This very night, if you like; and you will be doing me a great favour if you will let me sleep here. Then I shall not have to go to a hostel."

"It is you who are doing me the favour," said the lady. "And here is the key."

The Soldier took the key, fitted it in the lock, opened the door, went in, and searched the whole house; but he found no trace of anything wrong. It began to get dark, so he lit the lamp; he lit a fire in the kitchen, crossed himself to say the Rosary, and as he said his prayers he fried up a panful of bacon, red sausage, and black sausage.

As he was taking the pan off the fire and was dishing up his supper, he heard a voice in the chimney saying: "I am falling! I am falling!"

"Fall then," said the Soldier, "and be quick about it!"

And – *crunch!* – down the chimney fell a devil – God save us! – who at once began walking round and round the table. The Soldier, as if nothing had happened, put his plate on the table, said his Our Father, crossed himself, and tucked in. And I can assure you all his teeth were soon hard at work.

Then there was another voice in the chimney: "I am falling! I am falling!"

"Fall then," said the Soldier. "You ought to be down by now."

And – *crunch!* – there fell another devil – God save us! – who then followed behind the first one going round and round the table.

The Soldier went on eating his supper, with good mouthfuls, perfectly cheerful and taking no notice of the two horned walkers going round. Would you believe it, as many as nine devils came down the chimney, and they all walked round and round the table.

One of them, who was taller than the others, had bigger horns and a more curled tail, said to them: "Come on, take a slice of bacon from this young spark eating his supper so calmly!"

"Just a moment!" said the Soldier; "up to this point we can be friendly, but no further."

"Take a slice from him, I say!" the big devil shouted again.

"Let's see which of you bright fellows will dare try!" said the Soldier. "I fried this bacon for myself, not for you."

The smaller devils did not dare to carry out the order of the big devil, who was shouting louder and louder: "Take it, I say, and look sharp!"

The Soldier at this point said: "You give me a headache with all this noise. Why can't you let me have my supper in peace, you good-for-nothing idiots?" Then after a moment he exclaimed:

"But I don't have to put up with this!" He picked up his bag, opened it, and shouted as loud as he could: "Come on, all of you, *Into the bag!*"

And those devils had to go into the bag, willy-nilly. As soon as he had them in it he fastened the mouth firmly and went straight to the blacksmiths; there he said: "Master, a good hammering on this bag, please."

The master smith called his journeymen, they put the bag on the anvil, and then they took their hammers and sledges and – come on boys! *Bang-ti-bang! Bang-ti-bang!* till they were running with sweat.

"That will do," said the Soldier. He opened the bag, and you would have laughed like anything to see those devils, one with his horns broken, another without any, here one with his tail broken, there one with his head battered, all walking lame, breathing fire through their teeth and sending sparks out of their eyes; they all had their tails between their legs, and they fled as fast as they could.

The Soldier went and related the story to the lady of the house, and he stayed with her for a couple of weeks, with plenty to eat and drink. And the house was no longer haunted.

The lady was very grateful and wanted to load the Soldier with money, but she could not get him to take more than four guineas. And he went off as cheerful as a bird.

Walking and walking along, he came to another city and found it in a turmoil; you could not have heard yourself speak for the noise. "What is the trouble?" he asked.

"You may well ask, good soldier," they replied. "Our King was at war with another, but he was not winning. In desperation he called on the Devil. The Devil appeared and said to him: 'I will see that you win the war, but a year and a day from now we must settle the account, and you will have to give me what I demand.' So the King said: 'It's a deal.' And he won the war. But tomorrow will make the year and a day, and the King feels sure that what the Devil demands will be his soul. To protect himself he has surrounded his house with sentries; there are sentries at every door, and it is said that he is in the innermost chamber accompanied by all the lords and aldermen; it is as if he had been sentenced to death."

"Is that all?" said the Soldier.

"Don't you think it is enough?"

"It's hardly worth mentioning."

The next day the Soldier presented himself at the King's house. The sentries at the first door did not want to let him in, but he spoke so boldly and made such a fuss that eventually they let him through. It cost him more to get through the second door, and even more again for the third; but he did not give up until he stood in the King's own room.

They all looked him up and down from head to toe; nobody there knew him. "Is it possible this is the Devil?" they all wondered, and there they stood with their swords drawn. The King did not know where to put himself. He was wearing his crown, so the Soldier was able to recognize him.

"My Lord King," he said, "you need not fear anything; while I am here you can be easy. A lot of devils may come, but woe betide any that dares to touch even a thread of your robes!" When the King and the others heard the Soldier so confident, they plucked up courage a little.

After a while – *Whoosh!* – a platoon of devils appeared, saying: "Lord King, a contract is a contract. We made you win the war, and today makes the year and a day; we have come to settle the account, and the settlement is that you must come along with us."

"You are a bit presumptuous with your chatter!" said the Soldier. "The King go along with you? Whatever next!"

"A contract is a contract," the devils repeated. "Give us what is ours. And what we want is the King's soul."

"The King's soul is very well where it is, and it is not with him that you have to deal, but with me," said the Soldier, "and I shall be surprised if you come out of it in good shape."

When the devils heard him speaking so sharply they looked at him closely, and suddenly they cried out: "It's the soldier with the bag! Fly for your life." They took to their heels and did not stop running until they reached the innermost corner of Hell. Among the platoon were the nine who had had the hammering.

The King and his people heaved a sigh of relief, and they all embraced the Soldier; but while they were at it – *Whoosh!* –

another platoon of devils arrived, very determined and aggressive, and all talking fit to burst, saying: "Lord King, a contract is a contract; we made you win the war, and today makes the year and a day. We have come to settle the account; and the settlement is that you must come along with us."

"Not again, by Old Nick!" exclaimed the Soldier angrily. "How ill-mannered you are! Lord, what a bunch of oafs! Very well, come on you miserable creatures, you scum, you filth! Which of you will dare to touch the King?"

The devils were so sure of themselves and took so little notice of the Soldier that they came on at their prey, and they were about to dig their talons into him when the Soldier opened his bag and cried out: "Come on, all of you *Into the bag*!"

They squirmed and kicked furiously, but they all, one after the other, had to get inside the bag. When they were all in, the Soldier closed the mouth of the bag good and tight, and said:

"My Lord King, our next job is at a blacksmith's." They went to one and the Soldier said: "Master, a good hammering on this bag, please." They put it on the anvil and the master smith and his journeymen took up hammer and sledge and went at it with all their strength – *bang-ti-bang! bang-ti-bang! bang-ti-bang-bang* – till they were out of breath.

The Soldier then opened the bag, and those devils, all with broken bones, limbs out of joint, bruised, and mutilated, made off for hell as best they could, without any more argument; they did not want to know anything more about the King or his people.

The King gave loads of money to the Soldier, who went back to his home. He found his mother still living, and still single the girl he had been courting before he went to do his military service.

They were married and, with his mother, all three lived together for a good many years; whenever he needed a few guineas he had them in his pocket. We could all do with that if we deserved it. And may God not let us die unless he has forgiven us.

Amen.

Half a Pound of Flesh

A CERTAIN SHIP'S Captain once found himself in a Moorish port; he was unable to take a cargo on board his ship because he did not have the cash to pay for the merchandise. And there he was, thoroughly troubled and bewildered, not knowing which way to turn. To make matters worse, he did not know anybody in that place whom he could have borrowed money from.

While he was racking his brains trying to find a way out of this difficulty, he met a Moor with all the appearance of being a rich man, who addressed him in the language of Mallorca.

The Captain was greatly surprised that a Moor should speak to him in *mallorquí*; the man noticed this and said:

"It seems you are surprised that I should speak to you in your own tongue. You see, I spent seven years in Mallorca as a slave. I was in a ship that was captured by a man-of-war which seized us and made us all prisoners; then we were taken to Mallorca to be sold as slaves. I was there until my people at home could send me the money needed to redeem me. I did not have a bad time in Mallorca; I ended up with a gentleman and a lady who were the kindest of people and treated me as if I had been their son. That is why I have good memories of your land; and when I take a walk I usually come this way, and if I hear *mallorquí* spoken I come up to chat a little and recall things past."

The Captain was amazed at finding a Moor who was so amiable and friendly, and he at once had the idea of opening his heart to the man in the hope of finding a way out of the difficulty that he was in.

"Look, sir!" he said to the Moor. "What you have said has gone straight to my heart, and it makes me think you must be a good man and willing to help others."

"I have always followed the rule of doing what favours I can: but there is one thing that really makes me angry, and that is when somebody does not fulfil an agreement made."

"Very good," said the Captain. "I will be frank with you. It happens that I have not a penny to pay for the cargo that I should be loading on board. You are a good man; would you know anybody here who would lend me, only for three months, the amount of money that I need?"

"And what is the amount that you need?" the Moor asked.

"A thousand pounds," said the Captain, "and I would repay the amount within three months."

"If that is all," said the Moor, "don't worry about it any more. We will go to my house and you can pick up the money there."

"Good sir," the Captain said, "do you really mean that you will lend me a thousand pounds?"

"Would I be joking about it?" the Moor replied. "I will lend you this amount, not just for three months, but for half a year."

"And what interest must I pay you, good sir?" the Captain asked.

"Interest? I will tell you. Half a pound of flesh off your body if within half a year you have not returned the thousand pounds; and if you have returned them, nothing."

The Captain pondered it, and he had this thought:

"As my intention is to return the money within three months, I shall not have to pay any interest, and the deal is safe."

"Sir," he said to the Moor, "I agree to the terms you state."

"Then come home with me and I will give you the thousand pounds."

They went to the Moor's house, and he counted out – *ding-dong* – a thousand pounds. The Captain took the money and gave infinite thanks to the Moorish gentleman for the great favour, and promised that before half a year was up he would have returned the loan. Then he went off to buy a cargo for his ship, and he loaded it with merchandise; they weighed anchor, set sail, and took a course straight for Mallorca.

What do you think? The Captain made a profit of four thousand pounds out of that cargo.

He wanted to go back at once to that city of the Moors to return the thousand pounds, but the winter set in and there was very bad weather at sea, followed by more bad weather, and still more bad weather. He tried several times to set out, but the storms forced him to turn back.

After five and a half months of the half-year that the Moorish gentleman had set for the return of the thousand pounds, the Captain could wait no longer, and he set off in his ship for that Moorish port.

At first the ship made some headway; but the storm, instead of abating, worsened, and the sailors were exhausted with the work of keeping the ship afloat.

By dint of the greatest efforts the Captain brought his ship into the Moorish port, but it was a week beyond the end of the half-year that the Moorish gentleman had set for the repayment.

Since that gentleman always reacted by becoming very angry if somebody failed to fulfil an agreement, whatever it might be, the Captain found him furiously irate and flaming away because the Captain had not repaid the thousand pounds within the half-year.

In vain the Captain told him the blame lay with the bad weather at sea. But the Moor did not want to listen to arguments; he took his thousand pounds, but he also demanded the interest – that is half a pound of flesh off the Captain's body.

The Moor made such a row over this that the Authority came to know about it and sent for both of them – the Moorish gentleman and the Captain.

"What plea have you against this captain?" the Judge asked the Moor.

"I will tell you," the Moor replied. "I lent him a thousand pounds under certain terms: namely that within half a year he would repay the money, and if he did not do so I would exact interest by taking half a pound of flesh off his body. Well, the half-year ended a week ago, but he did not repay me the thousand pounds until today. Therefore I can by right take half a pound of flesh off his body."

"And you?" the Judge said to the Captain. "What have you to say?"

"I admit," the Captain said, "that everything this gentleman says is true. My point is that, although I am a week late in repaying the thousand pounds, this has been through no fault of mine but because of the storms and the bad weather at sea. Consider, my Lord Judge: it is three weeks since we left Mallorca to come here, when normally it takes four or five days at the most. The point is, my Lord Judge, I am asking for mercy since I have failed not because I intended to fail but because the weather at sea prevented me."

The Judge thought for a while and then turned to the Moorish gentleman, saying:

"My sentence is that in the rigour of the law you are entitled to half a pound of flesh off this man's body; but it must be you yourself who cuts it, and with this proviso: if you cut any too much I shall have that same amount cut from your body to be given back to the Captain, whose obligation is for no more than half a pound; and if you cut too little I shall have cut from your body the amount required to make up the half-pound that you are claiming."

When the Moorish gentleman heard this pronouncement he was thoughtful for a time, and then he said:

"My Lord Judge, please forgive the trouble. I renounce the right to collect that interest."

He turned and took his leave of the Judge and the Captain with a low bow to each.

The Captain thanked the Judge profoundly, returned to his ship, and set sail for Mallorca promising never again to borrow money with the obligation to pay interest of that sort. But for the judge's verdict he would have lost his good cheer and perhaps more than that.

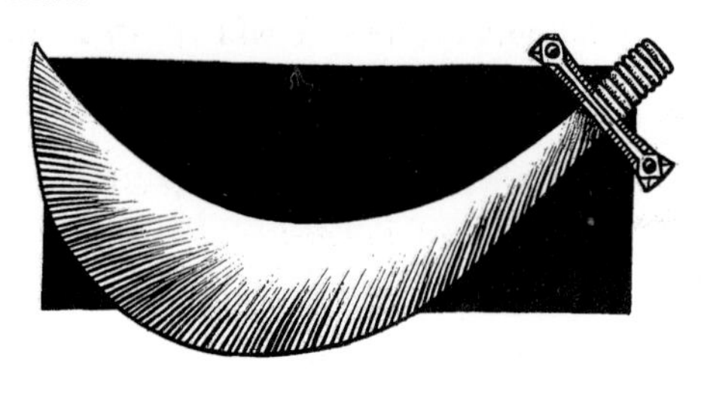

Maria Angela - a Resolute Girl

THERE WAS ONCE a girl called Maria Angela, as handsome in body and in spirit as she was short of money. Her mother had died giving birth to her, and her father had not wanted to marry again. They had a small-holding and kept a couple of pigs and two or three sheep.

One day a Knight passed that way as he was hunting. He saw Maria Angela, who at the time was aged seventeen; and he thought her such a beautiful and charming girl that he fell in love with her. He asked her a little about herself and, learning that she had a father, went in search of him and at once came out with:

"I have just seen this daughter of yours, and I don't expect ever to see a girl whom I could like so much. I am determined to marry her."

"Oh, sir," said the poor man, "my daughter is still a child and is not for a gentleman such as you."

"What do you mean?" replied the Knight. "Such a girl is good enough for a king, and certainly for a knight like me. I am single; she is single; we can be married."

"Sir," said the man, "the parsley is too green, as we say. Forgive me, but do me the favour not to talk about it any more."

"Very well," the Knight replied. "I will go away now and in a month's time I will come back and we can talk about it again; I wonder what you will say then."

A month passed and the Knight appeared again at Maria Angela's house and said to her father:

"I have come to say that I still feel the same; I like your

daughter, and I will marry her – or I will not marry at all. And what do you say to that?"

"I think it would be too unequal a marriage; you, sir, a knight, rich and well-to-do; and Maria Angela, daughter of a poor widower, owning nothing at all. There! It seems to me to be a mistake, and no small one. Forgive me; I do not say it to annoy you, but I have to say it. I have nothing in the world but this girl, and I cannot risk making her unhappy. I have to take care of her. I am her father."

"Very well," said the Knight. "Shall we wait another month?"

"It is never wrong to think matters over carefully," the man replied.

The Knight went away, and there was the poor man thinking and thinking over what he should do. On one hand he believed the Knight was in earnest, and that Maria Angela could not make a better match; but on the other hand there was the risk that the Knight could change his mind and make her very unhappy.

"What do you say about it?" he asked Maria Angela.

"I will do what you tell me," she replied. "If you tell me to say *Yes* I will say *Yes*, and if you tell me to say *No* I will say *No*."

The second month passed and the Knight appeared again. They sat down to discuss the matter, and in the end they agreed to think about it for another month, so as to make three months, and so that nobody could say they had been too hurried.

At the end of the third month the Knight arrived at the house, and Maria Angela's father at last said:

"Sir, for my part, if Maria Angela is willing to have you, you may marry her."

Maria Angela – and so I should think! – said *Yes*. They arranged everything and on the appointed day the Knight and Maria Angela were married; there was a magnificent wedding feast, a lively ball, and festivities galore.

Maria Angela was a very good girl, and the Knight was very proud of her; but one day a friend of his, a bad creature, said:

"Believe me, you are deceived. Your wife is like all the others."

"I will wager all I have that she is an honest girl, and that nobody can make her put a foot wrong," the Knight retorted.

"And I will wager all I have that if you give me a chance, within three months I can make her fall."

"Alright, the wager is on," said the Knight.

"Very good – it's on," replied the friend.

The Knight went off on a voyage and left Maria Angela alone with her maids and men-servants. When he had been gone three days the friend went to the house one evening quite late. He found it all locked up; he knocked with the knocker, and knocked again.

At length a maid looked out of a window and said:

"What do you want?"

"I came to see the lady of the house."

"Our mistress has ordered us, as soon as it begins to get dark, to lock up the house and not to open it for anybody, while the master is away."

The friend went off disappointed, but the next evening he went again. The maid said the same as before, and he began to complain and protest. The maid gave him no reply and shut the window.

The third evening he went again and knocked. The maid looked out of the window and, seeing it was the same man, she said:

"Sir, this is very impolite of you. We do what our mistress orders us, and that is that." And she shut the window on the rascal. Then he began shouting and raising the street.

An old woman – a thoroughly bad egg – came by and asked the crazy fellow what the matter was. He told her and she said:

"Don't worry, young sir; you can relax. I will make sure you win your wager."

He went away, but the next day when it was beginning to get dark, just before the house was closed for the night, the old woman appeared and asked to speak to the lady.

"Madam," she said, "I have come to tell you that today I went to confession, and I assure you I made a good and holy confession. The father confessor has given me a penance that I must spend the night kneeling at the foot of your ladyship's bed saying *Our Fathers*, but softly so as not to prevent your ladyship from sleeping."

"And does it have to be just at the foot of my bed?"

"That is what the father confessor imposed," said the wicked old witch, pretending to be as repentant as Mary Magdalene; "and your ladyship would not make me commit such a monstrous sin as to fail to carry out the penance given me by the confessor. I cannot believe your ladyship could be so heartless and uncharitable."

Maria Angela found it strange that the confessor had given such a penance, but she was shy of meddling in matters of confession, and in the end she resigned herself to that old scoundrel – whom she did not know but accepted as having been to confession and as being a real penitent – spending the night at the foot of her bed saying Our Fathers, but not to prevent her from sleeping.

She told her maids to let her be; and when she was in bed they let the old baggage into the bedroom, and there she knelt by the bed and began to do the penance she said the confessor had imposed.

The old witch began as if she were reciting *Our Father* after *Our Father*; but it was not in her heart that she did it – only from her mouth, with some wrong words here and there.

Maria Angela was soon asleep. The evil old woman, seeing her sleeping soundly, slowly got up, and moving as carefully as she could, so as not to wake her, looked at her hands, saw she was wearing a ring, took it, and hid it away. And then she went back to her pretence of saying *Our Fathers* one after the other.

In the morning, when the old woman heard the maids moving about, she went and asked them to open the door for her, as she had to go to Dawn Mass, because nothing in the world would make her miss it.

The maids believed her and opened up for her, and she went off like lightning – to Dawn Mass – straight to the house of that false friend of the Knight's, to give him the stolen ring. You can imagine how pleased the rascal was; he gave her a gold doubloon.

When Maria Angela woke up and was getting dressed, she noticed that she did not have the ring; she looked to see if it was in her bed, but of course she did not find it. She called her maids and told them; they all set about searching for the ring, and they nearly killed themselves searching and searching; but it was all in vain; they could not find it anywhere.

"It must have been that old woman who came and asked to spend the night at the foot of your ladyship's bed to do the penance the confessor had given her," said one of the maids, and the others thought so too.

Two of the maids went off in search of the old witch; but how could they find her? She had shut herself up in her house, and she did not come out for a week for fear of the consequences. Nobody knew any such old woman nor remembered ever having seen her.

The Knight eventually returned from his travels. The wicked so-called friend went to meet him and showed him the ring, that is, Maria Angela's wedding ring, saying:

"There you are, stupid! Do you recognize this ring? Do you want more proof?"

The Knight was aghast, dumbfounded. At length he said:

"Alright – you have won. But I shall take my revenge. Don't say a word to anybody."

"Don't worry," said the friend. "Nobody shall hear anything from me."

The Knight reached home. He revealed nothing. Secretly he had a box made, to his wife's size; he gave her a sleeping potion and, when he had her sound asleep, unseen by anybody he put her in the box and fastened it. Then he summoned a ship's captain and gave him a fistful of gold coins to take away the box and, when he was well out to sea, to throw it overboard. And he thought that was the end of the matter.

The captain did as he was asked. But, believe it or not, when the box was thrown into the sea, instead of sinking it floated and floated...

The sailors found this very strange, and they asked the captain to let them recover the box and open it,to see what was inside it. The captain said they could, and they did. When they had the box on board again they opened it, and they found a lady asleep.

They all stood with their hair on end in amazement, especially the captain.

Then the lady woke up and found herself on board a ship, in a box, and surrounded by the captain and his crew. She could not at all understand how she came to be there.

The Captain then related how he had been given the box, without being told what was inside it, with orders to throw it in the sea a long way from the shore.

Maria Angela, far from being overwhelmed and bursting into tears, summoned up her courage and asked the captain if he would let her have some sailors' clothing and, when they reached land, if he would let her go ashore to see if she could find out everything that had happened.

The captain gave her sailors' clothes and she began working as a sailor, as if she had always been one.

"And what name are we to call you by?" they asked.

"I will be called Angelo, since my name is really Maria Angela."

At the first port they entered Angelo jumped ashore, saying *Good-bye* to the captain and the crew – who were left bemused by the amazing lady, found in that way in a box, who dressed as a man and showed such courage and was so undaunted. The ship went on its way, and so did Angelo.

He arrived at a farmhouse and asked if they needed a hand; they said they did, so Angelo was taken on and did all the jobs they gave him. One day the farmer sent him with a message to the landlord. When the landlord saw the smart new hand he liked him very much, and he sent word to the farmer that he would keep the new hand for himself, if the farmer did not mind too much. The farmer resigned himself, and Angelo, who had done well at the farmhouse, did even better at the landlord's house, and everybody there liked him.

The landlord was a close friend of the General-in-Chief of the Kingdom. One day the General came to the landlord's house, where he saw Angelo and was much impressed by him. The General came two or three times more, and watched Angelo all the time. At length he said to the landlord:

"Could you let me have Angelo? He is just the lad I need in my service."

The landlord did not like to refuse the General, so Angelo passed into the service of the General-in-Chief of the Kingdom. But it did not stop there, since the King too was charmed by Angelo when he saw him a couple of times with the General-in-Chief. The King insisted on having Angelo in his service, and four days later he made him a General. Then the General-in-Chief died, and the King appointed Angelo in his place.

When Angelo found himself General-in-Chief he asked the King's leave to go to his home town to clear up a dirty trick that had been played on him.

The King said he should go, and that once he had cleared up the whole matter he should punish the guilty parties, without remission.

So Angelo, accompanied by the retinue proper for the General-in-Chief, came to his home town. He told the local Authorities he had come in the King's name to clear up a certain question, and to mete out justice. They all placed themselves under his orders, not suspecting anything nor recognizing who the General-in-Chief was.

The General began summoning people and asking them questions in secret, so none knew what he was asking of the others. After a couple of days Angelo had discovered everything that interested him: the wager between the Knight and his so-called friend over his wife's honesty; the device used by the evil old witch to steal his wife's ring with the pretence of doing a penance given her by the confessor; how she had taken the ring to the Knight's friend; and how, when the Knight came back from his voyage nobody saw his wife again, while he shut himself in his house and never went out into the street.

Then Angelo summoned the friend and the old witch; he questioned them very closely and he saw that these two were the guilty ones. He passed a sentence of death on them and they were straight away hanged on a gallows.

Then Angelo called the Knight, and Maria Angela revealed herself as his wife. He recognized her and, both in floods of tears like little children, they embraced. He begged her forgiveness, and she forgave him.

Then, still dressed as General-in-Chief, she returned with her Knight to the King; they told him everything, and he gave her leave to go home with her husband.

They went home, and I can assure you that they lived for years and years in great peace and harmony, and they are still alive if they are not dead.

And may we all meet in Heaven.

Amen.

Captain Peter

THERE WAS ONCE a ship's captain called Peter. He was returning from a voyage, rich and satisfied with what he had earned with his ship-load of goods, when a fearful storm got up; with every wave the ship nearly went to the bottom. Things looked so bad that Captain Peter in desperation made this promise:

"If the ship is saved I will marry the poorest girl in the port where we are able to disembark." He could make this promise since he was still a bachelor.

He had hardly said it when – phew! – the sea became calm, like a basin of oil. They soon found a port and went ashore. Captain Peter went to an inn and said to the inn-keeper's wife:

"Can you tell me, please, who is the poorest girl in this town?"

"Oh," she said, "there are plenty of poor girls here; as many as you want."

"No, that is not it," said the skipper. "What I am asking is who is the poorest of them all, in your opinion."

"Well," the woman said, "there was such a girl here just now; her name is Magdalene and she is a very good girl – the prettiest in the town, but also the poorest. She lives alone with her mother, who is nearing her end and has to be fed; they are quite destitute. And the poor girl has to go out to work to provide for her mother and herself, but what she earns is not enough. If some good people did not give them a little help they would die of starvation. I will tell you what kind of girl she is: being in the flower of her youth – she is about twenty – and girls' hair being, as you know, what they most value, she cut hers off and sold it – lovely fair hair that reached to below her knees – sold it to buy food for her mother."

When Captain Peter heard this he straight away fell in love with the girl – just from what the inn-keeper's wife told him; but to be doubly sure he went to see the Rector of the parish, and asked him if it was true that such and such a girl was the poorest in the town, and if it was true she was as good a girl as she was poor.

The Rector said he took her to be the poorest and one of the best girls in the parish.

Captain Peter wasted no more words. He asked the inn-keeper's wife to accompany him to the house where Magdalene lived.

Together they went to the house and found the girl at home. Captain Peter said: "If I don't tell you why I have come, you will never guess. The fact is I am a ship's captain; the other day we were in a most terrible storm, and we thought we were going to sink. I feared it was the end, but I made a promise that if we and the ship were saved I would marry the poorest girl in the first port we should reach. We were saved, and the first port we came to was this one; they tell me you are the poorest girl in the town; therefore, if you will have me, we can be married tomorrow."

You can imagine how Magdalene must have been taken aback. She asked for three days' grace to think about it, and Captain Peter said: "that is very wise of you. Being married is for life and is not to be entered into hurriedly, but sensibly like an old horse, treading carefully so as not to slip. Very well, I will come back in three days' time to see what you think about it."

Magdalene spoke to her mother, who said she should go to the inn-keeper's wife and find out what she knew about the man, and afterwards to the Rector. So Magdalene went, and the inn-keeper's wife said: "he seems to be a good man, and I don't think he is deceiving us; but I don't know him and I have never seen him before. He just turned up here and asked me who was the poorest girl in the town, and I told him I thought it was you. Would you like my advice, Magdalene?"

"Yes, please, indeed I should. What is it?"

"Well, if I were you I would take this skipper with both hands. He seems to be a good man; he clearly knows what he is doing; and he handles money by the shovelful – all ship's captains do. You are no longer a child, and you know the refrain:

When your girl is twenty-one
Get her married if you can,
For when she gets to twenty-three
It may be hard to find a man.

But you must do what you want to do; only you can know what suits you best."

Then Magdalene went to see the Rector to ask him his views; and the Rector said she should trust in God, but he thought the captain would suit her if she did not know a better man.

After three days Captain Peter went to see Magdalene to ask her what she had decided. Magdelene said *Yes*, and the next day they were married, and they had a good wedding feast and a lively ball. Captain Peter showed Magdalene a large bag full of golden guineas, telling her not to be afraid, as he was a man of substance.

Magdalene's mother died of joy when she saw her dear daughter's good luck and prosperity. May she rest in Heaven with all the faithful departed. Then Magdalene and Captain Peter went on board his ship and they set off for his home port.

When the people of this port saw the Captain's wife, so comely and seeming such a good woman, they all said: "Captain Peter made a good choice he has a good nose and good taste!" and they all congratulated him; he was very pleased and happy.

So as not to leave his wife alone too soon, he handed over his ship to another skipper, by name Ralph, who seemed very friendly towards Peter but was really a double-dyed villain. Captain Ralph was to make several voyages, on commission of course.

Captain Ralph made the first voyage, but it was a failure; he barely had enough money to pay the deck-hands. He made a second voyage, which turned out so badly that he could not even pay the deck-hands. He made a third voyage and came within a hair's breadth of sinking – ship, cargo and sailors.

At this point Captain Peter said: "There is nothing for it; if you have a business, manage it properly. I must skipper the ship myself."

"And I should like to come with you," said his wife Magdalene. "I don't want to be left all alone."

Captain Peter was a little reluctant, but seeing her so set on coming he said: "Alright, come on this voyage, but only this once."

The day of departure came, and the Captain's wife Magdalene and Captain Peter went on board. When the sailors saw the skipper's wife coming on board they said among themselves: "We shall see how this trip goes with a woman on board."

Anyway, they set off with sails spread, and away they went into the open sea. At first they had weather fit for a king, but on the third day there began to be gusts of wind, and soon it became a really bad-looking storm, with great waves, first from one side, then from the other.

The sailors then began saying among themselves: "There you are! The skipper's wife's storm; and it looks like being a skipper's wife and a half. Who does not know that a voyage with women makes bad weather certain? Who does not know that women to sea cannot go? If we don't throw this one overboard we shall all go to the bottom. There's no way out."

Captain Peter heard these threats, and he made a promise that if the ship were saved he would watch all night over the dead in the graveyard of the first port they should come to, come rain, come snow.

What do you think? He had hardly made the promise when the sea began to die down, and it was soon like a basin of oil. Then the sailors said: "Well, some saint protected the skipper's wife by calming the sea! If it had not died down she would not have escaped; we should have thrown her overboard, and no mistake."

They saw a port and put into it. Captain Peter and Magdalene went ashore. "Look, Magdalene," he said, "you cannot accompany me on any more voyages. We will buy a house here, and you will stay here with a maid, while I continue my work as a skipper." The same day he bought a good house, all furnished, with nothing to do but walk in and hang up your hat.

Towards sunset he went to the graveyard; he explained to the sacristan the promise he had made, and they agreed that he should watch. There was only one dead person, a woman. So Peter sat down near-by to watch; he told his Rosary with devotion for the soul of the poor woman lying in the coffin, who during her life had given rise to a lot of gossip.

If you will believe it, as the church clock was giving the last stroke of ten, Captain Peter began to hear a noise like something dragging along the ground. He looked about him, and he saw a large serpent, which was carrying in its mouth a small white flower; it went round and round the dead woman's coffin, and when it passed by Peter it paused for a moment as if showing him the flower. He was terrified; he did not know what to do and he dared not move. At length the serpent disappeared.

Captain Peter heaved a long sigh of relief; but when the church clock struck eleven – look! – the serpent appeared again, still with the flower in its mouth; and there it was going round and round the dead woman's coffin, and each time it passed by Peter it paused for a moment, showing him the flower.

He was once again terrified, unable to do anything, and he neither moved nor uttered a sound. At length the serpent disappeared, still with the flower in its mouth.

"But what the devil is this all about?" Captain Peter wondered. "What is this great serpent looking for? What is the reason for the flower that it carries in its mouth? And why does it stop in front of me as if showing me the flower? Anyway, if it comes again and shows me the flower, I will get up and take it. And I wonder what will happen after that."

Well, if you will believe it, twelve o'clock midnight came with Captain Peter still watching over the dead woman, and again there appeared the great serpent with the small white flower in its mouth, and again it went round and round the dead woman's coffin; and each time it passed by Peter it paused for a moment, showing him the flower. The third time round he summoned up his courage and took the flower from the serpent's mouth. The serpent disappeared at once .

"But what the devil can be the significance of all this?" he said to himself. "This little flower must have some great virtue. Let's try it out." He passed the flower over the face of the dead woman, and then again. He noticed that the woman's face was regaining colour, so he went on passing the flower to and fro across her face.

Would you believe it? The dead woman opened her eyes and breathed a deep and terrible groan. "Is it you, good sir, who have brought me back to life?" she said. "It is you, is it not?"

"I only passed the little white flower over your face," he replied. "I did nothing else."

"Oh, what good luck I have had!" the woman exclaimed. "I had died and the devils wanted to take me off with them to Hell – and I well deserved to go for the many sins I have committed – then there was a counter-order because I was not quite dead. With what you did with the flower, and with the Rosaries that you said for me, you have freed me from the clutches of those lucifers, and you have restored me to life. May God repay your kindness, good sir! May God repay it! And I promise I shall remember you for the rest of my life. Yes, while I live I will do nothing but penance, that God may forgive me and I may not again fall into the clutches of those devils. Believe me, they are ferocious!"

Captain Peter had his hair standing on end at all this. He was pinching himself to see if he was dreaming, trying to make out what was happening to him. The woman then got out of her coffin and on her own feet walked home to do a true penance.

Captain Peter went home to his wife and told her what had happened. They agreed to say nothing to anybody, and to keep the little white flower in case of need.

A couple of days later Captain Peter undertook a voyage with his ship, leaving Magdalene in the house that he had bought, and he told her to have nothing to do with anybody – only with her maid. The ship weighed anchor and with sails set went off into the open sea. Magdalene stayed in the house with only her maid, and had nothing to do with anybody. She went out only to go to Mass.

If you will believe it, that villain Captain Ralph, seeking his revenge, said to himself: "I will deal with Captain Peter, who did not want me to skipper his ship any more. I will punish him so that it hurts. I will steal away his wife."

He thought and thought about it – how to do it, how not to

do it – and eventually he had a devilish idea. He knew Magdalene went out only to go to church, and that she would have nothing to do with anybody; so what did he do? He found out the time of day when she went to Mass, and he began to go too. Normally the villain did not go near the church, even on Sundays and feast days; now he began taking up a position where Magdalene could see him; then he would bring out a great big rosary and would be there saying Our Fathers and Hail Marys galore.

At first he did not attempt to approach Magdalene when they came out of church, so as not to be too pressing, but after four or five days he began to leave the church when he saw she was leaving. Then he would go up to her and greet her, and ask her if she had news of Captain Peter; and he would say how he so much liked going to Mass because there was nothing better than to commend ourselves to God during the few days of our brief lives.

Magdalene thought Captain Ralph spoke nicely, and as he went to Mass and said his Rosary she believed he must perforce be a good man; and she was pleased by the friendly feelings that he seemed to have for her husband.

After a few more days Captain Ralph began saying to Magdalene, during the moments when he chatted with her coming out of church, how he wanted to show her the ship that he captained; it was such a fine ship, and she should do him the favour of coming to see it.

He asked her so often and begged her so earnestly that Magdalene, not suspecting any evil, consented to go and see the ship. She went on board with him, and he showed her everything; then he took her below deck to show her everything there. Meanwhile the sailors had been instructed that if the skipper came on board with a woman of such and such appearance they were to weigh anchor at once, and by the time she could be aware of it they were to be well out to sea. So now they weighed anchor and the ship headed out to the open sea.

What do you think? When Magdalene went up on deck to go home, she found they were some way from the shore and heading out to sea under full sail.

Imagine what a shock it was for the poor woman. She was

seized with trembling all over and she had to sit down, and then she swooned and collapsed in a dead faint. When she came to and found herself still in the ship, she burst into tears and there was nobody to console her. And who would have consoled her? The wretch Captain Ralph?

Well, if you will believe it, after some days Captain Peter's ship, returning from his voyage, passed quite close to Captain Ralph's. On Captain Peter's ship there was a devilish sharp cabin boy who descried Magdalene on board Captain Ralph's ship. Not for nothing is it said: *Beware of small eyes for they see everything.*

"Look," he said. "Look, there is Mistress Magdalene, our skipper's wife!"

The other sailors heard him and said: "Hey, you ass, don't talk nonsense!"

"I tell you," he repeated, "I saw our skipper's wife on Captain Ralph's ship."

"Impossible!" said the sailors. But he stood fast by it: that he had seen Magdalene. The sailors would in no way believe it, and they even threatened to throw him overboard if he said it again. Here Captain Peter heard about it and called the boy aside, saying:

"Let's be clear. Do you say you saw my wife Magdalene on Captain Ralph's ship?"

"Yes, I saw her," said the boy.

"Look," Captain Peter said, "this is a very serious matter. If you are not telling the truth and if I find you out, as soon as we reach port and disembark you will learn what it means to tell lies."

"Honestly, Captain," the boy insisted, "I am not telling a lie, and it is true, *true* that I saw Mistress Magdalene on Captain Ralph's ship."

Captain Peter saw the boy was not lying, and he became, as you can imagine, worried and disturbed. They put into port and disembarked, and Captain Peter went straight home. He found the maid distraught, and she said to him:

"It is so many days since Mistress Magdalene disappeared, and we have found no trace of her. One day she went to church, as was her custom, and she never came back. I went to the church, but I did not find her there; I went all over the town asking everybody about her, but got nothing. At length one man said he had seen her talking with Captain Ralph coming out of church; and another said he had seen them both going towards the harbour. I could not find out any more, and here I am, as you may imagine, half crazy with worry. She was a really good woman, she never had anything to do with anybody, and she only went out of the house to go to Mass. I cannot believe she has gone off with Captain Ralph of her own free will. I am sure he carried her off by deceit. Everybody knows what sort of man Captain Ralph is."

When Captain Peter heard all this he nearly died of sorrow and anger. On one hand he believed Captain Ralph had tricked his poor wife Magdalene, but on the other hand he thought:

"What if she had a bad moment and consented?"

These doubts were heart-breaking.

So what did he do? He ordered his sailors not to leave the ship, and he told the maid not to leave the house, until he came back. He dressed himself as a merchant and went off in search of Captain Ralph and Magdalene, determined to search until he found them, and determined to find out how his wife Magdalene had gone with Captain Ralph – whether tricked or willingly.

In his search, Captain Peter made for the city where the King was, because he reasoned: "Where the big sea is the big fish are; that is where everything happens, where all the news comes in. If anywhere I am to find clues of what I am searching for, it will be there."

He walked and walked, and after seven days he reached the city where the King was; and he found the whole place in a turmoil because the King's daughter had just died, an only child some fifteen years old. You can imagine what a state the King and Queen were in, seeing their dear daughter laid out in her coffin; they had no other children and no expectations because the Queen was no longer of that age. They were hitting their heads on the walls, they were tearing their hair with both hands, they were distraught.

When Captain Peter saw all the turmoil in the city, he presented himself at the King's house, dressed as a merchant, and asked to speak with His Royal Majesty.

"And who are you?" asked the attendants. "What makes you think you are worthy to speak with the King?"

"Who am I? I am Captain Peter. You can ask about me in all the ports of the kingdom; and wherever I go in the morning I can safely go again in the evening, if you want to know."

When the attendants heard this rigmarole they said: "Alright, we will tell the King that you want to speak with him; and we shall see what he says."

They went, and the King said: "Let him come in, whoever he is. Today is a day of mourning, and anybody who offers consolation is welcome."

When the Queen heard about it she said: "Heavens! A nasty sailor coming in here? A nasty sailor? They are bad people."

"Don't say that," said the King. "You know how in church we pray for those at sea. Perhaps this captain is a good man and one of those who wish us well. Show him in."

They showed him in, and he paid his proper courtesy to the King and Queen, and said: "Your Royal Majesties, please forgive my boldness in coming here without being summoned; but I was heartbroken at the sorrow that Your Royal Majesties must be suffering to see, dead in her coffin, your only daughter the Lady Princess. So I said: 'I will go and comfort my Lord the King and my Lady the Queen, who must be greatly in need of consolation'."

The Queen, on hearing this, found Captain Peter no nasty sailor, and the King thanked him for his kindness. Then he said to the attendants: "Show this man the Princess in her coffin, so that he may see her before she is taken to the tomb." And they did so.

While Captain Peter stood before the dead girl he said an Our Father, and then he brought out the white flower – the little white flower that he had taken from the mouth of the serpent in the graveyard when he was watching over the dead woman – and he did to the King's daughter what he had done to that sinful woman: He passed the white flower over her face four or five times. And what do you think? The King's daughter began to regain colour, and then more and more colour. He again passed the white flower over the girl's face, and then she opened her eyes and breathed a deep "Ah!" And then she said: "My God! Where am I? In a coffin to be taken to the tomb? No! I don't want to be buried yet!" And what do you think she did? She sat up in her coffin, then jumped out of it and began running about.

All the people there, as you may imagine, were amazed, with their hair standing on end, and crossing themselves. At this point the King and the Queen came in, to find out what the commotion was about. The Princess hugged them, and they hugged her, all weeping for joy.

For quite a time nobody could speak because of the shock, until at length the King said: "What has been happening? How is it our girl is alive again? Come on, who will give a clear account?"

Captain Peter was there watching, but he did not speak. Then one of the attendants who had been watching over the dead girl, and who had seen Captain Peter passing the white flower over her face, spoke up.

"I can give Your Majesty a full account, because I saw it all."

"Very well, tell us the story in detail," said the King. "And take care not to tell me any lies, for if I find you out I will cut your ears off, and no escape!"

"Never fear, Your Royal Majesty; I would never tell you a lie. Do you want to know who it is, after God, who restored your daughter to life?"

"That is just what I am asking," said the King impatiently.

"Well, you see that man dressed as a merchant?" and the attendant pointed to Captain Peter, who was there among the other people.

"Yes, I see him."

"Well, he is the one who, after God, revived your daughter."

Naturally they all turned to stare at Captain Peter, as if they would devour him with their eyes. They looked him over closely, especially the King, who at length said: "Are you not the man who came to console us in our great sorrow over our daughter's death?"

"The very same," said Captain Peter.

"Well, and what did you do to bring our daughter back to life?"

"May I say a word, my Lord King?" cut in the attendant.

"Say your word," said the King, "but keep it short."

"I am not an interested party, so I can tell Your Royal Majesty just what this man did to resuscitate my Lady the Princess."

"Well, what did he do?'"

"I will tell you. He brought out a white flower and began passing it over my Lady the Princess's face, again and again; she began to get back her colour, and more and more, and then she opened her eyes, and then she gave a cry and jumped out of her coffin; and then Your Royal Majesties came in and she hugged Your Royal Majesties and Your Royal Majesties hugged her."

When the King heard this he wasted no more words. He took

hold of Captain Peter and said: "You have restored to me what I most love in this world. How can I repay the kindness that you have done me? Ask me for anything; you name what you would have.

"Would you like my daughter, whom you have brought back to life, to marry her?"

"That cannot be," said Captain Peter, "because I am already married."

"Tell me then, what gift you would have. Ask me; don't be afraid."

Captain Peter thought for a while and then he said. "Well, I would ask you to make me General of Land and Sea and Commander of all the forces in your kingdom."

"Granted!" said the King. From this moment you are General of Land and Sea and Commander of all the forces in my kingdom."

Captain Peter straight away put on the uniform of General of Land and Sea and the insignia of Commander of all the forces in the kingdom. You should have seen the other generals and commanders of land and sea forces dutifully giving Captain Peter the proper salute. But don't imagine he was very taken with this . He at once issued an order that all skippers and captains of ships, boats, and all craft should present themselves with their papers in good order; otherwise they faced getting into trouble.

And there came skippers and captains of ships, boats and all craft, with their papers in as good order as they could manage. They handed in their papers to Captain Peter, who looked at them carefully and at once handed them back. He was trying to find Captain Ralph, and all this business was just for that. But Captain Ralph did not appear.

"Perhaps he is dead," said Captain Peter. He was not dead, but he was closer to it than he knew.

Captain Ralph was saying: "There is no way out. This time he will catch me and I shall have to pay for everything all in one go. It's all up with me!" And there was nothing for it but to show up before Captain Peter, who at once put him in prison and sent troops to arrest all the people they found on board the ship, and to bring them all before him. He told the troops to look carefully to see if there was a woman of such and such an appearance on board – his wife Magdalene – and if they found her, dead or alive, they were to bring her.

The troops went to Captain Ralph's ship and arrested all the sailors, but they found no woman; they looked thoroughly but found nothing. The troops brought the sailors before Captain Peter, and he asked them all kinds of questions about Captain Ralph and Magdalene.

He really grilled them, I assure you. They all told the same story: that Captain Ralph had tricked Magdalene, persuading her on board against her will, and arranging for the ship to sail without her being aware of it; and that when she realized it she burst into tears and did not cease to weep until one day, in a certain port, she managed to run away while they were not looking, and took refuge in a convent of nuns. They could not get her out from there, and they had not seen her again.

Then Captain Peter went to that port, and to the convent, where he asked to see the Mother Prioress. The Mother Prioress came, and Captain Peter asked her if it was true that in the convent there was a woman of such and such an appearance.

"Absolutely true," said the Mother Prioress.

"I am her husband," said Peter. "Would you be kind enough to bring her?"

The Mother Prioress went off and soon came back with Magdalene. When Magdalene saw this husband of hers, whom she had not expected to see ever again, she cried out:

"Oh, dearest husband! My soul!" And she swooned and fell to the floor in a dead faint.

They attended to her and brought her round; and when she opened her eyes again and found herself face to face with her husband – who was not looking at all angry but was crying like a child to see her overcome – she said: "Do you think I ran away with Captain Ralph of my own free will?"

"No, Magdalene, I don't think that," he said. "I know how it all happened! I know you were quite innocent of any such thing. I have found it all out."

Then they embraced each other, both in tears for joy. They almost swooned with the joy that flooded over them.

"Very well," said Captain Peter. "Don't move from here; I will come back within three days, and we will go home."

Captain Peter then went to where he had Captain Ralph and the sailors all locked up. As for Captain Ralph, he had him hanged from the mast of his own ship; the sailors he released, to go where they wished.

When the King heard about all this he thought it well done, and he told Captain Peter to fetch his wife from the convent; he said he wanted them to live at his Court for the rest of their lives.

So Captain Peter went to the convent and gave the Mother Prioress a big bag of golden guineas for having been so good to his wife Magdalene; then with Magdalene he went back to the Court. And there they lived all their lives with the King and the Queen and my Lady the Princess, loved and respected by everybody. And they must still be alive if they are not dead.

And may we all meet in Heaven.

Amen.

Three Skippers

THERE WAS ONCE a father who had three sons. He was well-off but he wanted all his sons to learn a trade by which they could earn a living if they ever found themselves owning nothing in the property register.

One son was apprenticed to a blacksmith, one to a carpenter, and one to a weaver. But the sons did not share their father's ideas, and learning a craft was not at all to their liking.

The eldest, who was called John, one day took his father aside and said: "Father, I don't like blacksmithing at all. Could you not fit out a ship for me with a cargo of wheat, which I could go and sell overseas?"

His father thought about it and said to himself: "What is to be done if this son of mine does not want to be a blacksmith? Ship's captain is a better calling than blacksmith." Then he spoke to John and said:

"So you want me to fit out a ship for you, with a cargo of wheat? You shall have it, but on one condition, which is that you never put in at the Port of the Queen of Hungary."

"And what is wrong with this port?" John asked.

"What is wrong? It is very dangerous."

"Because of the sea or because of the people?"

"They say there is a Queen there who knows everything, even where the Devil sleeps at night, and she can run seven circles round the sharpest of men and have them fleeced before you can say *Amen*. Anyhow, I don't want you to put in at this port, and that's that."

"Very well," said John; "I will bear it in mind."

So, they fitted out the ship with everything required, and they loaded a cargo of wheat; on the chosen day John, with a full crew of sailors, weighed anchor and set sail for the open sea.

"Where are we making for?" asked the helmsman.

"For the Port of the Queen of Hungary," John told him.

"Captain," said the helmsman, "that port has a bad name. But, if you want to go there, you are in command and I will do as you order me."

"I want to see if this port is as dangerous as they say it is," said the Captain. So the helmsman steered a course for the port, and on they went. In a week they were there.

The Queen of Hungary was single, but she had a horde of men-servants, and whenever they saw a ship approaching they hoisted a flag on the highest tower of the castle, to give the ship a welcome.

Seven of her men appeared at John's ship with an invitation from the Queen to the Captain to dine with her, and to take part in a wager on which of them should sleep the less: the Captain or the Queen.

When John heard this strange message he said to himself: "What shall we do? We must watch this smart lady carefully. Eyes open and no flies on me."

"Very well," he said to the Queen's men; "you may tell Her Royal Majesty that at mid-day I will be at the castle, God willing."

So at mid-day John presented himself at the castle, and the Queen gave him a great welcome. She chatted away without pause, and John was quite dazed as he listened to her prattling on and on.

When they had finished dinner the Queen said: "Captain, it is a custom at this castle that when a person comes to dinner if he is a respectable man – as you are – he will also have supper and will stay the night. I am sure you do not want to upset me by refusing to follow the custom."

John was not bold enough to say he did not want to have supper, nor to stay the night, so he accepted the invitation. Then the Queen said:

"I am very fond of making wagers."

"And what sort of wager would Your Royal Majesty wish to make?"

"I will tell you. If tomorrow morning you say *Good morning* to me before I say it to you, then all my ships, the port, the castle, and I myself, will be yours. But if I say *Good morning* to you before you say it to me, your ship will be mine; you will eat and drink here, but will receive no pay, and you will do whatever I order."

John was overwhelmed by all this from the Queen, and almost unwittingly he agreed to the wager. So he and the Queen had supper, and she secretly put a sleeping potion in his food. John ate a good meal, and he was soon so sleepy that he could not keep his eyes open; he went to his room and barely reached the bed. He did not even manage to undress, and there he lay, sleeping and sleeping away like a log.

The Queen was not so sleepy; she woke up before dawn; she got half dressed and went into the Captain's room, where he was still lying asleep as inert as a pile of sand. She went close and gave it to him loud and clear: "*Good morning, and a prosperous year, Captain!*" She had to say it three times, loudly, to wake him. He finally opened his eyes and saw the Queen standing there.

"I have wrecked everything!" he exclaimed. "My ship is lost and I am ruined."

"Captain," said the Queen, "I think there can be no doubt that I have won the wager."

"It would be pointless to deny it," he replied.

"Very well," she said. "My Majordomo will go with you; you will hand over your ship to him, and you will remain under my orders; you will have food and drink here, and if I order something you will do it. The sailors may all stay with the ship; I will give them the same wages as you have done, and they will do whatever I instruct them, within their calling."

Everything was done as commanded by the Queen. The sailors said they were willing to follow the Queen's orders just as they had followed Captain John's.

He, from that day on, went for walks along the quay and chatted with other captains; at the right times he went to eat and to sleep at the Queen's castle, but she never gave him any work to do and he lived a useless life.

The second son, called Tony, also got bored with his job as a carpenter, and one day he took his father aside and said:

"Father, could you not fit out a ship for me, with a cargo of wheat, as you did for John? I could try making a voyage overseas and I might earn some money."

His father needed to think about it for a few days, and at length he said: "Yes, I will fit out a ship for you, with a cargo of wheat, but on one condition: that you do not put in at the Port of the Queen of Hungary, because it is a dangerous port, and the Queen is even more dangerous."

"Very good," said Tony; "I will bear it in mind."

They fitted out the ship, loaded a good cargo of wheat, and took on the required crew of sailors. On the chosen day Tony ordered the anchor weighed and the sails set, and they headed out to the open sea.

"Captain," said the helmsman, "what course are we to take?"

"Straight to the Port of the Queen of Hungary!" Tony replied.

"Are you not fearful of that port, Captain?"

"Me, fearful?" said Tony. "Fear is nothing if you will only look at it close up. That's my rule."

"Alright," said the helmsman, "we will make straight for it."

And so, in seven or eight days' time they were off the Port of the Queen of Hungary.

The Queen's men saw the ship and hoisted a white flag in welcome. By Tony's order the ship put in and moored, and the Queen's men appeared asking to speak to the Captain. He came on deck and said:

"Tell me: what do you have to say?"

The men told him that the Queen welcomed him and invited him to dine with her, and to take part in a wager on who should sleep the less, the Queen or the Captain. Tony found this very strange, but at length he said:

"You may tell my Lady the Queen that at mid-day I will come to dinner. As for the wager, we can talk about it sitting down."

At mid-day Tony presented himself at the castle; the Queen gave him a great welcome. She chatted away without pause, and Tony was quite dazed listening to her prattling on and on. When they had finished dinner the Queen said:

"Captain, it is a custom at this castle that when a person comes to dinner – if he is a respectable man as you are – he will also have supper and will stay the night. I am sure you do not want to upset me by refusing to follow the custom."

Tony was too shy to say *No*, and he accepted the invitation. Then the Queen said: "I am very fond of making wagers."

"And what sort of wager would Your Royal Majesty wish to make?"

"I will tell you. If tomorrow morning you say *Good morning* to me before I say it to you, then all my ships, the port, the castle, and I myself, will be yours. But if I say *Good morning* to you before you say it to me, your ship will be mine; you will eat and drink here all you want, but you will receive no pay, and you will do whatever I order you to do."

Tony was overwhelmed by all these strange ideas of the Queen's and almost unwittingly he agreed to the wager. Anyway, he had supper with the Queen, and they ate a good meal, both of them; but she treacherously, unknown to him, gave him a sleeping potion. As you may suppose, he very soon could not keep his eyes open; they had to lead him to bed, and he did not even manage to undress, but fell onto the bed, and lay there sleeping like a log.

The Queen was not so sleepy; she woke up before the crack of dawn, she got half dressed and went into the room where the Captain was sleeping, still lying there as inert as a pile of sand.

She tip-toed up to the bed and flung at him:

"Good morning, and a prosperous year, Captain."

She had to say it three times, good and loud, to wake him. Tony opened his eyes, saw the Queen there, and exclaimed:

"So I have made a mess of it! I have lost my ship and I am ruined."

"Captain," said the Queen, "I think there can be no doubt that I have won the wager."

"It would be pointless to deny it."

"Very well," she said. "My Majordomo will go with you. You will hand over your ship to him, and you will remain under my orders; you will have food and drink, and if I order something you will do it. The sailors may all stay with the ship and I will pay them the same wages as you have done, and they will do what I instruct them, within their calling."

Everything was done as commanded by the Queen. The sailors said they were willing to follow the Queen's orders as they had followed Captain Tony's.

He, from that day on, began walking up and down the quay chatting with other captains. He soon met his brother John. They told each other what had happened to them with the Queen, who had cheated each of them of his ship. At the right times they would go together to eat and sleep at the Queen's castle, but she never gave them any work to do, and they lived useless lives.

And Sebastian, the youngest brother: what do you think? He got tired of weaving, and at length he said to his father:

"Father, what can I say? The craft of weaver does not interest me, not in the least. Could you not fit out a good ship for me, with a cargo of wheat, so that I could go on a voyage and with luck make a nice profit?"

"Like your two brothers!" said his father. "I fitted out a ship for each of them, with a good cargo of wheat, and we have heard nothing more of them. We don't know whether they are alive or dead. But so you shall not come grumbling that I have been unwilling to do for you what I did for them, I will fit out a ship for you, with a good cargo of wheat – but on one condition: that you are never to put in at the Port of the Queen of Hungary, because it is a dangerous port, and the people are more dangerous than the port itself. I would lay a wager your two brothers went there and have perished there, which is why we have had no news of them."

"Very well, Father, I promise to bear in mind everything you say. I give you my word on it."

So his father fitted out a ship for him, with a good cargo of wheat. Sebastian weighed anchor, and off they went into the open sea.

"Captain," said the helmsman, "where are we making for?"

"Straight for the Port of the Queen of Hungary," Sebastian replied.

"Are you not afraid of the bad name of that port, and of the people there?"

"Me, afraid? Hang me if I am afraid of anything or anybody." So they held their course for the Port of the Queen of Hungary. In a week they were there.

The Queen's men saw the ship and hoisted a white flag as it approached. Then they went to the quay to receive the ship; they presented themselves to the Captain saying:

"Welcome, Captain, on behalf of the Queen. She has instructed us to say that she expects you to dinner."

"But does she know me?"asked the Captain.

"We cannot tell you. We never ask such questions of Her Royal Majesty. Our job is only to do what she orders."

"Well said, my friends. Very good; you may tell my Lady the Queen that at mid-day I will be at the Castle, God willing."

And the Queen's men went off.

Captain John and Captain Tony were on the quay; they saw the ship and went towards it; they looked closely at the Captain, and together they said: "If that's not our Sebastian it's very like him." And they went up close and greeted him; sure enough it was their brother Sebastian. All three were greatly surprised at finding themselves together at the Port of the Queen of Hungary.

John and Tony told Sebastian what had happened to them with the Queen. "You must be careful," they said, "that she does not trick you the way she did us."

"Don't worry about me," Sebastian said.

At mid-day Sebastian presented himself at the castle; the Queen came out to meet him and gave him a great welcome. She chatted away cheerfully; she was tall, handsome, and comely, and she had her wits about her.

"Careful now, Sebastian!" he said to himself when he saw she was so wide-awake and friendly. "If I don't take care she will outwit me." He responded to her greeting as well as he could, but he kept a watchful eye on the lively lady.

They had dinner, and she did most of the talking. At length she said: "Captain, it is a custom at this castle that when a person is invited to dinner – if he is a respectable man such as you are – he will later have supper here, and stay the night. I am sure you do not want to upset me by refusing to follow the custom."

When Sebastian heard this rigmarole he thought about it a little and at length said: "Countless thanks to Your Royal Majesty for the invitation to dinner. As for supper and staying the night at the castle, I rather fear it may be too much hospitality for me. I should prefer to go and sleep on board my ship."

The queen showed she was greatly upset by the Captain's refusing her invitation. Sebastian realized it and since he did not want to anger her he ended by saying *yes* to supper and staying the night.

Then the Queen brought up the wager. "I am very fond of making wagers, and I should like to make one with you."

"And what is it?"

"I will tell you. The wager is that if tomorrow morning I say *Good morning* to you before you say it to me, then your ship will be mine; but if you say *Good morning* to me before I say it to you, then all my ships, and I myself, will be yours."

Sebastian thought about it a little and then said:

"The wager is on, just as Your Royal Majesty says."

Then Sebastian asked her leave to go to his ship to see if there were anything to be attended to. The Queen agreed but said he should manage to be back at the castle before dark, because she did not care to stay up late, but rather to have supper and go to bed, so as to be up early the next day.

The Queen did not feel quite sure about this Captain, and she said to herself: “How shall I deal with this sharp fellow? I am not so sure that I can get the better of him.”

Sebastian walked a little way along the quay, where he found his two brothers, and he told them how the dinner had gone.

“Look,” they said, “you must be careful in the evening. We think it was at supper we were tricked; the overwhelming sleepiness that came on us both could not have been natural. We are sure she gave us a sleeping potion, though we were not aware of it. So keep your eyes wide open, and be careful over what you eat and what you drink.”

Sebastian went his way; he went to a butcher’s shop and bought a bladder, which he fixed round his neck in such a way that it could not be seen. He was able to do this because of the great beard he had, as did all ship’s captains; his beard was very thick, dense, and large, and the bladder could not be seen unless one looked very closely.

As it was beginning to get dark he returned to the castle. The Queen had him shown in at once, and soon afterwards a footman came in and said:

“My Lady the Queen, supper is served.”

“Very good. Shall we go in, Captain?”

“As Your Royal Majesty wishes.”

They went into the dining-room and sat down at the table. Then Sebastian said:

“My Lady the Queen, not wanting to upset you, I agreed to come to supper; but at mid-day I had such a good meal with you that now, much as I should like to, I really cannot eat even a mouthful. If I did so I know for sure that I should spend a bad night.” The Queen begged him, but there was no way of making him take anything.

“Well, Captain,” said the Queen, “you will not refuse a glass of wine?”

In that glass was the sleeping potion.

Sebastian, strongly pressed by the Queen, finally took the glass and held it near his mouth; but instead of drinking it he poured it as best he could into the bladder that he had fixed round his neck, so he swallowed not a drop of the sleeping potion. So as to give nothing away, he said he was feeling sleepy and would like to go to bed. He said *Good night* to the Queen, and a footman accompanied him to the bedroom chosen for him.

"Is there anything you require, sir?" the footman asked.

"There is one thing I should like," said the Captain.

"What is that?"

"A basin of cold water."

"Now, at once?"

"Yes, now, at once."

The footman went away and soon came back with a basin full of cold water.

"Do you wish anything further, sir?" said the footman.

"Nothing more tonight."

"Then I wish you a good night."

"A good night to everybody," said Sebastian.

The footman went and told the Queen about the basin of cold water.

"And did he say why he wanted the basin?" the Queen asked.

"No, madam."

The Queen became uneasy about it, but finally decided to go to bed so as to wake up earlier than the Captain and win her wager, though she was still worried by the idea that this Captain might beat her at her own game.

And what do you think the Captain did with the basin of cold water in his bedroom? Well, first he bolted the door on the inside, then he sat down on a low table in front of the basin, took off his shoes, and put his feet in the basin. And like this he spent the whole night without closing his eyes – and so I should think, with his feet in cold water and with nothing to lean back on.

The Queen did not go to bed either, so as not to sleep too heavily, and she spent the whole night sitting in a chair; even so she dozed a little. At the crack of dawn she stood up, splashed her face with a few handfuls of cold water so as to be wide awake, and went towards the Captain's room. She found the door closed and she pushed it very gently to see if it would open. Sebastian heard this and, to be on the safe side, cried out:

"Good morning, my Lady the Queen!"

The Queen was struck dumb for a moment, but recovered herself and called back: "Good morning to you too, Captain! You have beaten me. Open up!"

The Captain took his feet out of the basin, dried them, put on his shoes, went and undid the bolt, and opened the door wide.

The Queen at once exclaimed: "I have been looking for you! You have won the wager and you have won my heart! I need a man like you, and I have been searching for many years. I am yours, and all I possess – the castle, the port, and all the ships in it – all of it is yours. I am single, and if you want me we can be married whenever you like."

You can imagine how Captain Sebastian at once said *Yes!* jumping for joy.

The Queen summoned the Court and related everything that had happened with Captain Sebastian, announcing she was resolved to be married to him.

All the people of the Court approved the idea and praised her good taste, and on the appointed day the great event took place: the Queen of Hungary and Captain Sebastian were married. There followed a magnificent wedding feast and a lively ball, and festivities and celebrations galore.

The Queen summoned Captain John and Captain Tony and gave them back their ships. They returned home and never again wanted to go navigating.

And the Queen of Hungary with Captain Sebastian and Captain Sebastian with the Queen of Hungary lived for years and years. And they must still be alive if they are not dead.

And may we all meet in Heaven.

Amen.

Two Skippers and a Wife

THERE WERE TWO ship's Captains, both very rich, still unmarried, and close friends. One was called Maurice and the other Caspar; each of them owned seven ships. Captain Maurice was once in a terrible storm and he felt death very close, just behind his ear. In the hope of yet saving his life and his ship, he made a promise to marry the poorest girl in the first port they should put in at, provided she was honest.

What do you think? He had hardly finished making this promise when the storm began to die down, and soon the sea was like a bowl of oil.

They came to a port and put in; Captain Maurice jumped ashore, and he came upon a girl carrying a bundle of fire-wood; she had hardly any clothes and was dressed in rags, she was barefoot and very poor-looking, but extremely pretty and well-shaped in all parts of her body.

Captain Maurice followed her as she plodded on, poor girl, loaded with the bundle of fire-wood, which was so big and heavy that it bowed her down. At length she went in at the door of a hovel. The Captain saw a tavern near there; he went in and asked about the girl. The people at the tavern said:

"She is a really good girl, the best in the town, but also the poorest. Consider: she has to maintain her mother, who is very old, and they are quite destitute."

"This is just what I was looking for," said the Captain. And what do you think he did? He went to that hovel, he spoke to the girl and to her mother, and told them his tale: that he had made this promise, and he had found out that she, the daughter, was the poorest girl in the town, and that he was obliged to fulfill the promise that he had made in the hope of being saved from that terrible storm.

The Captain put forward his case so well that Frances Maria, the girl, and her mother accepted it and said *Yes*. He gave them all the money they could need – a good bag full of gold and silver – and they soon had the wedding arranged. Captain Maurice and Frances Maria were duly married, and she thus became a proper skipper's wife. Then he took them both, his wife and his mother-in-law, on board his ship and they sailed for home without delay.

After some time Captain Maurice met Captain Caspar, and said:

Hello, Caspar! Do you know I am now married?"

"Oh, really?" said Captain Caspar. "And to whom, if one may ask?"

"To a girl from such-and-such a port."

"You certainly went some way to find her! And what is her name?

"Frances Maria," Captain Maurice replied.

"Daughter of a poor widow? Living in a broken-down hovel?"

"Quite right. Do you know her?"

"As well as I know bad weather."

"Are you trying to cast a slur on her, by any chance?"

"Well, I would not actually do so," said Captain Caspar, but what I say is she cannot be much – a girl as poor as that and having to work so hard to support her mother. The kind of life makes for sin."

"And what I say," replied Captain Maurice, "is that she is a saintly girl."

"What? A saint is she? Then you could go and order a niche for her and put her in it right away."

Captain Maurice became very angry at these taunts from Captain Caspar, and he said:

"Look here, mate, this sort of talk will not do. You are insulting my wife and insulting me, and I will not have it. I will prove to you that my wife is not what you would suggest, but is a woman of the very best. The day we were married I put a ring on her finger, which she promised she would never take off; she never has done, and she wears it always. Another thing: below her left ear she has three stray hairs. I will lay you a wager that you are not able either to take away her ring or to cut off those three hairs."

"And what are the stakes to be?" asked Captain Caspar.

"The seven ships that we each own," Captain Maurice replied.

"Very good; the wager is on."

"Alright; it is on."

Then each went his way; Captain Maurice angry at Captain Caspar's effrontery but not believing that he could ever win the wager; and Captain Caspar determined to win at any cost, even his whole fortune.

Soon afterwards Captain Maurice sailed away in his principal ship well loaded with merchandise, making for a very distant land. Captain Caspar went and shut himself in his house thinking and thinking how he was going to win the wager, how he could trick Frances into parting with the ring that she always wore and the three stray hairs below her left ear.

When he had done racking his brains over it he went off to Maurice's house, and he found it all locked up. He knocked once, and again, with the knocker, but without result. He knocked again, really hard, and still there was no response. Then a neighbour came out of her house and said to him: "Sir, do you not know who lives here?"

"Yes, I do. Isn't it the house of Captain Maurice, who owns seven ships all working for his account?"

"That's right," said the neighbour, "but the fact is the Captain is away on a voyage; and when he is away his wife does not come out of the house for anything in the world except to go to Mass; when she comes out of church she goes to the market and buys what she needs to eat; then, when she gets back here she bolts the door on the inside and does not open it again for anybody. You could knock until you battered the door down, but she will not open it until tomorrow morning."

"So she is there" said Caspar, "and hears the knocking, but will not open the door."

"She is there, right enough," said the neighbour. "I saw her myself early this morning when she came home and locked herself in."

"And do you think it is a thing to do," he said, "to hear somebody knocking and refuse to open the door?"

"I don't know," the neighbour replied. "Think of it: here she is, a young woman recently married and loaded with money. I have often heard it said rich people have their strange ideas, and so it must be with her. And what of it? After all, with this way of living she does nobody any harm; she is not very neighbourly, but she seems to be a good woman, and most devout. And above all, while she behaves like this there is no danger of any word of scandal about her."

When Captain Caspar heard these views he felt quite discouraged. He abruptly left the neighbour and went home to think out how and by what means he could get the better of this devil of a girl Frances. He thought and thought, and he pondered and pondered; then he went again to see the neighbour, asking if he could speak to her in secret. The neighbour took him into her house, and Caspar said to her:

"Good! Can we talk in confidence? You will not betray me?"

"Sir," she said, "I don't know you and I don't know who you are, though you seem to be a decent man."

"I assure you I am," he said. "And you seem to me to be a proper woman."

"I am second to nobody in the world. I have always been able to return in the evening to where I was in the morning. So you can begin telling me whatever it is you have to say."

"Very well," said Captain Caspar. "What I have come to say is that if you would like to earn, in one go, a thousand pounds, I have this amount here in my pocket."

"A thousand pounds?" she exclaimed, her eyes as wide as saucers.

"Yes," he replied. "You can pick up a thousand pounds if you are willing to do what I am now going to tell you."

"So long as it's nothing bad," said the neighbour.

"It's not bad if you look at it properly."

"Well, what is this thing?"

"I will tell you," said the Captain. "Have you not noticed Captain Maurice's wife wears a ring on one of her fingers, and also that she has three stray hairs growing below her left ear?"

"Yes, I have noticed," the neighbour replied.

"Well, if you can get the ring from her, and the three stray hairs, and put them in my hands, I will at once hand you a thousand pounds."

"Alright, but..." said the neighbour "...would this not be committing a theft from the Captain's wife?"

"Depending on how it was done," Caspar replied. "If you were to simply take her ring, just like that, it would indeed be a theft; but if you were to meet her in the street and were greatly to admire her ring, and you were able to persuade her to let you look at it, and you were to note it carefully, and were to have an exact copy made by the goldsmith; and if, while taking her ring, you were to give her the ring you had had made, the sin would not be at all serious, and it could never be said you had committed a theft, because at the same time you would be giving the same value to her."

"Yes, but who is going to pay for the ring that the goldsmith is to make?" the neighbour asked.

"I am ready to pay for it, to the last penny," the Captain replied.

When the neighbour had heard all this scheme it seemed to her that there was little harm in the trick she had to play on Captain Maurice's wife, especially as, without doing her any real hurt, she herself could pocket a thousand pounds, which would keep her in comfort for the rest of her life.

Anyway, in the end she said *Yes* to Captain Caspar, and the following morning she was on the watch for when Captain Maurice's wife opened her door to go to church, so as to give her a really friendly greeting by way of preparing the ground.

So it was that as soon as Frances came out into the street the next morning the neighbour appeared, saying:

"Good morning, madam! How early you are! Going to Mass, are you? Lucky the husband who has you for wife! And do forgive me for saying it in front of you; I am so happy with you that it just will out!"

Well, of course Frances was rather surprised at this effusive greeting from a neighbour who earlier had done little more than raise her eyes and just say "Good morning", but she was far from thinking ill of it. Praise always pleases us, and that's a fact.

What do you think? The next day, and the next, and the day after that, and the next after that, as soon as Frances came out early in the morning to go to Mass – *snap!* – the neighbour appeared and greeted her and smothered her with praise and flattery; Frances was soon quite taken with the woman, and would stay there for some time chatting with her and laughing at the things she said and the jokes she made, and all with a great air that she had.

Some days later this deceitful neighbour, after praising to the skies all the clothes that Frances was wearing, and her earrings, and her string of pearls, and the cross with precious stones that she wore round her neck, and the gold bracelets she had on each arm, began to admire the ring she wore on one of her fingers.

"Oh, what a beautiful ring!" said the wily woman. "Where did you get it? There cannot be a more lovely ring in the whole world! Oh, I do admire it, and no joke! I would bet even the Queen herself – who after all is the Queen – has no ring to compare with it."

And every time this cunning woman met Frances, coming out of the house to go to church, she sang the praises of the ring more and more vehemently.

"Would you let me see it close up, madam?" the neighbour would say: "Will you let me look at it closely? Don't deny me that pleasure, madam." And Frances would hold out her hand so the woman might look at the ring; but she never took it off.

But the neighbour, after having looked at it closely three or four times, said to herself: "That will do me!" Then she went off to the goldsmith's and said to him:

"Make me a ring like this and like that, in gold, with such and such stones set in it."

"Neighbour," said the goldsmith, "I wonder if you are overdoing it a little. You might find it very dear."

"Well, how much will it be?"

"It will not be less than two hundred pounds."

"Do you think you can daunt me with two hundred pounds? Come on! Get to work on it at once, and tell me when I can come and fetch it."

"When?" said the goldsmith. "In a week's time."

"Good," she said. "In a week's time I will come with the two hundred pounds."

She went off to Captain Caspar's house and told him about it, and he said: "In a week's time come again and I will give you the two hundred pounds."

What do you think? At the end of the week the neighbour turned up at Captain Caspar's house, he paid out two hundred pounds, she went off to the goldsmith's, he gave her the ring, finished, which was a joy to behold; she counted out – *ding-dong!* – two hundred pounds and handed them to the goldsmith, and then off she went with the ring, straight home.

Thinking and thinking how she could manage to get hold of Frances's ring, she devised a wicked plan, which she began to carry out the next morning when she saw Frances coming back from church. She greeted her and told her a friend had brought her a bottle of Malmsey wine, the most delicious thing that anybody had ever tasted; and Frances absolutely must do her the favour of drinking a little glass of it. Frances at first said *No*, but the neighbour praised this Malmsey so highly, and begged her so pressingly to taste it, that Frances finally consented. She let the neighbour into her house and brought a small glass; the woman filled it. Frances raised her elbow, and the Malmsey was so good that she drank it all.

In that Malmsey wine the treacherous neighbour had put a sleeping potion, so that poor Frances no sooner had that drink inside her than she lost consciousness and fell asleep like a log.

And what do you think the neighbour did then? She exchanged the rings, and with a pair of scissors she cut the three stray hairs that Frances had below her left ear. Meanwhile she was saying to herself: "Right! Now I will take the ring and the three hairs to that Captain, I will collect the thousand pounds, and I will come back here and wait for this girl to recover; then I will tell her it was the naughty Malmsey that overcame her. If she says her ring has been changed, I will say it has not, and if she swears that the ring she is wearing is not the one she was wearing before, I will swear it is. I wonder how it will all work out."

Well, if you will believe it, this wicked neighbour went off to

Captain Caspar's house. She found him there and handed him the ring and the three stray hairs from below Frances's left ear, and he – *ding-dong!* – counted out a thousand pounds. She gathered up the money and went straight home to stow it away safely, well hidden so that nobody should steal it. Then she locked up her house and went over to see Frances; she found her still slumped on the table, fast asleep.

The neighbour sat down beside Frances and waited for her to wake up; and there she waited and waited. Mid-day came and Frances was still asleep; the afternoon became evening, and still she was asleep, while the neighbour waited and waited. Then the woman went over to her own house to have a bite to eat, and she came back quickly to watch over Frances, who did not wake up until the next morning. At first she did not know where she was.

"But what happened, madam?" said the neighbour. "Was that little drop of Malmsey enough to overcome you?"

"My dear," said Frances, "I don't know what happened to me! I just don't know. Do you think it was the Malmsey put me out?"

"Well, what else could it have been?" the neighbour said. "It cannot have been anything other than the Malmsey."

Frances could not make out what had come over her. Then she happened to glance at her ring, and then she stared at it. She thought it looked very bright and shiny, and she said:

"Now why the devil is my ring looking so shiny?"

"Naturally it is shiny," said the neighbour. "It is solid gold."

"Yes, but why is it that yesterday, and the day before, and the day before that, it did not shine like this?"

"I think you are mistaken, madam, or have you polished it?"

"Not I," Frances replied. "That's the last thing I would do."

"Then forget about it, madam. It must be the same as it was before."

Frances did not know what to reply, so she did as the neighbour advised and forgot about it, believing the woman must be right.

She did not notice that she was without the three stray hairs below her left ear, and she was as calm as you please. She went on living her life as before, only leaving the house to go to Mass and to buy what she needed for housekeeping. She shut herself up at home like a nun; and she resolved never again to taste Malmsey wine, because, as she said: "What if my husband came back from his voyage and I was tipsy? What would the good man say if he found me half-seas-over? Why should I ever want to taste that treacherous Malmsey? May I turn into Malmsey myself if I ever taste it again, ever!"

Now we leave Frances to lead her well-ordered life away from the world, and we turn to Captain Caspar and Captain Maurice.

Caspar, as soon as he had possession of Frances's ring and the three stray hairs, went straight to the ship that he was skippering, upped anchor, and with sails set to the wind, went off to where he guessed he would find Captain Maurice.

After a few days' sailing with the wind astern, the devil put in at a port where he was lucky enough to find Maurice; he just caught him as he had weighed anchor and was setting sail for home.

Caspar called to him to stop, for Heaven's sake, as he had something important to say to him. Maurice hove to and Caspar went on board, where he took him aside, saying:

"Well, Maurice, didn't I tell you I would win that wager?"

"Yes," said Maurice. "I remember very well you said so; but you have yet to win it."

Here Caspar brought out the ring and the three stray hairs and showed them to Maurice, thrusting them under his nose.

Captain Maurice looked at them and looked at them again very closely, and he stood as if turned to stone, dumbfounded, with his hair on end.

"You have won..." the poor man said at length.

He had to sit down, and he broke out in a sweat, a cold sweat, and huge tears sprang from his eyes and rolled down his face.

He made an effort to master himself, and he said to Captain Caspar: "My seven ships are yours now; will you at least do me the favour of taking me home?"

"But of course," said Caspar "I would not just leave you here. Do me the favour of staying on this ship and skippering it until we get to our own port."

They did that, and when they reached their port Captain

Maurice handed over his seven ships to Captain Caspar and went home, determined to have it out with his wife. He came to his house, found it all locked up, and knocked on the door. Frances heard him, recognized him, and ran to open the door for him.

She opened it, and when she saw him with such a changed face she could not help saying:

"But, Maurice, is there something amiss? What is the matter? What is wrong with you?"

"Don't you know?" he said.

"How could I know if I have had no news of you since you went away?"

Then Maurice noticed that she was wearing the ring on the same finger of her left hand, where he had placed it when they were married. You cannot imagine how strange he found this and he could not help saying: "Let me see your ring."

"Take a look at it; it has become a little brighter than it used to be, but nothing else."

He looked at it closely for some time, and then said:

"It is true it is a little more shiny, but it seems to be the same ring."

"I can assure you," she said, I only take it off to wash my hands, and afterwards I always put it on again."

Then he looked to see if she had the three stray hairs below her left ear. She had them, certainly, but they were quite short; it was clear they had been cut.

By this time the poor man was more confused than ever. When Caspar had shown him the ring he had recognized it at once as being his wife's, but here she was wearing the same ring, or at least he could see no difference except that it was a little brighter; but this brightness could be from many causes. As for the stray hairs, it was quite clear they had been cut, but she could have cut them herself, and Caspar could have got his three hairs from somewhere else. Captain Maurice's head was a can of worms, thinking and thinking, here, there, and everywhere, trying to puzzle out what had been happening.

What he did was to bottle up his worries over the strange affair, and he refused to discuss it, neither with his wife nor with anybody else; he spent his time cudgelling his brains over what he should do and which direction he should take.

Poor Frances! You can imagine how she felt, seeing her husband so preoccupied and silent, she could not get a word out of him; he did not want to be spoken to, and she could see he was distraught.

Days and days went by like this with no improvement and no promise of any, until one morning Maurice turned to Frances and flung at her:

"My girl, you have got taller since I went away."

"I cannot have done," she replied; "I should have noticed it by my clothes."

"Anyhow," he said, "I am going to measure you."

"Alright!" And she stood against the wall as straight as she could so as not to conceal her height.

Captain Maurice took her measurements and, without saying a word, left her there and went straight to the carpenter's shop. "Master," he said when he got there, "make me a box with these measurements." And he gave him the measurements of Frances.

"These measurements, are they for the inside of the box or for the outside?" the carpenter asked.

"For the inside," said Captain Maurice. "Now tell me when you will have it ready."

"When? In three days' time," the carpenter replied. "What you must tell me is where you want it delivered."

"Where? You let me know when the box is ready, then I will come and pay you and tell you where to take it."

"Agreed, then," said the carpenter.

After three days the carpenter sent word to Captain Maurice that the box was ready; Maurice went round to the carpenter's and looked at it; he liked it, he paid for it, and he told the carpenter to take it to a certain place on the sea-shore; and he said that the man who carried it to this place should stay and guard it until he himself arrived there, which would be at once.

The carpenter's man went off carrying the box, making for the place on the shore, while Maurice went home and said to Frances:

"Come on, let's take a walk along the sea-shore." She agreed, she got dressed in no time, and off she went with her husband towards the shore. Walking and walking along, they reached the place where the man was waiting with the box. Captain Maurice told the man he could go, and then what did he do?

He said to Frances: "I am going to see if I can get into this box." he tried, but he was too big for it. "Let's see if it is big enough for you," he said. "Try it, for fun."

She got into the box, suspecting nothing ill, and of course she fitted in. And what did the Captain do? He shut the lid down, fastened it, and threw the box into the sea, saying:

"If you gave your ring and the three stray hairs to Caspar, let the sea swallow you! If you are innocent, may you float and come to port!"

Believe it or not, that devil of a box, instead of sinking at all, rode the waves, which carried it out to sea, farther and farther out, floating as if it knew how to swim.

Then Maurice realized his wife was innocent of all that business of the ring and the three stray hairs. He took his clothes off and plunged into the sea, and he swam and swam as hard as he could after the box, trying to catch up with it and bring his wife home again. But not a hope! The box went as fast as a hare, farther and farther out to sea.

If you will believe it, when the box was a long, long, way out to sea it came near a ship. The sailors saw it and told their skipper about it; he hove to, had a boat lowered, and sent two sailors to get the box and bring it alongside. The sailors got hold of it and it was hoisted on board. Then they opened it and inside they found that beautiful and graceful young woman Frances Maria.

You can imagine how they stared, the skipper as well as the sailors. They could not understand how inside that box there could be anything so lovely to look at.

"How, the devil did you come to be in this box?" the skipper asked Frances.

"That is something I don't know," she replied.

"And who put you in it?"

"That is a secret," she said, "which I shall never tell." The good girl did not want to mention her husband because she could see that somebody had hoodwinked him with a calumny against her, which was why he had done what he did.

The skipper saw there was some mystery here, but he was a prudent and considerate man, and he asked no more questions.

Instead he asked her where she would like to be taken; and she replied that the greatest favour he could do her would be to take her to the city where the King had his Court.

"That will suit us perfectly," said the skipper, "because we are making for that very city."

The wind was favourable and they made good headway; so after a couple of days they were in the port of this city. The skipper was such a good-natured man that he would not accept anything for having rescued Frances; so she gave him abundant thanks for his great kindness and promised to commend him to God every day of her life.

What do you think Frances did as soon as she was ashore? Well, she went to a goldsmith to sell one of the gold bracelets she was wearing; and with the money that she received for it she went to a tailor's and had man's clothing made for herself.

The next day she fetched the clothes and went to an inn, where she shut herself in a room and dressed herself as a man; she made a bundle of her woman's clothing, hiding inside it her other bracelet, her rings, and her earrings; and then she set off for the King's house to see if a servant was needed there.

The Majordomo appeared and when he saw this fine young fellow, handsome and winning, with all the appearance of being a good lad, he said he could stay and they would always find work for him.

"Very good," said the Majordomo. "That is settled. And what are you called?"

"Frank," she replied.

"Frank? That's a nice name." And the Majordomo went to tell the King and Queen about it. When they heard his praises of the fine appearance, good style, and handsome looks of the new servant, they wanted to see him.

The Majordomo presented him, and the King and the Queen were very pleased with him, saying to each other: "If his work matches his fine appearance and handsome looks we shall be very happy."

What do you suppose? Frank's work certainly matched his looks. He excelled at every kind of work; jobs that he was told to do he did quickly and with great pleasure; he enjoyed his work and had no thought for anything else.

The Majordomo was delighted with Frank and was for ever talking about him, and the King and the Queen the same, to the extent that the other servants became envious when they saw Frank so willing and able in everything, and so handsome in spirit and body. From the King down to the least courtier, everybody made much of him and chatted with him.

But what nobody could understand was why a young fellow like that never looked at a girl – as if he were not made of flesh and blood like other boys.

"Could it be that he wants to be a monk?" people said. "It is very strange that girls don't seem to move him or interest him in the least. What can it mean?"

Those who were most upset by this were the maidservants at the King's house, and all the other girls who went there. Would you believe it, they were soon more than half in love with Frank, and each of them, on her own, was watching for an opportunity to declare her feelings; and they were all too ready to squabble and snatch off each other's caps rather than allow any one of them to win the prize and make a conquest of Frank.

The most serious thing was that the one who fell most deeply in love with Frank was the Queen. One day she approached him, but he did not respond and afterwards avoided her.

The Queen took this very badly and turned furiously against Frank, wrongly accusing him to the King in the most horrible manner, turning things round to the very opposite of the truth.

You can imagine how the King felt when he heard this tale from the Queen. He never thought his Queen would deceive him so brazenly; he never imagined she was a woman to tell him blatant lies. He wasted no time; he had Frank imprisoned and he signed a death sentence by which, in three days' time, Frank would be tied to the tails of four horses pulling in different directions and quartering the indecent culprit for having been so bold as to commit such a shocking crime.

So they put Frank in the condemned cell. He asked for a friar to come and confess him, and he told the friar the whole of his story. At that the friar said: "I offer to go and see the King, to tell him the facts, and ask him to arrange to have you physically examined by two of the most honourable ladies in the kingdom, who will say whether you are a man or a woman."

"Oh, Father!" said Frank, "Indeed I would have you go to the King and ask him to do that! I beg you, as a favour! Please do it, for the love of God!"

The friar went at once and asked to speak in secret with the King. The King took him into a remote inner chamber, and when they were alone the Friar said:

"My Lord King, I have to communicate something really horrifying, if you will allow me. It is a charge of conscience."

"Well, what is it?" said the King. "Explain clearly."

"I will explain," the friar replied. "I have come on behalf of the poor fellow whom Your Royal Majesty has condemned to death, and who is already in the condemned cell, to tell you that he is wholly innocent of what he is accused of."

"That is what all criminals say. They always say they are innocent."

"Yes," the friar replied, "but there are ways and ways of saying it."

"And what do you mean by this?" said the King.

"What I mean is: the accused offers proof of his innocence, which, if it is as he says, makes it impossible not to recognize that he must be innocent."

"And what is this proof?" asked the King.

"I will tell you," answered the friar. "The poor fellow says he is not a man but a woman; and that he is willing to be examined whenever you like. That will settle the matter."

When the King heard this he was thunderstruck, dumbfounded, as one who sees visions, until at length he exclaimed:

"Do you mean he says he is a woman, not a man?"

"That is just what he says," replied the friar, "and he asks to be physically examined."

"Alright! We will have it done now."

"May I say a word?" the friar put in.

"Say on."

"Well, I think Your Royal Majesty should summon two of the most honourable and trustworthy ladies in the kingdom and have them examine the accused. If he turns out to be a man, then let Your Royal Majesty's sentence be carried out. If he turns out to be a woman, then the accusation cannot be true."

"You are right," said the King. And he at once summoned two of the most honourable and trustworthy ladies in the whole kingdom, and he said to them:

"Ladies, we have sentenced this poor fellow to death because he assaulted the Queen in a shocking manner; he now says he is not a man but a woman, and we have summoned you two ladies to examine the prisoner and afterwards to declare on oath whether it is a man or a woman."

Then the two ladies went to see the accused in the condemned cell; they turned out everybody else, and then they examined the prisoner; and of course they found it was a woman they were examining. How could she be anything else if that is how she was born? Then these two honourable ladies went to the King and declared on oath:

"Lord King, Frank is not Frank but Frances. The Queen and all the ladies of the Court may go and see for themselves, to clinch the matter."

This declaration left the King as if turned to stone, with his hair standing on end, dumbfounded, overwhelmed. He had to sit down, his head was spinning, and he almost swooned away. It is understandable that all this should happen to him because if Frank was innocent – not being Frank but Frances – then the Queen's accusations were false; and in this Kingdom there was a law whereby anybody who falsely accused another would receive the sentence passed, or about to be passed, on the person thus calumniated.

The Queen was so upset by the Frank business that she had to go to bed; meanwhile the King summoned the whole Court and asked them to advise him what to do.

"Unless the person calumniated," said the Lords of the Court, "pardons the slanderer and pleads for clemency and absolution of the crime, Your Royal Majesty knows what he must do if he wishes to uphold the law that we have received from our forebears."

"Your advice is all too sound," said the King.

So what did the King do then? He gave orders for the accused in the condemned cell to be brought before him. When Frank was in the King's presence the King sent everybody out and the two remained alone.

"Well," said the King, "I understand what has occurred, and I see you are innocent of the false accusation made against you; but it happens that this calumny was made by the Queen. According to a law that we have here, it is the Queen who should now be sentenced to death and put at once in the condemned cell to be executed, unless you, the person falsely accused, pardon her and plead for clemency and absolution for her."

"My Lord King," said Frances at this point, "for my part, my Lady the Queen is pardoned from this moment; I see it was a bad moment she had, such as we are all exposed to." And as she said it she fell on her knees before the King saying, with tears in her eyes:

"My Lord King, clemency and absolution for my Lady the Queen. Kill me rather than her.'"

Then the King too burst into tears and wept copiously, and it was as much as he could do to refrain from embracing Frances, still dressed as a man, in his heartfelt gratitude for the immeasurable kindness that she had done him.

"Wait for me here just one moment," the King said. And he went to tell the Queen how Frances had pardoned her and had pleaded for clemency and absolution for her – in other words that Frances had saved her life.

You can imagine how happy and grateful the Queen was when she heard. She asked for the dear good Frances to be brought to her bedchamber, and she hugged her, all in tears, and begged for her forgiveness in God's name and in that of his Mother.

At length the King took Frances aside, still dressed as a man, and went with her into a closed room; there he said:

"Frances, ask me for anything in the world that I have and I will give it to you. If there is a marriageable son of mine whom you would like, we will marry you at once."

"Thank you, my Lord King," said Frances, "but I am already married."

"You don't mean it!" exclaimed the King.

"It is true, my Lord King," said Frances. "And now, if you will allow me, I will tell you in a few words my life story, and why I came here dressed as a man. I was the poorest girl in my town, and one day there came a ship's captain called Maurice, the owner of seven ships, who asked me to marry him. We were married and he put a ring on my finger telling me never, ever, to take it off. And I obeyed him. But when he came back from his first voyage he one day took me down to the sea-shore; there was a box there and he made me get into it; then he threw me, in the box, into the sea. The waves took me far, far, out to sea. Then a ship came along and took me on board, and the captain asked me where I wanted him to take me. 'To the city where the King is', I said. So he brought me here. I asked him to do that because I thought the quickest way of finding out why my husband had done what he did was to approach Your Royal Majesty. And how was I to approach you unless I came as a servant to this house? If I had presented myself as a woman I should have met only the Queen, and that was not what I needed. So, my Lord King, you see my motive in dressing as a man to get a job with Your Royal Majesty in the hope, one way or another, of finding out what happened to my husband."

The King could not make head or tail of all this; he found it altogether amazing. Then he said:

"Well, if you are married what gift can I make you? Tell me, and whatever you want is yours."

"What gift do I want from your Royal Majesty?" said Frances. "Will you give me the rank of General of Land and Sea, just for a couple of weeks until I have found out the truth of what I told you about my husband?"

"Granted here and now!" said the King. "From this moment you are General of Land and Sea."

Then the King called for the uniform of General of Land and Sea to be brought; Frances put it on, and they came out of the room. All the people of the Court saluted the General, and they all went cap-in-hand and were politeness itself.

The King gave Frances a platoon of soldiers in case of need, and with them she set off for her husband's city. By good luck Captain Maurice was there; the General of Land and Sea summoned him, and when he appeared said to him:

"Are you single or married?"

"I am a widower."

"And your wife?"

"Dead. "

"And how did she die? Where, how, and when?"

At this point the Captain began to be confused, and the General said:

"If you want to save your skin, tell me everything that happened to your wife. If I find you deceiving me over anything it will be the worse for you."

Captain Maurice saw he was getting into stormy water, and he concluded that the best and safest thing to do was to come clean and tell everything, without adding or leaving out anything. So he told his story like this:

"I will tell you in a few words the whole of my story. I married, to fulfill a promise, the poorest girl in the town, a lovely girl, beautiful, and a very good woman. The day we were married I put a ring on her finger and told her never to take it off; and she began doing just what I had told her. She had a mole below her left ear, with three stray hairs. I boasted about her everywhere as the finest woman on God's earth, but one day another skipper, a friend of mine, said she was not so good as I made out, and he said he could get hold of the ring and the three stray hairs. We made a wager on it of the seven ships that I owned against seven ships of his. After some time this skipper turned up with the ring and the three stray hairs. I went home intending to take it out on her, but I found her as cheerful as could be, with the ring on her finger, but the three stray hairs shortened. This plunged me into a mire of confusion; I did not know what to do. At length I had a box made, big enough to contain her, and I had it taken down to the sea-shore; I told her to lie down in the box, which she did; I shut the lid of the box and locked it, and then I threw the box and my wife into the sea, saying: 'If you are innocent you will float! If you are guilty you will go to the bottom'. The box, far from sinking, was carried out to sea by the waves and floated away. Then I realized my wife was innocent. I plunged into the sea to rescue her, but it was no good; the box was moving away too fast, without slowing down at all. I could do nothing but swim back to the shore and go home, without the box and without my wife, and I have heard no more of her. And there, sir, General of Land and

Sea, is all my story."

"Good," said the General. "We now know your part; but we need to know about the part played by the captain you say you laid the wager with. What was the name of this skipper?"

"Captain Caspar," said Captain Maurice.

"Have him brought here with all speed," ordered the General.

They found him on the point of setting sail for a voyage to very distant lands. "The General of Land and Sea demands your presence," they said.

"I don't have any business with him," said Captain Caspar.

"Captain," they said, "don't play about with a General of Land and Sea!"

He thought for a little and then saw it was best to obey the summons. He went to where the General was and presented himself, saying: "Here I am. What do you want of Captain Caspar?"

"Ah!" said the General of Land and Sea. "So you are Captain Caspar?"

"The very same," he replied.

"Good! I am interested to know what device you used to win the wager you had with Captain Maurice that you would get hold of a ring and three stray hairs from his wife."

When Captain Caspar heard this he was struck dumb, speechless, and he went as white as a sheet.

"Did you not understand me, Captain Caspar? Why don't you answer?" said the General. But Caspar stood with his mouth shut, as if he had been bewitched.

"Captain Caspar!" said the General of Land and Sea. "I am determined to clear this matter up. If you want to save your skin, speak up openly and relate everything as it was. If you do not speak the truth, I can assure you there will be no remission; you can regard yourself as being in the condemned cell."

Then Caspar saw there was nothing for it but to come clean, and he said:

"Sir, to tell you the truth, pride and the desire to win the wager with Captain Maurice blinded me. I saw that Frances, being the good woman she was, would never, ever, let me approach her near enough to take her ring or to cut those three stray hairs she had below her left ear. So I got the help of a neighbour near Captain Maurice's house; she contrived to look very closely at the ring that Maurice's wife wore, by stopping her in the street when she saw her going to Mass or returning from it. This neighbour then went to a goldsmith and had him make a ring just the same as Frances's. When she had this ring, she used the pretext of having Frances taste some Malmsey wine that she said had been given to her, in which she gave Frances a sleeping potion. When she saw Frances thoroughly asleep she exchanged the rings and cut off the three stray hairs. Then she came round to bring me the ring and the hairs. All this cost me a thousand pounds, as well as the cost of the ring that the goldsmith made."

"So you never saw nor spoke with Frances in all this time?"

"No, sir," Captain Caspar replied.

Captain Maurice was present and heard all this, and you can imagine how the poor fellow felt when he saw what a dirty trick Captain Caspar had played on him.

"Good," said the General. "Now we need to have the neighbour here. Tell her to come immediately."

With the directions that Captain Caspar gave them, they went to fetch her, and the poor woman had no choice but to go along and present herself, which she did with much trepidation, trembling like an aspen leaf.

The General of Land and Sea began asking her questions, and the poor woman confessed it all, agreeing in every detail with what Captain Caspar had said.

Then the General of Land and Sea turned to Captain Maurice and said: "Do you see now that your wife was innocent?"

"All too well I see it," he said. "Oh, if only she were alive! Oh, if only I knew her fate!"

Then the General said to all the people present:

"Nobody is to move until I return."

The General then retired into a chamber and Frances put on her woman's clothes – the same as she was wearing when her husband made her lie down in the box on the sea-shore – and she came out and stood before Captain Maurice, Captain Caspar, the neighbour, and everybody else, and said to the three:

"Do you recognize me?"

Captain Maurice certainly did recognize her; he took her in his arms and gave her a great embrace, in floods of tears for sheer joy.

Captain Caspar and the neighbour fell on their knees before her, also in tears and begging forgiveness with anguished cries.

When the platoon of soldiers in attendance saw that the General of Land and Sea had become a Generaless – because Frances had put the General's sash and other insignia over her woman's clothes – they were amazed and kept crossing themselves, their hair stood on end, and they could not understand how they had not recognized, nor even suspected, that their General was no General but a Generaless; and they looked at her all over, I can tell you, when they saw how handsome she was.

Where the Generaless of Land and Sea was in great doubt was over what should be done with Captain Caspar and that neighbour.

Captain Caspar took hold of Captain Maurice and said:

"I will give you back your seven ships, and I will hand over mine, because it is you who have really won the wager."

And then the neighbour spoke up saying: "Captain Caspar, I will return your thousand pounds because I don't want to have money from a bad deed."

Then Frances said to them: "Captain Caspar, and you my neighbour, you really did play a very cruel trick on me, and you both deserve to hang; but this time, and because you have confessed your guilt, I pardon you. Captain Caspar, you must return my husband's seven ships to him, and you my neighbour shall take the thousand pounds to the local hospice for poor people."

Captain Caspar and the neighbour gladly accepted the sentence passed by the Generaless of Land and Sea, and they carried it out straight away. The Generaless and Captain Maurice, with the platoon of soldiers, went back to the King's house.

When they arrived there the King came out to greet them, and the Generaless presented her husband, Captain Maurice, who was weeping for joy, and she said:

"My Lord King, I have discovered and cleared up everything I wanted to know; I have found my husband; I have uncovered the dirty trick that was played on us. The guilty ones confessed their crime with tears, and begged for pardon; so I pardoned them. Now I return to you the sash of the General of Land and Sea, which I no longer have any use for. I have enough with my husband and what God has blessed us with."

"My Lord King," said Captain Maurice then, "what my wife has just said is perfectly true. Our heartfelt thanks are to God and to Your Royal Majesty for all that you have done for us. If you have no further tasks for us, and if you will give us leave, we will return home. If ever you should need us, you know where you have two subjects willing to serve you in any way they can."

The King loaded them with money, so grateful was he to the Frank who turned out to be Frances. And then Captain Maurice and Frances set off for home. And they lived for many years in blessed peace and harmony; and they must still be alive if they are not dead.

And may we all meet in Heaven.

The Port of the White Onion

THERE WAS ONCE a ship's captain; he was very rich, and he had a son called Robert. One day this captain said to his son: "I am old now and the years weigh heavy on me. You are young; you can take over the ship and do the navigating. But there is one thing I command you, and that is: Don't ever put in at the Port of the White Onion, because people fare badly there."

"Don't worry, father," said Robert.

Then Robert's mother said: "My son, take this advice from me: Always, wherever you may be, *Do good and never question for whom.* Who does good will find good."

One day before dawn, with his ship in perfect order, Robert weighed anchor, and with the wind astern sailed away. He found a suitable port where he sold his cargo for more money than he expected, and then he began the journey home, rich and satisfied. One day he asked his sailors: "Do you know the Port of the White Onion? Where is it?"

"We are not far from it," the sailors replied.

"Good. Let's go there and see if one fares so badly as my father says."

"We will never put in at that port."

"Come on! Don't be such cowards! That is where we are going."

The sailors had to obey orders, however much against their will. They were soon outside the port; they put in, and they saw there was a large city. They moored, and Robert impatiently jumped ashore and went off to see the place.

He soon found himself in a large square; in the middle of it there was a White Onion so big that its leaves were like the sails of a windmill, and its stalk was as thick as the stoutest of ships' masts.

Below this Onion there was a crowd of people; Robert went near and saw there was a dead man surrounded by people, some of them spitting on him. When Robert had watched for some time he could not contain his curiosity any longer, and burst out:

"What the devil is this you are doing?"

"What are we doing?" they replied. "Why do you ask? Were you born yesterday and baptised today, or do you come from another world?"

"I have never before been in this country, and this is something that I have never in my life seen."

"Well, let us explain," they said. "Here it is our custom, when somebody dies with debts, to put him beneath the Onion; and he cannot be buried until all his debts are settled. The people he owed money to have the right to come and spit on him until they feel paid and satisfied. This man here made the mistake of dying with more debts than credits; that is why he is here and why they are doing what they are doing. Serve him right! He deserves it! He should have paid what he owed. What right has anybody to borrow and to get into debt at other people's expense? And those who have done the favour of lending and have carried the burden, should they just have to slap their own faces and put up with it? Therefore, if you don't want to be brought here beneath the Onion when you die, pay up what you owe, to the last penny."

When Robert heard this rigmarole he remembered his mother's words: *Do good and never question for whom;* and he exclaimed:

"And if there were somebody to pay his debts for him, could not this dead man be buried?"

"Most certainly," they said, "and very quickly too, but who would be fool enough to go in for that sort of business?"

"I would," said Robert.

The moment he uttered this, the people who were spitting stopped doing so.

"What did you say? What are you saying, friend?" they cried, crowding round him. “Pay up; pay us to the last penny and you shall see how quickly this rascal will be covered with earth.”

“Now, now,” said Robert. “Don’t insult the dead, because God has already passed judgment on them.”

“Alright; pay up, and we promise not to ask for more.”

Robert brought out a tremendous bag of golden guineas, and *ding-dong* he paid out until he had covered all the debts of the dead man; and they amounted to so much that he was left high and dry; the money bag could be turned inside-out like a sock, with no danger of the odd golden guinea or doubloon falling out – they had all gone – just to bury the poor devil of a dead man.

So Robert had little to laugh about. He started back for his ship dejected and worried, and thinking: “This has been a rather bad joke. Clearly my father was right to warn me not to put in at the Port of the White Onion, but there is also my mother’s advice always to *Do good and never question for whom.* Never mind; but I wonder what will come of it in the end. It was well done; so no more complaints or forebodings, for this or for any other reason.”

He arrived at his ship quite cheerful, and the sailors saw nothing amiss.

“Did it go well, Captain?” they asked.

“Yes, very well,” he replied. And they set sail and made straight for their home port. When Robert went ashore he found his father and mother waiting for him, and you can imagine the embraces and the kisses they must have given him, and the joy they had in seeing him fit and well, and as cheerful as a bride.

But when Robert told them what had happened at the Port of the White Onion they stopped laughing and were as if stunned. His father gave him a tremendous dressing down, because, as he said, he had warned Robert beforehand not to go there, and it was through his own obstinacy that Robert had brought such a calamity on himself. Robert’s mother, considering that in paying the dead man’s debts he had done no more than follow her advice, accepted the blow and said:

“Doing good has cost us rather a lot this time, but it cannot be helped; who does good will find good; and worse things could have happened, from which may it please God to protect us."

After about a month Robert approached his father and said: "Father, are we not going to arrange another voyage?"

"Yes, but not if it means you are going to put in at the Port of the White Onion. I wonder if you learned your lesson when you disobeyed me. If you go there again don't come back to this house; I shall throw you out."

"For God's sake, Robert,'" said his mother, "don't go there. Obey your father; and your mother too: *Do good and never question for whom*, my son."

"Don't worry," he replied. "All will go well if God and the Blessed Virgin so wish it."

He went on board his ship, well loaded with goods; they weighed anchor and under full sail with a following wind they were away. They searched for a port to put in at, and by God's grace they found one; Robert sold the whole cargo, and he made more money than he expected. He had a tremendous bag full of doubloons, guineas, and crowns.

Then he set off for home rich and satisfied, but – if you will believe it – he was filled with a strong desire to put in at the Port of the White Onion; and this desire became so intense that he could not resist it, and he said to the sailors: "Make for the Port of the White Onion."

"But what will your father say? He, who knew so much and was so wise, would never put in there."

"To the Port of the White Onion, I say. The Captain is boss here." And the sailors just had to bow their heads and obey orders. Within seven or eight hours they were in this famous port; they moored up and Robert jumped ashore and went walking about the city. He soon came to the same square he had been in before, with the enormous Onion, and this time the crowd of people there was really huge.

"What is going on?" said Robert. "Not another dead man loaded with debts?"

He went up close and saw it was not a dead man that the crowd was surrounding but a young girl. She was in floods of tears but, although she was looking miserably unhappy and showed in her face the agony that was gnawing at her heart, she was clearly the prettiest and most lovely creature you ever saw. She was leaning against the trunk of the giant Onion for support; beside her there was a tough-looking gentleman with his mouth shut and his eyes wide open. A huckster with a face just like Caiaphas was moving to and fro in the space left open by the people and saying in a voice that scorched your ears and resounded in your brain:

"A thousand pounds I am offered! Come, who will raise the bid? The goods are worth more than that! One thousand pounds – going..."

"What the devil is all this?" said Robert when he had taken in the scene.

"What do you think?" said a bystander. "Open your eyes. They are auctioning this girl, and if you want to bid, hurry up in case you are too late. The corsairs came in today with a boat-load of captives, male and female, and they have sold out so quickly that only this girl is left. They kept her till last so there should be more time to look at her, and more interested buyers."

This bystander had hardly finished his account when a voice was heard saying "A thousand pounds more". And the huckster, encouraged by this, nearly burst himself shouting out: "Two thousand pounds I am offered! Come, who will raise the bid? Quick, if you want to be in time. You can see this girl is worth all the money in the world! Enough to drive you mad. Two thousand pounds I am offered – going... Who will raise the bid?"

"Captain," said the bystander to Robert, "you can hear the way it is going. If you want to bid, do so quickly, because the price looks like rising. They will get more money out of it than they expected. And to tell the truth, I have never seen such an attractive girl."

At this point they again heard a voice saying "A thousand pounds more"; and the huckster of course was like a madman, dashing to and fro like a shuttle, and saying:

"Three thousand pounds – going... Come, who will better this? Wake up! Don't be idle! Anybody with money, bring it out now – this is the moment! Don't you see what a lovely girl this is, even though just now she is distressed. You can see she is beyond price! Three thousand pounds – going... Who will advance on this?"

"There is no doubt about it," said the bystander; "the corsairs have struck gold today. What a sale! Come on, Captain! If you are interested, don't hang back; the bidding may go higher, and then it would cost you a lot more."

Robert did not answer; he was preoccupied, deep in thought. He was filled with compassion for the young girl, and he thought it horrible that she should be condemned to slavery for the rest of her life, and that her mother and father should be weeping for her as lost for ever. He was deeply moved by her tears and her cries, and he was convinced he would never deserve God's forgiveness if, with all the money that he had, and had so easily earned, he did not rescue her from a horrible fate. He was further urged by his mother's words: *Do good and never question for whom*; but then he remembered his father's threats and the treatment he would get if he again came home with an empty purse. The poor chap was between the Devil and the deep sea; if he did one thing, bad; if he did the other, bad too.

At that point he heard another voice saying "A thousand pounds more". The huckster then went completely mad, deafening everybody with his shouting and bellowing.

"Four thousand pounds – going... Any advance on that? Come, hurry! You will be too late if you delay. Come on, this is the cream! The prettiest girl on the market – knocks spots off all the others! Four thousand pounds – going... Any advance?"

Robert could hold out no longer. "Here goes, and come what may!" he said loudly. He forced his way into the crowd, and by elbowing to right and left reached the huckster, when he pulled out his money-bag, as fat as a large black pudding. With his eyes flashing and his whole body trembling, he said:

"This bag, full of gold, for the girl!"

The huckster was dumbfounded; the corsair sat with his mouth hanging open; the crowd of bystanders were with their hair on end; those who had been bidding, stunned, began to back out saying, if not with their tongues at least with their eyes and faces: "This has beaten us."

"Finish it off," said the corsair to the huckster.

"This bag of gold," cried the huckster. "Going... any advance? Going... Gone!" And after a short pause he turned to Robert and said: "She is yours."

The corsair stood up and Robert emptied his money-bag into a large handkerchief spread out; there was a tremendous pile of gold.

Then Robert turned to the girl and said: "Don't cry any more; you are no longer a captive or a slave. It is true that I have bought you, and I have given all I had to buy you; but I did not do it to make you mine, but rather to be able to return you to your father and mother. Tell me where they are, and we will set off at once."

The girl thought she was dreaming; she heard what Robert said, and he did not seem to be the sort to play a trick on her; but still she could not get into her head that it was true. It cost Robert quite an effort to make her believe it; he had to talk hard. Then she could not restrain her happiness; she wept for joy; a great rejoicing came over her and she was crazy with delight.

"Are you single or married?" she suddenly asked Robert.

"Single," he replied.

"Then I must tell you: I am a king's daughter. I was captured by the corsairs and brought here. I too am single, and if you will have me we could be married, and the sooner the better. I am yours, and everybody should have what is his."

I need not tell you how much Robert liked the sound of these words; he certainly thought it was a great idea.

"My dear," he said, "you can see for yourself: to free you from the clutches of the corsairs I have parted with all the money I had, all my capital. I am captain of a ship, but it belongs to my father, and when he sees me returning without a penny, I don't know what he will do. That's the position we are in; if you can face it, I assure you I don't want to discourage you."

"You have rescued me," she said, "and you have risked everything to give me back my freedom. I can well take a risk too; I want to share your luck, good or bad. Let's be married and not discuss it any more."

They were married and they went on board his ship. The

sailors opened their eyes wide when they saw that girl arriving with the skipper, and she so pretty and comely.

"This is my wife," said Robert. "Please respect her as such."

"So you got married?"

"I did, and don't you think I have good taste?"

"Wonderfully good! Marvellous!" said the sailors, all amazed.

"My dear," said Robert to his wife, now you must tell us which is your father's kingdom and where it lies."

"Don't ask me," she replied. "When the corsairs captured me I lost my senses, and what with having cried so much and having suffered so much anxiety – and God alone knows how much – I don't know where we went, nor where I am, and even less which way we should go."

"Then the best thing is to go to my home, and from there we will take steps to find out." She thought that was a good idea, and they sailed for Robert's home port.

When they arrived and Robert's father saw the two of them and heard their story, and when he saw how his son had again returned without a penny – and with a wife into the bargain – he was so angry and took it so badly, that he did not want to know if she was the daughter of a king or of a kingfisher, nor whether she had or had not fallen into the hands of corsairs; he threw them out on their ears and told them never to appear again while he was alive.

So Robert had to leave home in disgrace, and you can imagine how he felt.

"There is nothing for us to do," he said, "but to go about the world like pilgrims, and keep on going until we find your father's house."

So walking and walking, on and on, they went through one land after another, asking everybody for news of the place they were trying to find. Many people had never heard of such a king nor of such a kingdom. People who had some idea all said it was so distant, so very far away, that you could die walking before you got there. But the two never lost courage, and they kept going in the direction that people said.

The poor king who had lost his daughter – and he had no other – nearly died of grief. He sent courtiers from his court to go looking for her in every direction until they should find her, and he gave them a plan to follow:

"You are not to say straight out that it is my daughter you are looking for, because this might bring complications and altogether muddy the waters. Here is what I have thought of to get round this difficulty. My daughter, as you know, is the best embroideress there has ever been – where she puts her hands let no other come, lest she should make a mess of it. I will give you a flag embroidered by her; you will take it with you and you will go from town to town and from city to city, and all you will have to do is this: show the flag to everybody and say: 'The girl who can embroider a flag like this will inherit our King's crown. She who can present an embroidered flag to equal this one has only to come with us, and as soon as she arrives here she shall have the crown on her head; she will be Queen. As nobody other than my daughter is capable of embroidering a flag to equal this one, you cannot go wrong. If she is alive you will eventually come to where she is living, and then you will find her at once. Off you go now, and don't come back without her."

He handed them the flag – which was a marvel, the most exquisite thing you can imagine – and they set off straight away.

They walked and walked, and tramped and tramped, through land after land and kingdom after kingdom. They showed the flag to everybody and they said their piece. Wherever the courtiers went the girls did nothing but embroider flags, and I can tell you they put their five senses into it, and all their endurance. But they were disappointed because they all failed; the flags they embroidered were rubbish beside the flag that the courtiers carried.

They had been going about the world for seven years, searching for the embroideress who could produce a flag to match theirs. None had even approached it; all their efforts had failed to yield any result. They were on the point of giving up when God so arranged it that they came to the city where Robert and his wife happened to be, in the course of their pilgrimage.

They caught sight of these courtiers, and she recognized them; but she said nothing and decided to play it her own way.

"Would you like me to try and make a flag like that one?" she said to Robert.

"If you dare to," he replied.

"I certainly do dare to."

"Then go ahead."

They found a kind soul who gave them the cloth and the thread needed; then she went and looked closely at the flag and asked for two weeks' grace, which they agreed to. She threaded her needle and within the two weeks she had the flag finished. She took it to the courtiers, and they put it beside the flag that the King had given them, and it was exactly the same, neither more nor less. After a while, when both flags had been passed from hand to hand to be looked at, nobody could tell which was one and which the other.

The courtiers got an explanation from the girl and her husband, and then they saw clearly that their search had succeeded; they had found the King's daughter.

You can imagine what great joy they all felt – both parties. The courtiers said: "The quickest way home would be by ship, and we must return to the King as soon as we can." So they took ship, and with the wind astern away they went.

When they had been sailing for a couple of days, the devil Envy, who is never idle and will worm his way where no other does, began nibbling at those courtiers and, before they knew it, had got inside them, where he kept saying to them:

"And will you consent to seeing this miserable Robert – penniless and useless, who has had to go begging from door to door, *some little thing in God's name?*, just to have something to eat – will you consent to such a person being our King? Can't you see what will happen? As soon as we arrive home the King will give them the crown and you will not be able to prevent it. Are you so feeble that you will submit to such an insult?"

These thoughts took a firm hold of those courtiers and they sniffed each other out and said among themselves: "The best thing will be for a couple of us to engage him in conversation in a dangerous place, and then two or three of us give him a push overboard – so by killing the cow we wean the calf. We will say he fell overboard by accident; one of us will marry her, and everything will be as we want it."

What do you think? They carried out their scheme. That very same day they engaged Robert in conversation; chatting and chatting away, they led him to the side of the ship, and as soon as they saw him a little inattentive they gave him a push; the poor fellow fell straight into the sea and they lost sight of him.

"Robert has fallen overboard!" these villains cried, shouting and making a lot of noise. "Oh what a misfortune! What a disaster!"

The King's daughter heard them and came out on deck. She looked at them, she looked all round and everywhere, and nowhere did she see Robert. She swooned and fell down in a dead faint.

They bathed her temples with brandy, and they fanned her, but they could not bring her round. Then those courtiers found themselves in a real quandary, deep in the mud.

They arrived back at the Court, the King came out to meet them, and he saw his daughter unconscious. He did not know what was happening to him; on one hand he was overjoyed to see her when he had believed her lost for ever; on the other hand he was choked with anguish seeing her stretched out senseless, motionless, hardly breathing.

"Lord King," said the courtiers, "it was the joy of knowing that she was coming home that brought on this fainting fit. Don't worry; it will soon pass, God willing." But it did not pass at all, and the King and all the Court were in despair, not knowing what to do; there were tears and lamentations everywhere.

The poor girl was laid on a bed, and all the doctors with any reputation came to see her, and they kept having consultations and trying things to bring her round, but it was all in vain.

Robert, as soon as he hit the water, felt he was clasped in two arms and carried along, faster than a dolphin. After three days he came to a beach; and when he was on the sand he realized that the arms bearing him along belonged to a body; he was in the arms of a man.

"Don't you recognize me?"said the man.

"I don't remember ever having seen you before," Robert replied.

"I am the man whom you saw dead at the Port of the White Onion, and whose debts you paid so he might be buried. I have come to return the kindness you did me then. When you hit the water it was my arms that received you and have borne you along these past three days. You were thrown overboard so you should not be made King. Your wife went into a dead faint, and she is still in it. She is at her father's house, and all the doctors together are unable to bring her round."

Then the man produced a guitar. "Take this guitar," he said, "and go and play it outside the King's house." Robert took the guitar and went and did so, and I assure you he played for all he was worth. He played very well and made the finest music.

The Queen, hearing these sounds, looked out and saw Robert with his guitar. "Have him brought up here," she said. "Since nobody can find a cure for my daughter, perhaps the sound of this guitar will be good for her." They brought Robert up and took him into the room where the King's daughter was lying; he began to play, and he put his heart into it. Then he began to sing:

> The song of the Skipper,
> Who as a captive found you;
> The song of the Skipper
> Who bought you and unbound you.

At this point the King's daughter began to regain her colour, and more and more.

"Don't stop! Play some more!" said the King and the Queen, feeling encouraged. And Robert played on – and so I should think!

"Sing, sing again!" they said. So he sang on:

> The song of the Skipper
> You were joined with in marriage;
> The song of the Skipper –
> Seven years in pilgrimage.

Then the King's daughter opened her eyes and looked and looked around, especially at Robert and at her mother and father. The King and the Queen were about to embrace her and smother her with kisses.

"Nobody must touch her, for Heaven's sake." said Robert. "Let me finish."

The King and Queen restrained themselves. "Come on, then," they said. "Sing your song and make haste!" So Robert went on playing and continued his song with as good a voice as he could muster:

> The song of the Skipper
> Who was thrown in the sea;
> The song of the Skipper
> Whom God has made free.

At this point the King's daughter opened her mouth and said with a sigh:

"Ah, beloved of my soul!"

"For goodness' sake, not a word!" cried Robert. "Don't move, anybody!"

Nobody spoke or moved, and Robert, softening his voice as much as he could, sang:

> The song of the skipper
> Who is here to revive you;
> See your father and mother
> See the man who has saved you.

He had hardly sung the last words when the King's daughter suddenly sat up, jumped out of bed, fit and well and lively, and threw herself into Robert's arms. The King and the Queen embraced them both, weeping for joy like little children, and they hardly knew what they were doing or where they were going.

Robert and his wife recounted everything that had happened to them, and everybody was astonished and amazed. The courtiers who had committed the crime confessed to it with tears of blood; their lives were spared but they were shut up in the dungeon of a castle and never again saw the sun or the moon.

The King said there were to be three days of high festivities and a dinner every day for all his vassals – but a dinner of the sort that leaves a man flat on his back – and I can tell you they all enjoyed it and there was merry-making and dancing of the best.

The King gave his crown to his daughter and Robert, who were a King and Queen of the first order, and they lived for years and years at peace with themselves and with everybody; and they are still alive if they have not died.

And may we all meet in Heaven.

Amen.

Postscript

THE CATALAN TONGUE current in Mallorca during the nineteenth century was, in its spoken form among country people, vigorous and picturesque; it was the ideal medium for narrating *Rondaies*. The island's geographical position in the western Mediterranean made it a busy staging port for maritime traffic, both material and linguistic. In Mossèn Alcover's time the tales included European and North African legends and some that were no doubt indigenous. Mallorca must then have been a folklorist's delight; indeed there were several learned Europeans in the field, but Alcover was the only native collector and writer of *Rondaies*. He was, by birth and upbringing uniquely fitted for the task, and he became passionately absorbed in it.

Alcover's love of *Rondaies*, began in his childhood, and continued for the rest of his life. He saw that the task of hearing them, writing them down, making good their deficiencies, and producing smooth flowing narratives, had virtually no limits, and it was characteristic of him that he embarked on the project despite his important ecclesiastical and academic commitments.

He recognized that his gathering of tales would have been more comprehensive if he had been able to go in person from village to village and to all the corners of the island in his search for narrators, but his other obligations made this impossible. Even so, he succeeded in hearing, writing, and editing over three hundred tales told by two hundred and twenty narrators, including twenty-three *Rondaies* from his mother, twenty from his father, and twenty-six from their friend Toni Garrit.

If any criticism of Alcover's relentless work were admissable, it might be that his insistence on the strictest propriety led him to reject tales that were at all salacious or conducive to lewd thoughts. His response to such criticism was that the good should be preserved and the bad forgotten. His friend and biographer Francesc de Borja Moll has observed with a touch of regret that this exclusion means there is no material for a *Decameron* of Mallorca.

Alcover was criticized for his method of selecting the best passages and the most dramatic wording when he had more than one version of a *Rondaia*. The professional academic folklorists claimed that this practice produced "corrupt" versions tainted by erudition rather than authentic folk-lore. To this Alcover could reply that he was not erudite, that he wrote down the tales for his own pleasure and to save them from extinction through neglect, and that as he was himself a countryman, what he wrote was as authentic as any other source. He was convinced that oral transmission was disappearing, that *Rondaies* were being forgotten or not passed on from one generation to another; he did more than any academic folklorist to rescue the tales from oblivion. He was assisted and inspired by the Catalan literary revival of the second half of the nineteenth century.

There were other folk-tale hunters in the field, though there was no other native islander, and none made great efforts to record and disseminate the tales they heard. The most prominent among the visitors was the Archduke Ludwig Salvator of Habsburg-Lorena, who collected *Rondaies* chiefly as a hobby. He had his versions – some translated into German – bound in leather and deposited in the libraries of several European cities. This did not greatly contribute to the survival of the tales by dissemination. By contrast, Alcover printed and published his dozen volumes of *Rondaies* as cheaply as possible in his attempts to save the tales from extinction.

Towards the end of the nineteenth century, when the revived study of Catalan linguistics was in its early stages, Alcover became a prominent figure in the field. He was criticized as being an amateur, but what he lacked in formal academic training he more than made good by the volume, solidity and comprehensiveness of his philological studies.

When the *Institut d'Estudis Catalans* was set up in Barcelona in 1907 it was natural that Alcover should be associated with it. When the *Institut* set about compiling a definitive, comprehensive Catalan lexicon, Alcover was able to contribute the linguistic material and the personal experience of ten years' work in this field. It should have been a great collaboration, but disagreements between Alcover and other members of the *Institut* – exacerbated by his blunt, not to say pugnacious, manner – caused no little resentment in the academic circles of Barcelona.

In 1918 Alcover withdrew from the *Institute* his dictionary material of hundreds of thousands of entries, and ended his personal membership. He renamed his project *Diccionari Català-Valencià-Balear* instead of the former and more correct title of *Diccionari de la Llengua Catalana.*

For Alcover this split meant a severe reduction in official subsidies. For the Dictionary to advance he had to impoverish himself. Characteristically undeterred, he set up at his own expense a printing press equipped with the special type-faces that the Dictionary called for.

In 1920 he enlisted the collaboration of his friend Francesc de B. Moll, who contributed his time and his great erudition to the progress of the Dictionary.

The first of ten volumes appeared in 1930; it was the only volume that Alcover was to see, as he died in January 1932 before the second volume appeared. The subsequent sections of this massive work, based on Alcover's wealth of dictionary entries, have been written and published by Moll, who thus achieved Alcover's ambition and has produced a definitive lexicon of the Catalan language in its several forms.

Note on Corsairs

TWO OF THE TALES in this book involve the nefarious doings of the Corsairs, also known as the pirates of the Barbary Coast – now the coastal regions of Algeria, Tunisia, Tripoli, and part of Morocco – Muslim territory that for a couple of centuries was dominated by the Turkish Empire. The Corsairs' depredations began to be a serious menace to the Europeans soon after the reconquest of Granada in 1492, and were thought to be inspired by the animosity of the many Moors whom the Christians expelled from Spain to the Barbary Coast.

The rapine was vigorously conducted, and these coastal communities became so rich and powerful that in the seventeenth century they broke away from Turkish rule and became independent states subsisting chiefly on high-seas robbery, pillage, abduction, and the trade in Christian slaves.

Of the several ports along the Barbary Coast from which the Corsairs operated, the richest and most powerful was Algiers, so much so that *Algerine* became a synonym for Barbary Corsair. At the height of the pirates' activity in the seventeenth century it was said there were twenty thousand captives, mostly Christians, in the slave market of Algiers.

The European governments failed conspicuously to put a stop to the plunder and kidnapping, and although the Corsairs' activities declined in the eighteenth century they were not finally suppressed until Algiers was taken by the French in 1830; even then, incidents continued to occur. Although religious orders were very active in collecting money for the redemption of captives, their efforts benefited relatively few victims.

When Mossèn Alcover was collecting *Rondaies* around the end of the nineteenth century, the Corsairs' assaults and abductions seem to have been fresh in the people's memory. The Port of the White Onion must be somewhere on the Barbary Coast, and could be Algiers itself. In The Rivals, when James returns rescued to Mallorca, he states clearly that he has been held captive in Algiers.